HOW SMALL A PART OF TIME

*The Biography of the Two
Beautiful Miss Lynchs of Cabragena*

To Rivy and Lyna, with my love

And for Lady Reid, with loving thoughts.

HOW SMALL A PART OF TIME

by

MAGDALEN KING-HALL

"How small a part of time they share
That are so wondrous sweet and fair!"
WALLER

LONDON: PETER DAVIES

FIRST PUBLISHED 1945

AUTHOR'S NOTE

The author asks her readers to have the kindness to imagine that in writing this " biography " of the two Miss Lynchs she had access to the following sources:

The Private Journals of Dorothea Marchioness of Mandlesham

Household Accounts of the 4th Earl of Aintry

The Moffat Papers

as well as to other unpublished journals and letters in the possession of the Mandlesham, Aintry, de Lapalisse and Kilrush families.

Her real and grateful acknowledgements are particularly due to the following: *Dublin under the Georges* and *Country and Town in Ireland under the Georges*, by Constantia Maxwell, M.A., Litt.D., and *Irish Beauties of the Last Century*, by Francis Gerard.

PRINTED IN GREAT BRITAIN FOR PETER DAVIES LTD
BY J. AND J. GRAY, EDINBURGH

THE BACKGROUND

THE RIVER BLACKWATER rises in the Kerry mountains and follows an easterly course across Ireland for some fifty miles till it reaches the town of Cappoquin, where it turns south to flow another fifteen miles to the sea through a singularly beautiful and solitary countryside.

It is like a tarnished mirror, or mother of pearl, between the reedy banks where a lonely figure cuts rushes for thatching; at its meeting place with the river Bride it is set in a background of soft hills and distant dreamy mountains; dawn throws rosy clouds, sublime as the wings of archangels, across the tender sky; the river gleams like blue enamel in the sunshine, reflecting with infinite devotion the changes of the sky above. Elsewhere the river banks are steep and thickly wooded; the water is jade or olive green and glassy, winding between little islets of grass-covered mud. There is quietness here, space, remoteness, a certain languor in the air, very soothing to the fretted modern mind.

Do not be deceived. This Munster countryside has a past of indescribable suffering and strife. Gunpowder and fire reduced that castle and that abbey church to their present pleasing state of ruin. FitzGeralds and Butlers convulsed the countryside with ferocious internecine warfare. The Elizabethan and Cromwellian planters clung grimly to their conquered acres. Oppression and despoliation bred rebellion and savage massacres, rebellion bred savage retaliation. Famine, fire and sword swept periodically through the country, reducing it to utter desolation. Spenser records that its surviving inhabitants "spoke like ghosts crying out of the graves".

Strangely enough out of this lawlessness and chaos a civilisation and a society evolved; a civilisation alien to the country and violently imposed upon it, and yet produced by the mysterious absorption of these alien elements into the country itself; a society that was founded on injustice and bitter race and religious hostility, and yet contributed richly to Ireland's heritage, that though often extravagant, dissolute, reckless and callous produced brilliant men of letters, famous soldiers and statesmen, benevolent land-lords, eminent theologians and beautiful women—so many beautiful women!—whom Ireland must acknowledge as her children, for to deny them would be to deny part of herself. No other country could have given birth to them. Their ancestors came from Scotland, Wales and all parts of England, and Ireland seduced them from their old allegiances and subtly crept into their hearts, for this is Ireland's way with strangers. "Lord! how quickly that country doth alter men's natures", Spenser said in bewildered exasperation.

This absorption, however, was incomplete. Irreconcilable forces of class, politics and religion set them apart from the conquered race whose lands and privileges they enjoyed. The memory of past wrongs smouldered beneath the surface, bursting every now and then into flames. Ireland was their home, and yet they were still in a sense England's garrison in a hostile country and proud of their trust. This bewitching country turned a secretive, resentful face towards them. This has been the tragedy of the Anglo-Irish, who can claim with justice that they have added immeasureably to Ireland's renown.

The eighteenth century was their high noon. Secure in the fine mansions and their demesnes, absolute in their power over their tenants, with the gaieties of Dublin and the mimic pomp of its Viceregal Court to console those of them who were not absentees for the distant amenities of London, with gambling, duelling, drinking and every

6

kind of sport and amusement to fill their leisure moments, they had no doubt of their divinely appointed role in the life of the nation. Everything had been given into their hands, it seemed, and whatever may be said against them it cannot be denied that they enjoyed life with a lively zest and an extravagant appetite that has never been surpassed.

As the Blackwater approaches the sea it widens out almost majestically into a broad, strongly flowing expanse of water, before merging into Youghal Bay. There is a tang of salt in the freshening breeze, seagulls wheeling and squawking, a band of sparkling light on the ocean horizon.

The "New and Correct Map of the County of Waterford" in *The Ancient and Present State of the County of Waterford* by Charles Smith, M.D. (1774), gives no indication of how the eighteenth century traveller could pass from the western or Youghal side of the river to the eastern bank. There is no bridge marked on it further south than Lismore. Dr Smith himself says loftily, "I shall now cross the Blackwater and proceed to the barony of Decies within Drum," later adding the information that "Between Youghal and this barony is communication by a ferry boat, which in bad weather is hazardous and difficult to pass." Imagination will convey us across the river more conveniently.

A change has come over the scene. Gone are the "very entertaining landscapes" which Dr Smith admires on the banks of the Blackwater. This coastal country is bare, unsheltered and windswept, lit by soft and variable lights, and backed by boggy, mountainous land and the blue darkness of the hills. There is no friendliness in this uncompromising country or intrinsic charm, only the desolate beauty lent to it by the sea and the constantly changing sky.

It is blotted out by sea mists and drizzling rain; then the

7

sun breaks through the clouds, illuminating the headlands with a refined, unearthly light. A fragment of rainbow dips into the sea. At evening the light streams down on to the sea from beneath the clouds in Old Testament splendour. Or the sea is peacock or hyacinth blue and the horizon is banded with lemon-coloured light. In all weathers, even the calmest, a curl of white surf marks the foot of the cliffs. Wild thyme and furze grow on the steep promontories; there are little crimson and yellow shells and azure mussel shells on the beach and, very rarely, lumps of ambergris; sea birds nest in the cliffs and cry like lost souls in the stormy air.

This strip of coast is lonely, even nowadays. The little seaside resort of Ardmore—formerly a Danish settlement— which scrambles up a headland, lends some animation to the neighbourhood's summers in present times. In the eighteenth century it was not much more than a fishing village, with "a stump of a castle" to serve as a reminder of past importance, and a round tower, a holy well and the crumbling remains of an ancient church to attract the attentions of the faithful on St Declan's feast day.

Between Ardmore and Youghal Bay is the high headland of Ardnabannagh, and on this headland stood Cabra House, the home of two sisters whose beauty was a brief wonder in an age renowned for its beautiful women— Dorothea and Jenny Lynch.

PART I

CHAPTER I

THE HOUSE

CABRA (or Cabragena) House was not one of those Irish Georgian mansions—often gaunt and gloomy but with their own austere beauty—which are the chief marks left by England's domination on the half-tamed Celtic countryside. It was both older and less imposing—a semi-fortified house dating from the early seventeenth century, of a type to be found in Ireland, Scotland and the Border country where life remained unsettled and insecure till a later date than in England.

It had been converted gradually, haphazardly, and without any marked success, into a more comfortable residence, but its curious round towers and small barred windows showed its origin. It is marked on Dr Smith's map but, significantly, is not thought worthy to be included in the text among the "gentlemen's seats".

Nothing but self-protection of the most urgent kind could surely have induced its original builder to place it in this wildly desolate spot. Only a rough, sloping field separated it from the cliffs. It was exposed to every Atlantic gale that battered at the coast and every squiff of mizzling rain. Silvery gleams of sunlight on the sea, its sudden changing from lead to sapphire blue, the path of dappled moon-light across the water, or sunsets of fire and aquamarine, could hardly have compensated, except to the most ardent lover of seascapes, for the general bleakness of the scene.

This is one of nature's battlegrounds—wind and waves and rain tormenting themselves eternally and senselessly against the grim rocks, always repulsed and always returning to the assault. There is a feeling of stress and restlessness here that is subtly exacerbating to the nerves. The house can never have been quiet. How the wind must have thundered and raged like the guns of an attacking army round its windows in the winter or during the spring and autumn gales—its fierce breath laden with the salt moisture of the sea-spray, as though a wild beast had learnt to shed human tears—dying down to a mournful sobbing, rising again to a frenzy. Even on summer days there would be a breeze teasing the coarse grasses and thyme of the headland, and there would be the endless murmuring of the sea. The trees, except for the stalwart firs, are bent landwards, their attitude and stunted growth testifying eloquently to the weathering endured by the now ruined house.

The early history of Cabra House is obscure, only to be glimpsed now through a mist of half-forgotten local tradition. It belonged in the seventeenth century to an Anglo-Irish family of some consequence called Kyle, and the impression that one gets from the little that is known of their family life there is one of unrelieved violence and gloom.

It is said that the master of the house coming home unexpectedly from a journey found his young wife in the embraces of a lover. The gallant escaped out of a window and leapt on to his horse pursued by the husband, who called out his servants and bloodhounds to join in the chase. In the darkness of a stormy night the hunted lover lost his way on the cliffs. According to one account his horse lost its footing, slipped and was hurled with its rider on to the jagged rocks below. Another version says that the horse stumbled, rolled down the incline, and the young man, becoming entangled with his reins, was hanged from a natural bridge of rock. This place is still shunned by the local people after nightfall when, it is said, unearthly shrieks and wails can be heard above the sound of the wind and waves.

The husband, no doubt filled with a satisfaction which

it is unpleasant to contemplate, rode home and completed the horror of the night by secretly hanging his wife from a beam in her room. This part of the house, of course, had the reputation afterwards of being haunted, and strong support is given to the story by the fact that years later, when alterations were being made to the house, the skeleton of a woman was found walled up in this room.

It almost seems as though ghosts share misfortune's dislike of singularity. One house in a neighbourhood will make a corner, as it were, in supernatural happenings. Not satisfied with the spirit of the poor murdered wife and her lover, Cabra House had several other minor, rather obscure "haunts"—a loose board on the back stairs that would never stay fastened down—a common enough thing no doubt in many of the ill-kept Irish houses of the time, but in this case the body of a new-born child had been found beneath it (a sordid little tragedy believed to be the result of some maid-servant's illicit amours); while the shadowy figure of a woman in a black shawl was occasionally seen near the door of the walled garden, an appearance for which no one was able to account.

Enough has been said to show that the house was considered, with some reason, to be sinister and unlucky. It seems unlikely that the Lynch family would have chosen to take up residence there if it had not passed into their hands by a strange chance. Early in the eighteenth century, Luke Lynch, the grandfather of Dorothea and Jenny, while visiting a gentleman in the neighbourhood, won Cabra House off its owner, the last of the Kyles, in a single night of cards. It was not known for certain what happened to the ruined man. It was believed that he went abroad, where he committed suicide.

There are some houses that really seem to be inimical to the small, warm joys and comforts that garrison a family against the indifferent cruelty of the outside world. These houses seem to have a forbidding life of their own, as though a melancholy fatality emanated from their actual stones. Built to be lived in, one feels that they would much prefer *not* to be lived in, that it suits them very well to be deserted and crumbling into ruin. It is impossible to say what gives them this atmosphere, whether there is something inauspicious inherent in their situation or structure, or whether it is stamped on them by the lives and emotions of their inmates. In either case one fancies that any effort to create a happy community life within them must be doomed to failure, as surely as other houses remain beloved and gracious through a series of family sorrows and misfortunes.

Cabra House must certainly have been one of these unblest houses even in its prime. But the buoyancy of the human mind is remarkable. The Lynch family, undeterred by its sinister history and the unpropitious way in which they had come by it, no doubt entered into possession with confidence, even with jubilation. Alterations were made, furniture and pictures arranged, the rambling back premises swarmed with barefooted servants, tenants and beggars hung round the back door; there were roaring fires in the winter, hogsheads of claret were fetched up from the cellar through a trapdoor in the dining-room; on spring days daffodils and primroses were planted by feminine hands in sheltered corners.

It was the Lynchs who built the lofty garden wall. This garden is ruined now like the house. It is an uncanny thing to open the garden door and to find behind it nothing but a desolation of long grass and straggling trees. But formerly the massive walls must have given good protection even from the prevailing south-westerly gales to flowers, vegetables and fruit trees.

In the early days of the Lynch occupancy of Cabra, when money was comparatively plentiful, and the master of the house anxious to establish himself in his newly acquired property as "a gentleman every inch of him", life there was modelled on the luxurious lines prevailing in the larger country houses. But as time went on and reckless expenditure (chiefly on cards, wine and horses) exceeded the rents extracted from a starveling peasantry, the standard of living declined. The fine furniture became shabby and dilapidated, ceilings leaked, doors swung loose on hinges, bell ropes could be tugged at till they came away in the hand without ringing a bell, a mirror here was cracked, a carpet there was stained with the port spilt during a drinking orgy; the cavernous kitchen was frightening in its smokey squalor.

What did it matter? The stables were always filled with half-broken horses; servants, friendly and familiar, tumbled over each other; there was an abundance of wine and food (practically everything except wine and groceries was produced on the place) and of hospitality to friend and stranger on the lavish Irish scale that always confounded English visitors, and which the erudite tried to explain as a relic of the ancient Irish tribal custom of "coshering".

These, in the estimation of the lesser gentry of that period, were the essential things. A mixture of reckless ostentation and happy-go-lucky slovenliness took the place of refined comfort. Of culture there was practically none. The library at Cabra House was a dark, musty-smelling room on whose shelves rows of leather-bound sermons, copies of the *English Magazine*, some books on sport and farriery, and a few novels, such as *Robinson Crusoe* and *Hudibras*, collected the dust. Guns, foxes' brushes, fishing rods and sporting prints on the walls of the hall and parlour were expressive of the tastes of the owners.

It is related that neither Dorothea nor Jenny Lynch had a long mirror of their own till they married. They had to run into their mother's bedroom to have a full length view of those charms that were to dazzle their contemporaries.

This was the house in which the sisters were born and spent their early youth.

CHAPTER II

THE FAMILY

THE LYNCH FAMILY came originally from the West of England. One of the younger sons was a soldier of Cromwell's, and was rewarded for his services during the Irish campaign, at the subsequent "settling" of Ireland, by a grant of land in Galway. Nothing much is known about him, but it can be safely concluded that he was tough physically and mentally. Otherwise he would soon have been murdered or chased out of his newly acquired possessions.

Nothing could have been less "settled" than Connaught (or any other part of Ireland for that matter) at that time. It required nerve, energy and ruthlessness for an interloper to exist in the middle of a wild country of bogs, lakes and mountains, surrounded by despoiled and revengeful natives. Every morning Ebenezer Lynch must have wondered, as he rose from his bed, if he would be alive at sunset, and every night, when he went to bed, if he would be murdered in his sleep. But perhaps this hardy soldier of fortune never thought of such things at all and in that lay his strength. At any rate he survived and founded a fine family (six sons and five daughters).

In a generation or two the Lynchs became acclimatised, absorbed into their adopted land by that strange process already alluded to. Ireland seeped into their bones; the sharp edges of their energy and ruthlessness wore off. They became "Irish", that is to say easy-going, open-handed, improvident and impatient of authority. They were still tenacious of their own rights, but it was social aggrandisement that they now coveted. The acquisition of Cabra

House in the early eighteenth century was a distinct lift up for them, raising them, in their own estimation at least, above the category of "half-mounted gentlemen". For one thing, Cabra House was larger and had more land attached to it than their ramshackle dwelling in Joyce's Country. For another thing they were strangers in County Waterford and could hope to be accepted at their own valuation.

Jonathan, the elder son of Luke Lynch, had all the tastes of the gentry, a passion for hunting, horse-racing and sport in general, gambling and duelling (he had "smelt powder" before he was seventeen and was a duellist of some renown by the time that he was thirty). He could carry his wine like a gentleman, having "made his head", as the phrase went, when he was young, and he had an aptitude for the boisterous practical jokes fashionable at that period.

In person he was extremely handsome with a fine figure and an easy swaggering air, and was known to the day of his death as "Beau" Lynch. In character he was good-humoured as long as his will was not crossed, hot-tempered when opposed, generous in a rather ostentatious way, boastful and extravagant. When he had money he immediately spent it. When he was short of money he ran up more debts. This was his idea of maintaining his position as a gentleman. No notion of attempting to improve the miserable condition of his tenants ever entered his head—he would have considered it mere moonshine—but when he was in the mood he could be very kind to an individual peasant, and there was always a drink of milk or a bowl of potatoes in the kitchen of Cabra House for a beggar.

Looks and manner count for a good deal in Ireland. A fine upstanding man, a lovely woman and a good horse will never be without their admirers in that country. Jonathan Lynch's handsome air and bantering, familiar ways gave him a certain popularity among the country people. They were proud of his exploits on horseback and with sword and firearms, and greeted him when he rode round the neighbourhood with more genuine pleasure than they might have felt if he had been the most estimable of "improving" landlords.

Jonathan had a less personable and sophisticated version of himself in the person of his younger brother Oliver. There was no reason why Oliver, who was perfectly healthy and fairly intelligent, should not have supported himself, except that he was too lazy to study for a profession and too pretentious to enter a trade. As one of the Lynchs of Cabra he considered that he had the right to live the life of a country gentleman, and so he remained on at Cabra House, even after Jonathan's marriage, hunting and drinking and borrowing money off his tolerant elder brother—a loud-voiced person, always dressed in buckskin breeches and riding boots.

It was probably Jonathan's fine looks and his reputation as a buck that gave him the opportunity to marry somewhat above him. His wife, Hester Pinkerton, niece of the Earl of Kilrush, was a striking young woman whose relations expected her to do better than to throw herself away on a spendthrift squireen. If Hester, who had been brought up in fashionable circles in Dublin, regretted the decision which made her the wife of "Beau" Lynch with his debts and his duels and his drinking, and the mistress of a shabby house on a remote headland in the south of Ireland, she was not the woman to admit it. The head-strong vitality which had enabled her to marry Jonathan Lynch in the teeth of her relations' disapproval, carried her more or less triumphantly through the vicissitudes of her married life.

A friend of her girlhood, visiting her at Ardnabannagh, comments in a letter on her changed appearance. She had become portly, and careless in her dress ("wearing her fine diamonds of a morning with the horridest looking old

16

powder mantle or dressing jacket with an effect which you may readily imagine"). But with her well-bred features and piercing dark eyes she must always have been an imposing-looking figure, even in an old powder mantle.

Though the friend was devoutly thankful to be conveyed away from Cabra House and its gales in a springless farm cart with a mattress in it (the roads round there being impassable for any other kind of vehicle) there is no evidence that Hester Lynch wished that she were going with her. Jonathan Lynch's looks and facile, boisterous charm may never have palled on her. And then she had her daughters.

Three girls (and a stillborn son) were born to Jonathan and Hester Lynch—Dorothea in 1750, Jane, always known as Jenny, in 1751, and two years later another daughter, Laetitia.

Dorothea and Jenny from their earliest childhood gave promise of that remarkable beauty that has given a lasting fragrance to their names. Laetitia the youngest was an idiot.

The cruelty of fate in dealing so bountifully with the two elder sisters and in withholding from the third even the gift of reason, might well have filled their mother with the most bitter sadness. Mrs Lynch, one suspects, was a woman of more sense than feeling. She accepted Laetitia —known in the locality as "little Miss Tishie"—as a life-long burden, made the best of her—she was tiny, wafty, twittering and quite harmless—kept her well fed and clothed, and concentrated her energies and hopes upon her creditable children.

The two elder sisters, though so close in age, were strikingly dissimilar in appearance and character—it was said of them later that they had nothing in common but beauty, their love for one another and their brogue—and it was this perhaps, taken in conjunction with their many undeniable graces, that may account for the extraordinary impression which they made on their contemporaries.

Dorothea, even as a gawky young girl (her proud father alludes to her as "my long-legged, golden filly") had a certain air of composure, which later was to develop into that dignity that made her one of the most queenly-looking women of her time. The dark-haired Jenny must have been as enchanting as a child and girl as she was as a woman; her wonderful sea-blue eyes with their "eyelashes a yard long" were no doubt busy with their work of bewitching all around her before she could speak plainly.

No wonder that Mrs Lynch, occupied in rearing her two treasures amid the harsh airs of Ardnabannagh, and watching their development with delight and wonder, could afford to ignore the patronising pity of her fashionable friends, and could even bear with fortitude the vacant stares and senseless chatterings of the idiot Tishie.

Jonathan Lynch may have been disappointed at having no son, but he was inordinately proud of his lovely daughters. He taught them to be fearless riders, to be able to doctor a sick animal and to enjoy a bawdy joke. Here his contribution to their upbringing ended.

Mrs Lynch knew better what the education of young ladies of good family entailed, and it fretted her sorely that she was not able to give her daughters all the advantages that they deserved. She taught them to embroider and to dance, and gave them a smattering of French which was not to stand them in very good stead in later life (Jenny's incurable malaprops in this and her own language were a source of derisive amusement to her aristocratic friends).

Their book learning was imparted to them by one, Bat O'Hallohan, a local hedge-schoolmaster. When he was not teaching his ragged, barefooted peasant scholars in a barn or, in fine weather, under the shelter of a hedge, Bat, dressed in his rusty black coat and breeches and stockings of homespun sheep's wool, toiled up the hill to Cabra House to instruct the young ladies in "reading, spelling,

18

writing, arithmetic, book-keeping, geography, use of the globes, natural and moral philosophy, divinity, geology, classics, the manners and customs of the ancient Romans and Greeks, prosody composition in English, Irish, Latin and Greek and a small taste of Hebrew" (for these were some of the subjects that Bat claimed to teach).

The result of this wealth of instruction, as far as the Miss Lynchs were concerned, was briefly as follows: Dorothea spent her whole life trying to conceal and improve the deficiencies in her education, while the frivolous Jenny never even learnt to spell.

Bat, who was a pompous, long-winded person with a keen sense of his own importance, fostered by the exaggerated respect paid by the peasantry to his supposed learning, was sadly tried by his lively young pupils. To think out new ways of teasing him was their chief form of home-work, Jenny being the main instigator of the plots against his dignity and peace of mind, with Dolly abetting her in more sedate enjoyment. Bat, goaded beyond endurance, would break into a flood of Gaelic oaths and even brandish his blackthorn stick at his pupils, who would sit before him, blonde and dark heads bowed in mock repentance, looking as innocent as the angels themselves in their white muslin gowns. The moment that Bat had left the room they sprang up laughing and chattering and, flinging their books to one side, ran out into the open air, and perhaps Bat, as he trudged away down the steep muddy lane, would glance back and see them standing there on the cliffs, linked arm in arm, no doubt giggling at his recent discomfiture, the sea wind tossing the fair and the dark curls about their faces, and whipping their skirts round their long legs—bad luck take the bold, unbiddable girls!

Yet when Bat was a very old man, the memory of his hoydenish pupils stirred a latent strain of poetry in his pedantic mind, and he wrote some verses on "My Countrywomen the Notable, the most Exquisite and Bright Miss

Lynchs of Cabragena House" which, in spite of the high-flown and stilted phraseology, bring us across the years a far-away gleam of the radiance of their youth.

A more important influence than Bat on the girls was their foster-mother and nurse, Kathie McCarthy. She was the wife of a cottier and the mother of nine upstanding sons. The two youngest had conveniently arrived at the same time as Mrs Lynch's elder daughters, and Kathie McCarthy had been honoured to extend to the young ladies the bountiful hospitality of her breasts. She worshipped them ever after, and put down Miss Tishie's sad condition to the fact that she had not been able to foster her.

When her husband died she handed over her own family to the care of a sister, and came to live at Cabra House as the little Misses' nurse. She was a big-boned woman, with the shrewd, kindly blue eyes of the Irish peasant; her lap was a haven of refuge from childish troubles; her soft lilting voice was the perfect lullaby. She was full of talk and blessings and lively observations. She knew everything that was happening in the neighbourhood almost before it happened, and when Kathie dressed herself up in her best quilted petticoat and her two hooded cloaks, the inner one of fine blue cloth and the outer one of black broadcloth, and went off to a wedding or wake or to visit her children, the Lynchs knew that before morning they would be cognisant with all the matchmaking, births, deaths and quarrels of the countryside.

Dorothea and Jenny, though they did not know it, really loved Kathie better than their mother, in the sense that they were happier and more comfortable with her. Kathie was the link between them and native Ireland. From Kathie they imbibed a number of superstitions from which they were never able wholly to free themselves. Even Dorothea, with her good sense and dignity, once caused a sensation at a private supper-party at Versailles by springing up and blowing out one of the three candles burning on the royal supper table. Her apologies and blushing explanations (were not three candles a portent of death?) were graciously received, but there were raised eyebrows and smiles at the eccentricity of "La Belle Anglaise".

Kathie's supernatural acquaintances were as numerous as her earthly ones. On stormy winter nights she told the girls about the "little people", and could say for a certainty which thorn trees in the neighbourhood were the scenes of their midnight revels, about banshees and the Leprechaun, magic bulls and horses that haunted the mountain lakes, and fairy cities to be seen at sunset on the western rim of the Atlantic. She also told them about the ghosts of Cabra House, so that when the girls went to bed the familiar house seemed to take on a strange and alarming aspect, the dark passages were full of queer rustlings and creakings, they hardly dared look in their mirrors for fear of what they might see in the shadows behind them, and went to sleep snuggling against each other in delicious terror.

Kathie was a natural sick-nurse; she also believed in a variety of charms and superstitions relating to the healing art. There was nothing like crushed snails, in her estimation, as a remedy for bruises; certain herbs gathered by moonlight in the name of the Holy Trinity were most efficacious against disease; she always had a philtre of holy water from St Declan's well handy in case of emergencies (it was said to ward off evil spirits, sickness and misfortune), for the fact that the family she served were Protestants did not worry her in the least.

St Declan's feast day—July 24th—was a great occasion every year for Ardmore and its neighbourhood. St Declan, who lived before St Patrick, landed at Ardmore and built a round tower and a church there in a single night, thus establishing himself beyond dispute as the patron saint of the locality. His grave and a massive lump of rock on the seashore (said to have swum all the way from Rome with vestments for the saint, a lighted candle and a bell for his tower), also a holy well, attracted a crowd of pilgrims every summer.

There were the remains of two churches in this spot— one, completely in ruins and perhaps the first to be built, was on the edge of a cliff near St Declan's stone; the other up on the hillside was in a more interesting state of preservation. The remains of figures in high relief, representing Adam and Eve, the judgment of Solomon between the two harlots, and other Old Testament scenes are still to be seen on the West end of the church; in the eighteenth century the chancel of the church was roofed over and used for Mass on occasions such as this. Near by is the beautiful round tower.

For several days before the pattern (or pardon) tents and booths were set up in this holy spot, casks of whisky and beer arrived, for the pilgrims were a thirsty lot. The old hag who did the honours of St Declan's grave took up her position in it, where she slept and ate till the pattern was over, rather than risk losing such a lucrative post.

As the morning of the feast day dawned, the mile between the two churches swarmed with people as though an anthill had been disturbed. This much the Miss Lynchs could observe from the headland of Ardnabannagh, but further acquaintance with the delights of the pattern was rigorously denied them by their mother and even by the indulgent Kathie, who would have been horrified at the thought of her refined nurslings mingling with the praying, jigging, drinking, fighting and largely unwashed mob of pilgrims.

One year when the sisters were fifteen and fourteen years old they determined to see the fun and, disguising themselves in the coarse red flannel petticoats and hooded cloaks of country girls, slipped out of the house and ran down towards the shore, taking off their shoes and stockings and hiding them under a hedge before joining the crowd.

The scene in which they found themselves was one of great excitement, fervour and hilarity. The calm evening air jangled with a variety of noises. There was a loud, continuous gabbling as the devout counted the beads of their rosaries or threw pebbles from one hand to another to record the number of their prayers; beggars whined and displayed revolting deformities, other voices were raised in lively badinage and dispute, sellers of drink and food bawled their wares, the enticing music of a jig wooed the young people to dance.

Dorothea and Jenny, all astonishment and glee, made their way to the strand where hundreds of believers were kneeling round the Holy Stone, crawling round it on their bare knees, under it on their bellies (a feat only possible at low tide), kissing it, bumping their backs three times against it, and holding babies and children in arms up to it. Dorothea (so she relates in her private memoirs) would have been content to have watched these rites, but Jenny insisted on participating in them and, throwing herself on her face, wriggled swiftly under the stone. Dorothea followed her, but being larger and less agile, and perhaps being suddenly assailed by thoughts of Mrs Lynch, stuck half-way and lay panting on her stomach, Jenny, in peals of laughter, pushing her from behind. She was dragged out at last by friendly hands, amid cries of "Glory be to God! she's through!"

Both Dolly's and Jenny's hoods had fallen back during these contortions. Their looks, even at this immature age and in these rough peasant clothes, were remarkable, and attracted as much attention now as they were to do in later years when set off by powder, rouge and the finest of jewels and satins. They became aware of curious stares and, suddenly shy, pulled their hoods over their faces, pushed their way out of the crowd and slipped away up the hill to see the grave.

Here another crowd knelt in postures of utter abasement, waiting their turn to be let into the little dormitory over the grave where the old woman sold the miraculous clay

23

and displayed a skull said to be that of the saint himself. She was a horrible figure, so emaciated as to look hardly human and, only half of her appearing above ground, she seemed to the girls like a resurrected corpse. Her tongue, however, was animated enough. She kept up a continuous patter, extolling the merits of the clay and recommending her clients to take a piece of it and eat it with faith as it would afford them protection against fairies, fire and drowning.

Dorothea, fixing her candid blue eyes on her, asked her politely how it was that the supply of clay never came to an end, as the sides and bottom of the grave were of solid rock. A malevolent glare was her answer, and the old woman was showing the skull to a devotee when Jenny asked pertly if it was true that the original skull had been sent to a silversmith in Youghal who, having dropped and broken it, had replaced it with a new one. This question drew down such scandalised and disagreeable looks upon the sisters that they thought it best to edge their way hurriedly out of the throng.

While they were looking round wondering what next to do, an old woman, bent double and wrapped in a filthy ragged cloak, seized their hands and, calling down blessings on their sweet faces, offered to tell their fortunes. Dorothea drew back—her more serious turn of mind gave her a kind of awe of the future—but Jenny, flippant, gay and already, in a childish way, confident that her powers of fascination would bring her everything that she desired, accepted the offer eagerly.

The crone, without troubling to look at their palms, assured them that they would both make grand marriages before they were many years older and would wear coronets on their brows. The dark girl, she said, would be loved without loving and would be starved of love at her ending. The fair girl would love without being loved and would be rich in love at the end. The dark girl would break her own heart and the fair girl would make her own

24

soul, and their names would be remembered long after the house of their birth lay in ruins.

All this, except the part about making grand marriages (how their eyes must have met in startled delight), seemed like nonsense to the sisters, but they thanked the old woman and giving her a coin received the customary blessing, "May the Great King speed ye and the blessed Patrick go with ye." Then, for they were hungry, they stopped a man who was walking around with a boiled leg of mutton, crying out "A cut for a penny!", and bought a couple of slices off him.

Next they drew near a group of young people dancing a jig. They were both passionately fond of dancing. They were not old enough yet to appear at balls, and envied their mother's maid-servants who footed it on summer evenings at the cross-roads. A wistful glance must have passed between them now. The more decorous Dorothea hung back, but Jenny, small foot tapping, eyes gleaming between the long lashes, urged her forward. ("Where other women danced with their bodies my sister Jenny seemed to dance with her whole soul" remarks Dorothea.) The magic of the jig was too much for them. They joined the young people—girls in one line arms akimbo, boys opposite with arms hanging loosely by their sides, feet tapping out the tantalising measure, eyes beckoning to eyes across the dividing space. The sisters were to dance in Dublin, in all the grandest ballrooms of London, at St James's and Versailles, but did ever any dance music thrill their young hearts like the wild, unappeasable music of the jig that summer's evening at Ardmore? There are moments, trivial in themselves, that are so intensely felt, that they live in the memory as long as life itself.

The fiddles ceased; the dancing youngsters, flushed and sweating, strolled away together, arms round waists, whispering and giggling. Overhead the evening sky was clear as water, a star hung low on the horizon, but here in the dusky fields the noise and confusion was unbelievable. Drunken men reeled out of the boozing and gaming tents to sprawl on the ground, or join in one of the faction fights which always sprung up at these affairs. Cause for offence, quickly followed by blows, was easily found when nearly everyone "had drink taken", but if a fight did not develop naturally it was quite usual to see a hefty fellow strutting about with a spare trusty (or grey woollen cloak) trailing over his shoulders, shouting: "Touch that by Jasus if you dare!"

Dorothea and Jenny were suddenly scared, conscious, rather late in the day, of their gentility and of the impropriety of their being alone in the middle of this jostling, rowdy mob. How unaccountable the peasants were—soft-spoken and respectful to your face, knowing their place, and yet with a pleasant natural dignity of their own, but when you saw them thus, fighting, drunken, cursing, praying with an abandon that was never seen at Protestant devotions, you realised how untamed they were, half-savages, wildly gay and despairingly melancholy, alien—or, disconcerting thought! were you the alien in a sullen, hostile country?

There were shrieks of "Fire!" A couple of cabins were blazing fiercely. Half-naked children rushed out of them screaming. Men and women ran to and fro. The old guardian of the grave, with remarkable presence of mind, scattered handfuls of clay on the ground safely out of reach of the fire, in order to demonstrate its miraculous powers.

Dolly and Jenny, clutching each other's hands, ran like frightened fowl, but wherever they turned they were blocked by the crowd. A hand caught Dorothea's elbow and a voice asked, "Miss Dolly! what are you and Miss Jenny doing here?"

Dorothea looked up and saw to her relief her foster-brother, Conn McCarthy, regarding her with shocked eyes. He was a finely-built lad, tall and broad-shouldered even at fifteen, whose appearance Dorothea has recorded in some detail. She says frankly that he was the most beautiful youth that she ever saw. He evidently had that air of noble distinction sometimes achieved by the Irish peasant. His finely chiselled features would have graced a prince, his black eyebrows met above amber-coloured eyes as mournful as a dog's between their long straight lashes. Dorothea, ashamed, asked him how he had recognised her. "By the whiteness of ye two bare feet, Miss Dolly" he replied.

Dorothea remembered his answer all those years, and so it may be concluded that she recognised, with the half-amused, half-wistful indulgence of the older woman for the vanished emotions of her girlhood, that she had felt for Conn McCarthy the first intimations of love. But at the time she would never have allowed such a thought to enter her mind. She was Miss Lynch of Cabra House and a young lady of her quality (for Mrs Lynch had brought her daughters up with some idea of their own consequence) did not fall in love with a young fisherman, even if he was her foster-brother and descended (according to Kathie) from the old kings of Ireland.

She was very thankful all the same for his protection as he shepherded her and Jenny out of the mob and, suddenly ashamed of her prank, hoped that she had not lowered herself in his good opinion, for Conn McCarthy was a grave and seemly lad. She was too proud to ask him to keep silence about the escapade. Jenny, who had no such scruples, had soon extracted a promise from him that he would not say a word to his mother or to anyone else.

As they climbed the hill to the headland of Ardna-bannagh the turmoil below them died away to a confused murmur. The moon had risen (Dorothea remembered vividly many details of that night—was it because of the old woman's prophecy, so strangely to be fulfilled, or because of some unavowed thoughts of Conn?). An ashy

27

radiance bathed the formidable cliffs; the sea was silvered and scaley with moonbeams. Cabra House must have looked dark and unpleasant, embowered in its stunted, tormented trees, against that cold and lifeless brightness. But probably no thoughts of its gloomy associations depressed Dorothea's and Jenny's spirits, only the fear of being discovered as they crept up to their room.

Of course their misdemeanour was found out—though Conn kept faithful silence. Dorothea's incapacity for subterfuge and Jenny's imprudence was the worst possible combination for such an adventure. Mrs Lynch was outraged; even Kathie's eyes looked stormy. The girls were locked into their room and kept on bread and water for a day. Mrs Lynch, who knew her own weakness where her daughters were concerned, sent their father up to them with strict injunctions to chastise them with a hunting crop.

Dorothea does not say exactly what happened—(how could you describe with pen and ink the witchery of Jenny's eyes?) but when Mrs Lynch came up with smelling-salts and lavender water to administer comfort to her penitent daughters, she found them both sitting on their father's knees, listening with rapture to his description of the fine ball that he meant to give at Cabra House for their début.

CHAPTER III

HARD TIMES

THE MOTHERS of beautiful daughters have satisfactions but also anxieties unknown to the parents of less remarkable-looking girls. The delicate contours of cheek and chin, the velvet bloom of the skin and starry gaze cannot

28

fail to arouse in the maternal mind hopes that life will pay her darling a bonus of happiness and success. But these physical allurements may bring dangers and temptations too, unless she has managed to inculcate into her daughter an extra allowance of stability and common sense. The lovely one stands like a young deer on the edge of the world's wild forest. Her comeliness invites pursuit; she may run headlong into disaster; she may be trapped too young by an importunate suitor into an indifferent marriage or, dazzled by her own vanity, delay too long and miss the cosy domestic happiness achieved by her less personable friends.

As it became obvious to Mrs Lynch that her two elder daughters were going to be not merely pretty but conspicuously beautiful, she became much concerned for their future. This is indicated by letters which she wrote at this time to Lady Kilrush, who seems to have kept up a desultory correspondence with her husband's first cousin. It is clear that Mrs Lynch is trying to interest her influential relation in her young daughters:

"I hope that I may be absolved from improper pride when I say that I do not believe you could find a prettier pair of young misses in the length and breadth of Waterford than my Dolly and Jenny. Dolly at 16 has an air and a carriage which would not disgrace a woman of fashion and yet with the look of perfect modesty and bashfulness proper to her age. She has the fine white and pink bloom of the Lynchs in her cheeks, hair fair, nose pretty good like my mother's. Her good understanding and quick, steady sense, and the best temper in the world, should make her an excellent wife for any man. But I believe most people will reckon Jenny the greater beauty of the two, for she unites a darkness of hair and brows with a whiteness of skin not often to be seen, and has a thousand prettinesses in her eyes and face which may prove very captivating. Her manners are less prudent than her

29

sister's, but she has a warm heart and is greatly disposed to love those who show her any kindness."

In a later letter she laments that her remote situation and circumstances will prevent her from giving her daughters, when they grow up, all the social advantages that she would wish for them, "so the poor girls must be satisfied to be admired by seagulls and curlews" she concludes, "and find their happiness and contentment in their affection for one another and for their parents, and in peaceful domestic occupations." Both the humour and the resignation are strained.

It does not appear what impression Mrs Lynch's panegyrics of her daughters' excellencies made on Lady Kilrush, or her thinly-veiled hints that she should take some notice of them. When the names of the beautiful Miss Lynchs were on everyone's lips, Lady Kilrush was very ready to own them as cousins, in fact to claim that she had "discovered" them, but meanwhile the hoped-for invitation to Dublin did not materialise.

Mrs Lynch had exaggerated when she suggested that her daughters led a life of complete seclusion, at Ardnabannagh. Their father kept open house as far as the limitations of local society allowed, and the girls were as accustomed to the sound of tipsy laughter and convivial singing coming from the dining-room, as they were to the more romantic cries of those seagulls and curlews of which their mother made mention. So given to hospitality, in fact, was Jonathan Lynch that when he was unable to collect any of his cronies round him he rode out into the highway, and stopping any likely-looking traveller offered him supper and a bed at Cabra House. This was all very well for Jonathan and his brother Oliver. These chance encounters provided them with many sportive and riotous evenings (Jonathan had his decanters made round at the bottom so that, as the only stand for the decanter was at the head of the table, the guest had to

30

refill his glass at once and pass it on), but it did not seem to Mrs Lynch a very hopeful way of finding eligible husbands for her girls.

Admiration of a kind no doubt they would have in plenty when they were old enough to attend the military balls at Youghal, or any other gaieties afforded by the neighbourhood, but what were their chances of meeting marriageable men of any rank or consequence? Were they fated to marry local squireens, illiterate, loud-voiced boors in muddy hunting boots—these rare creatures whose like might not be seen again for a hundred years? For Mrs Lynch's description of her daughters in her letter to Lady Kilrush was studiously restrained; she was too intelligent and worldly-wise to make a fool of herself, and invite spiteful ridicule, by giving way in public to the rapturous amazement that her daughters' looks evoked in her. In a letter to Jenny, shortly after the latter's marriage, she reveals her true feelings: "If I shall meet Leda, mother of Helen of Troy, in the shades, I assure you that I shall not toady to her one whit, for she only had one surpassingly beautiful daughter. I have two!"

It was this duality of beauty that inspired Mrs Lynch with such pride and a yearning to display it to the admiration of the outside world, for she judged, rightly, that though her daughters, taken singly, might have rivals, together they would make a conquering effect. They seemed to have been born to display one another—the fair, stately Dorothea, the dark, coquettish Jenny. Dorothea's air of serenity, Jenny's light and wilful sweetness and changing moods. It was pleasant to see their mutual devotion—a devotion so deep and sincere that it struck the beholder at once though the sisters seldom kissed or fondled one another.

No wonder that Mrs Lynch brooded over these things as she sat with her family of an evening by the drawing-room fire—Jonathan and Oliver dozing after their heavy

31

supper and many glasses of port and brandy, Tishie tying scraps of ribbon and rags round her dolls (an occupation that was to afford her amusement even in extreme old age), her bird-like glance darting from one face to another, now and then breaking into a nervous, inconsequent titter—and the luxuriant blonde and dark curls of Dolly and Jenny close together as they bent over their needle-work, talking together in low confidential tones, sometimes giggling, their faces glowing like roses in the candlelight, a picture of girlish sweetness and grace. A silence would fall. The stentorian breathing of the men would mark the passing of time. The wind would howl, hostile and inconsolable round the house, rattling the windows, sending gusts of smoke down the chimney and draughts under the doors, and outside, muffled by the wind, but not more than a field's-length away, was the eternal, long drawn-out sob and sigh of the Atlantic rollers. At such moments Mrs Lynch must have known that feeling of defenceless nakedness that at times assails the bravest mother's heart, and wondered in hope and dread what life held for her darlings.

These hypothetical worries were soon to be engulfed, as so often happens in life, by more urgent and practical cares. Hard times were coming to Mrs Lynch and her daughters.

Jonathan Lynch, as already mentioned, had an easy way of disposing of financial difficulties. He never paid anything that he owed except his "debts of honour", in other words his gambling debts. Living as he did on a remote and lonely headland he could defy his creditors with impunity. His bonhomie did not extend to the rare process-servers who ventured to Ardnabannagh. In fact any attempt to serve him with a writ roused him to a fury of indignation and, as his detestation of officers of the law was fully shared by the local population, he could act in as high-handed a way as he pleased without any fear of the consequences.

Dorothea never forgot the alarming scene that took place one May afternoon, just before her seventeenth birthday, when a process-server arrived at Cabra House and tried to serve a writ on its master. Sounds resembling the bellows of an infuriated bull came from papa's study. Suddenly a little man rushed, like a hunted hare, into the drawing-room where the ladies were sewing and, throwing himself at Mrs Lynch's feet, implored her to save him from her husband who was threatening to shoot him and throw his body over the cliffs. Dolly and Jenny screamed, Tishie tittered. Mrs Lynch, with her usual presence of mind, seized him by the hand and, with a speed surprising in one of her portly figure, dragged him out of the room by the opposite door to the one by which Jonathan Lynch entered a moment later, gun in hand, shouting out that he would have the damned blackguard's life. So violent was his rage that he threw his elder daughters off roughly when they tried to put restraining hands on his arm. It was terrifying to them to see his handsome face transformed into a flushed and ugly mask. Nor would the assurances of Mrs Lynch, who had reappeared, that the man had escaped down the avenue, appease him. He stamped about round the place for at least half an hour searching for his victim, followed by the whooping Oliver and a mongrel pack of dogs.

By supper time he had recovered his good humour, and after his fourth bottle of claret was boasting to his brother and his women-folk of the fright he had given the impudent scoundrel.

At daybreak the next morning, Dorothea was startled at being awoken by her mother, a compelling figure even in a nightgown and nightcap, and told to get up at once and dress, as she was to escort the process-server, who had been hidden all this time in one of the towers, to safety. It seemed natural to Mrs Lynch to choose Dorothea for this task, not only because of her year's seniority, but because she could be relied upon to carry it out with discretion and dispatch.

The hunted man, dusty, dishevelled and abjectly frightened, was fetched out of his hiding-place, and Dorothea and he stole out of the house by a side door. Dorothea knew every yard of the way and led him unerringly along the precipitous path. Below them, even in the calm of this pearly summer dawn, could be heard the sullen murmur of the ground-swell. As they walked the man clung to the skirt of Dorothea's dress. This tall young girl with the golden hair and wide, steady blue eyes, seemed to him, in his present state of nerves, as blessedly reassuring as an angel. Could she really be the daughter of that murderous ruffian up at the house? When they were within sight of Ardmore, Dorothea said goodbye to him, and, hurrying back to the house, slipped back into bed beside the sleeping Jenny.

At the time the event seemed natural enough, if rather exciting, to Dorothea, but she never forgot it, and perhaps it was that strange walk along the cliffs at daybreak that first awoke in her an intense yearning for security and the beauty of an orderly and seemly life.

A few weeks after this episode a writ was served on "Beau" Lynch by a process-server who would not be denied. Lynch had gone up to Dublin on "business affairs", which with Jonathan Lynch was a way of saying that he wanted to gamble and drink with a fresh set of acquaintances. As he came out of Lucas's Coffee House he found his way blocked by a notable buck and duellist, Edward Molesworthy, known to his intimates as "Blue Blaze Devil Ned". This gentleman had so stationed himself that Jonathan Lynch was obliged either to jostle him or to walk in the mud. Lynch, his naturally quick temper inflamed with wine, pushed brusquely past him. Molesworthy immediately challenged him to a duel. Two friends offered themselves as seconds. The four men repaired to Phoenix Park, where a double engagement was fought (the seconds, after some hot words, deciding to fight a duel on their own account), during which Jonathan Lynch fell to the ground with a fatal wound in his chest. In a few seconds he was dead. "Blue Blaze Devil Ned" could add another to the many nicks which decorated his silver-mounted "barker" recording the number of opponents whom he had brought down in "self-defence", for so the majority of duels were designated by complaisant juries (many of whom were themselves enthusiastic duellists).

The body of Jonathan Lynch was brought back to Ardnabannagh for burial. No one can know the thoughts that passed through Hester Lynch's resolute mind as she kept watch in the darkened house by the coffin of the man who had been her husband and the lover of her youth. The tablet that she erected to his memory bears the conventional tributes to the deceased customary at that period—"A devoted husband and careful parent, a benevolent landlord . . . faithful friend . . . assiduous in his religious duties and all good works . . . in life much respected and in death sincerely lamented." The picture conjured up by these fulsome words does not bear the faintest resemblance to the swaggering, boastful, devil-may-care "Beau" Lynch whom we have learnt to know through more reliable sources. Probably it was not the recollection of his virtues, fancied or real, that agonised his widow, but the thought of some physical characteristic, some trick of raising his dark eyebrows, the fine bold line of his jaw, his rollicking laugh as he entered the house— these trivialities clutch with frightening tenacity at the bereaved heart.

Dorothea has left a description of her mother's silent grief, of the darkness and gloom of the mourning house, of Tishie's idiot bewilderment (her morbid interest in the details of the funeral—"What will poor Papa wear?"—

must have been a considerable trial to her mother and sisters), of Uncle Oliver drowning his sorrow in brandy and port, of her own and Jenny's feeling of astonished disbelief that their boisterous father who had petted them and romped with them had vanished from their lives.

Kathie, with her warm Celtic acceptance of death, was the only source of comfort in the shrouded, dismal house. Death to Kathie was as natural and, in its solemn way, as good a thing as birth and mating, to be received with tears but with a kind of exalted joyfulness too. Life without the supreme climax of death, the triumphant bursting of the soul into immortality would, after all, be a very dull affair.

Dorothea felt that the native wake, with its lamentations mingled with social pleasures, its gossiping, ghost stories and match-making going on in one room while next door the professional mourners raised the Irish cry or keen over the corpse, would have suited her father's roistering spirit much better than this muffled grieving, this frustrated sorrow expressing itself lugubriously in drawn curtains and mourning rings.

There was a gale the day of Jonathan Lynch's funeral. It seemed as if the wind was trying to sweep the house right off the headland. The Atlantic breakers broke thunderously against the savage rocks below, sending up clouds of spray into the air. Seagulls battled to and fro, their wild cries coming in torn snatches on the wind. The storm lasted all that day and continued unabated throughout the night. Dorothea and Jenny clung together in bed for comfort, forlorn and frightened. Everything that they knew of their home's sinister and unlucky tradition crowded into their minds, their father's untimely death giving it a new and terrifying meaning. It seemed to them that in taking possession of the home of the Kyles they had inherited the bad luck of that doomed family.

The next morning a perfect calm brooded over land and sea, as though nature was a woman exhausted but peaceful after childbirth. The sun shone hazily, the blue sea was as mild as milk. Only great masses of sea wrack thrown up on the rocks, high above the usual line, told of last night's turmoil. Life began again at Cabra House.

Practical considerations soon forced Mrs Lynch to rouse herself from her grief. Jonathan Lynch had left his affairs in a state of hopeless confusion. Money was owing on every side, and his death was the signal for his creditors to clamour for their dues. Mrs Lynch lived in dread that the sheriff's officers would penetrate to the seclusion of Ardnabannagh and take possession of her home. She and her daughters hardly dared put a foot outside the place for fear of meeting a creditor or a bailiff.

Mrs Lynch had few near relations, and those she had (an elderly aunt and a younger brother who was a clergyman, married, with thirteen children) were not in a position to help her. Her cousin Lord Kilrush was the only one of her relations able to afford her financial help, but she was determined, for reasons connected with her daughters' future, not to appear before the Kilrushes in the ignominious role of a suppliant.

She must have felt friendless and desolate indeed as day by day she sat in her late husband's study, surrounded by his sporting trophies, his duelling pistols and his swords, trying to bring some order into his papers, appalled by the rapidly mounting pile of unpaid bills. Her brother-in-law Oliver was useless to her in this emergency; he had all Jonathan's insouciant disregard of responsibility without his buoyant charm. His parasite life at Cabra had made him thoroughly selfish. As long as there was a horse to ride in the stables and a bottle of wine to drink in the cellars he was quite content.

To add to her difficulties Mrs Lynch was burdened with the large and, in this case pretentious, household, usual in Irish country houses. It had gratified Jonathan's vanity to see a quantity of retainers in the back premises and

37

hanging round the yard. As far as can be gathered from Dorothea's description of the "family", it consisted of a "butler" and a "footman" (the inverted commas are necessary for it appears that neither of these men-servants was of a very polished type, the butler "Neller the Black" being an amiable negro or half-caste whom Jonathan had found stranded on the docks at Waterford and had attached to himself as a personal servant, while the foot-man was only a country lad in livery), a cook (a barefooted kitchenmaid or two may be presumed), several raw girls who acted as housemaids, Jonathan's valet, a dairymaid, a laundrymaid, and of course the "gossoon", without whom no Irish household was complete, a small boy who was the slave of the upper servants and who ran on errands, barefoot, at incredible speed across the countryside. Kathie ruled over the indoor servants in the capacity of housekeeper and personal maid to Mrs Lynch and the girls. Out of doors there was a coachman, and a fluctuat-ing and quite unnecessary number of stable boys and gardeners.

None of these people received, or expected, large wages, but they had to be clothed and fed. Any attempt on the part of "Madam", as Mrs Lynch was called by the servants, to reduce her household would have been con-trary to the almost feudal tradition in which she had been reared, and which she had endeavoured to maintain at Cabra House. One servant dismissed would have spread dismay and dissatisfaction among the others. As every-body did a little of everybody else's work and preferred it to their own (in the manner of Irish servants), it seemed impossible to eliminate any one servant without disturbing the whole structure of the household. One person who might easily have been dispensed with was Jonathan's valet, but Oliver flatly refused to do without his services.

The servants realised and sympathised with Mrs Lynch's embarrassed circumstances and, with the instinctive good

38

breeding of their race, took no advantage of it (Dorothea records despairingly in her journal that some of the servants had not received wages for nearly a year), but it was impossible to make them realise the need for economy. A class of people who have never had to pay for their own household expenses cannot easily be persuaded to be careful with their employer's money. Everything had to go on as usual though credit had practically ceased, and ready money was more scarce than ever.

How Mrs Lynch managed during the first year of her widowhood to keep the family financially above water must remain a mystery. Oddly enough, money details are harder to salvage from the past than those most elusive things, motives and emotions. We read in the biography of, say, some famous poet, that he was reduced to his last five-pound note. Two chapters and six months later he is still alive, with no apparent means of support besides that fabulous five-pound note.

Mrs Lynch may have sold some of her jewellery or her horses, she may have borrowed from friends or money-lenders. All that is clear is that the family passed through a period of harassing and sordid worry.

Dorothea, proud and reserved, suffered intensely from the dreary shifts that insolvency, and particularly indebtedness, must entail. She was never greatly interested in clothes (though she afterwards gained the reputation of being one of the most superbly dressed women of her day, she used to say that clothes were a matter of concern for ladies' maids and milliners) and her personal vanity was small, so it is unlikely that she minded the patching and turning and darning, the denials of little luxuries and adornments, that made Jenny flare up rebelliously, but she admits that she was sorely fretted by the disorder of their daily life.

Surprisingly enough it was Jenny, capricious, vain and pleasure-loving, who was the chief solace of her family during these difficult months. It is probable that it was Dorothea (though she does not say so) who helped her mother to disentangle her father's papers, and who tried to bring some order into the shabby confusion of the household. But we have Dorothea's assurance that it was Jenny who provided what laughter and gaiety there was in their family life. "Even in a patched muslin she was the most sprightly and the prettiest thing you ever saw," says Dorothea, trying to record in bare words that youthful radiance of looks and spirits.

Debts and unpaid wages, shabby furniture, leaking roofs and darned clothes had no power to depress Jenny for more than a few moments: not because of any hidden reserves of strength in her character—alas! poor Jenny she had none—but because she skimmed light as a dragon-fly over the surface of life, and because her naïve vanity gave her an almost unbounded confidence in her destiny. She would throw a darned dress on the floor, declaring that she would as soon go naked as wear such a shabby old thing; a few moments later she had found a rose or a ribbon to put in her hair and, gazing into the mirror, would be all aglow at the sight of her own beauty.

Dorothea confesses frankly that she found Tishie almost unbearably trying. It required all her self-control to enable her to show her idiot sister the steady kindness and patience which her lamentable condition demanded. She pitied her deeply, and the effect of this pity on her self-contained nature was to produce a kind of irritable revulsion against its object. She managed to conceal her feelings, but it was a daily effort and, with her usual honesty, she admitted to herself her failure. Jenny, on the other hand, with the effortless sympathy and sweetness that was one of her greatest charms, was prodigal of little attentions to Tishie, would dress her dolls for her, answer her meaningless questions and assure her solemnly of her belief in Protestant doctrines (a subject on which Tishie's

wandering wits showed unexpected and surprising concentration).

There are strange contrasts in the scene at Cabra House
at this time—the stout, harassed mother sitting in the dark
study brooding over legal documents and her children's
future, the sodden Oliver bragging interminably of the
gay times that he and Jonathan had had together when
they were young buckeens, poor little idiot Tishie and her
dolls, the feeling of oppression and loneliness accentuated
by the gloom of the house and the bleakness of the windy
landscape outside and, moving against this depressing
background, the bright figures of two young creatures,
lovely in their shabby black dresses, brimming over even
in their boredom and solitude with the unquenchable
hopefulness of youth.

About a year after Jonathan's death there was a
marked improvement in the circumstances of the family
at Cabra House. The girls, their mourning ended,
astonished their neighbours by appearing in stylish silks
and muslins, ribbons and laces that had the look of being
not only new but of the most expensive quality. Neller
the Black was seen in Youghal on his weekly shopping
expeditions buying lavishly for the household, and wearing
a new suit of clothes, his black face beaming with childish
gratification. Most wonderful portent of all, several of
Mrs Lynch's most pressing creditors received payment.

Mrs Lynch let it be known among the county ladies
that she had stocks of brocade, taffetas, paduasoys and
other materials, as well as a choice selection of ribbons and
lace, over and above what her daughters required for their
adornment and, as a great favour, was ready to dispose of
them to her friends. It became quite a usual habit among
Mrs Lynch's neighbours to send a servant to Cabra House
when they had a daughter's wedding, or some other festive
occasion impending, with a request for a length of material
or some other piece of finery from Mrs Lynch's "magic

store chest". So one lady tactfully alludes to Mrs Lynch's mysterious source of supply. Naturally gossip was busy on the subject. The nature of the goods—all contraband— and the peculiar situation of Cabra House made it obvious to everyone that Mrs Lynch had dealings with the smugglers.

Smuggling might almost be said to be one of Ireland's most flourishing industries at this date. Several respectable and even titled families owed their prosperity to the illegal importation of claret, madeira and fine silks. British cruisers patrolled the southern and western coasts but were not able to do more than hamper the illicit trade. Ships continued to slip to and fro from France to Ireland. Most of the country people were in sympathy, and many in active league, with the smugglers (even clergymen were known to buy smuggled goods) and every possible device was resorted to in order to outwit the revenue officers.

When Kathie conveyed to her mistress that her son Conn was working with a gang of smugglers, and that his friends would be glad to recompense the Madam for any assistance she might give them, Mrs Lynch did not hesitate to accept the offer. She had often deplored the lonely and exposed situation of Cabra House; now she could derive some benefit from it and ease the situation a little for herself and daughters.

Kathie, who knew everything, was always able to keep Madam informed of the movements of the revenue officers and their men. When the coast was clear and the slow summer dusk had deepened into night, Dorothea or Jenny would go to a window in one of the narrow towers, and hold up a lighted lantern as a signal to the boat which lay in wait out on the dark waters.

To the men watching out there in the boat in the silence of the summer's night, broken only by the lapping of the water against the boat's sides and the sound of their own lowered voices, that light suddenly appearing high up on the headland was a welcome release from tension, a sign that they could land their dangerous goods in safety. It may be guessed that to one of them, Conn McCarthy, that grave and handsome boy, it meant something more, that with a strange lifting of his heart he wondered each time if it was his foster-sister the golden Miss Dolly who stood there shining the light out across the sea.

"My foster brother Conn McCarthy had the highest esteem and, I may say, a most respectful devotion for me", Dorothea writes with careful propriety and dignity. "He assured me, and I believe it to be true, that he would have been very happy to have laid down his life for me." Conn's "esteem" seems to have been carried to unusual lengths. A few pages further on it is manifested in an even more remarkable way. "Conn told me, in the picturesque language typical of the Irish peasantry, that when he saw my light at the window he knew how the blessed dead felt when they approached the gates of heaven. Of course", she notes, "it was often my sister Jenny who held the light but in Conn's imagination it seemed to be always me."

Up at Cabra House Mrs Lynch and her elder daughters were busy in the cavernous kitchen arranging eatables and drinks on the table. When all was prepared they set a light on the table, left the postern gate, which was the outside entrance of the kitchen, ajar, and going up the stairs locked the dividing door between the kitchen quarters and the rest of the house before retiring to their beds. In the very early morning, before any of the other servants were astir, Kathie came down to remove the traces of last night's meal. Food and drink were gone; in their place were packages containing a present of silk and lace—and sometimes a keg of foreign brandy as well.

Neither of the girls seem to have had the slightest qualms about this mode of living. This is not surprising in giddy Jenny, but even the more thoughtful Dorothea looked upon her mother's connection with the smugglers as proper and natural. She had been brought up by her father to regard the Government and authority in general with an impatient contempt that she was never to outgrow completely, and to which later, as one of the great Whig hostesses, she was able to give almost regal expression. Moreover, she was only eighteen, had grown apace during the last year, and it had hurt her proper pride to have to wear dresses that were too short at the hem and at the elbow. Anyhow her dear Jenny's rapturous delight, as the packages of illicit finery were unpacked, would have eased any prickings of conscience that Dorothea might have had.

This pleasant state of affairs came to an abrupt end one night in October when the revenue officers, with a guard of soldiers, descended on Cabra House and informed Mrs Lynch that signalling lights had been observed from the windows of her house, and that in consequence she and her household were under suspicion of being in league with the smugglers.

Mrs Lynch must have been a picture of widowed pathos as she faced the officers of the law, her arms protectively round her two lovely young daughters, her idiot child clutching at her skirts. With calm dignity she asked them if they seriously accused her, Mrs Lynch of Cabra House, of being the friend of smugglers. Confronted with this direct question and the look in her piercing dark eyes, the revenue officers yielded ground. They assured her that such an idea had never occurred to them, but that they could not feel so satisfied about her household.

Mrs Lynch immediately summoned her sleepy servants to her and, in front of the revenue officers, gave them a very edifying lecture on the iniquities of smuggling, warning them that anyone in her service who had truck with such people would be dismissed immediately. Meanwhile the sight of so many strange faces had sent Tishie into one of her fits of inane tittering. This gave Dorothea,

44

who had already received an urgent look from her mother, the excuse to lead her sister from the hall. Once out of sight she bundled her unceremoniously into a bedroom, locked the door on her, and hurried down the back stairs to warn the smugglers who at that very moment were coming to the house for their usual meal.

She found Conn McCarthy, who had come ahead of the others, standing in the kitchen. She warned him of the danger and urged him to escape at once. But he stood and gazed at her as though unable to move. "He would not go, in spite of my earnest entreaties, but stood looking at me as if he understood that this was to be his last sight of me."

How strange a setting it was, that dark and squalid kitchen, for this parting between two beautiful young creatures who were physically so suited to love one another, but were irrevocably divided by every consideration of birth, race and religion. The lighted candle that Dorothea held in her hand must have illuminated her golden hair and fair skin with a soft radiance, her candid blue eyes must have shone with a tenderness which she dared not admit to herself. As for Conn: "He was the most beautiful and indeed noble looking young man that I ever saw or ever hope to see."

She urged him again, with tears, to leave her. Did he hold her for a moment in his arms, laying her head against his shoulder, and kiss her gentle mouth, his ardour and longing hidden with pathetic clumsiness beneath a foster-brother's kindness? It would seem so, for those few minutes in the kitchen of Cabra House were imprinted unforgettably on Dorothea's memory.

He was gone and she was left (she admits) weeping. Unlike Jenny who was easily moved to laughter or tears, Dorothea cried seldom, never in public, and only in moments of deep emotion.

Next day she learnt that Conn and his companions had

45

been seized by a press-gang who, working in conjunction with the excise men, had been lying in wait for the smugglers, and had attacked and overpowered them as they tried to put off in their boat.

Kathie's grief at this calamity was as bitter as though her son had died, in fact possibly more bitter. It seemed to her that, in being removed in this violent way from his home, he was as lost to her as though he were dead, while, to her simple mind, the dangers and hardships to which he would be exposed in his new life were more appalling than the pains of purgatory, a belief to which living conditions in the Navy at the period lent some support.

Dorothea, with her restrained but tender heart, must have suffered considerably at this time. First love is none the less agonising for being unacknowledged. To the mature judgment, calloused by contact with life, the anguish of young love seems out of all proportion to reality. The memory of middle-age looking back cannot recapture its raptures or torments, can only marvel at emotions that were so fresh, so foolish and so piercingly alive.

To the family at Cabra as a whole this break-up of the smugglers' band was a disaster. The old problem of how to live from day to day, how to keep up the standard of gentility which, to Mrs Lynch's ideas, was scarcely less precious than life itself, returned with harassing force. Dorothea and Jenny were now eighteen and seventeen respectively, fully marriageable ages according to the ideas of the times. The sight of their rapidly unfolding beauty and charm must have filled Mrs Lynch with a feeling of desperate frustration. Were they to waste the fleeting days of their wonderful youth on the waves and gales of Ardnabannagh and on a few bucolic neighbours?

Dorothea was silent and grave since the disappearance of her foster-brother. Even Jenny's volatile spirits were subdued by the dismal and monotonous outlook. Mrs Lynch knew that the loveliest girls needed laughter,

46

gaiety, and above all admiration, if their bloom was to endure. Something must be done and without delay.

It was in the autumn of 1768 that Mrs Lynch took the bold decision which was to have a profound effect on the destinies of her elder daughters. She sold the rest of her jewellery, put Kathie in charge of Oliver and Tishie, and took Dorothea and Jenny to Dublin.

CHAPTER IV

DUBLIN

I

THERE ARE few cities where the outlines of the eighteenth century can be more easily discerned beneath the deposits of time than in Dublin. The light of the setting sun lends a soft glow, almost a bloom, to houses whose bricks have mellowed to the colour of claret. In the apricot haze of a winter's afternoon, or on a gusty spring day of blue sky and high racing clouds, nobly proportioned streets and squares take on the spacious yet minute aspect of an eighteenth century print. Modern eyes, accustomed to the shoddy and the tasteless, look with surprised delight on balconies of iron work as delicate as Spanish lace, each one different in design yet sinking their variety in an exquisite uniformity, on elegant spider-web fanlights and finely wrought lamp arches and bell-pulls adorning houses whose severe façades and tall windows are witness to the prosperous dignity of their long-dead owners. Even in the slums there is the crumbling beauty of old staircases, medallions and stucco ceilings.

It is night, the traffic is hushed; the timeless moon rising over the roof-tops invests the empty streets with mystery. Now from that dark passage-way a cloaked figure may swagger, there will be the rumble of distant coach wheels on the cobble-stones, the flare of links, the hurrying trot of the chairmen, the watchman's cry. . . . With a delicious, yearning pleasure that is half pain one deludes oneself fleetingly into the belief that lost time can be refound.

What is all this but a dream within a dream, the whisk of something glimpsed, or perhaps only imagined, out of the corner of one's eye, the reflection of a ghost seen in a mirror?

Who can imagine Dublin, all alive-oh, as it was in 1768 —the year that Dorothea and Jenny Lynch came to town? Dublin, noisy, gay, sad, splendid, stinking, busy, idle, luxurious, squalid—the reflection of all the myriad complex emotions and activities of its inhabitants.

There were the pestiferous fever-ridden quarters of the Liberties, as well as the stately, new-built houses of Merrion Square; garrets where starving human beings huddled together on heaps of verminous rags, as well as the spacious wainscoted halls where the chairmen waited while their patrons danced and gambled upstairs; the red-cheeked girl bawling, "Fresh herrings, large Dublin bay herrings alive here! Here's a large fresh Cod here, Here's large Soles and Plaices alive or fine Boyne salmon!" and the masked lady in french brocade applauding a concert in the Rotunda Gardens. The rich drank claret and port, and ate Turkey Pout and Crab Fricassée and Cheese Cakes and Plumb Crocart and strawberries and cream and a dozen other dishes all jumbled together in frightening juxtaposition (we must salute the digestions of our ancestors); the poor washed down their nauseous scraps with copious draughts of whisky. There was gambling, betting, drinking and gossip at Daly's and other resorts of the well-to-do, and betting, drinking and equally lively talk at the innumerable gin shops of the city.

There were routs and riots, elegant supper parties and ridottos, and bloody battles which lasted for days, to the terror and inconvenience of the respectable citizens, between the Ormond and the Liberty Boys, as the Butcher and Weavers were called. The statue of "King Billy" in College Green, symbol of the Protestant ascendancy, was honoured with feux-de-joie and parades by the loyalists, to be daubed at night by their opponents with pitch and grease. Duels were fought in the famous "Fifteen Acres" in Phoenix Park or in the fields behind Merrion Square, not only between reckless buckeens but between such staid personages as Chief Justices, Chancellors of the Exchequer and Provosts of Trinity. The streets were crowded with hackney coaches, private chariots, chairs, turf carts, and the jingles and noddys peculiar to the Irish capital. Beggars, whose language entertained or shocked English visitors according to temperament, swarmed round the coaches of members of the Viceregal Court. Bullies swaggered about the town ogling the women and picking quarrels with the men. There were many book-shops, a Society, patronised by the nobility and gentry, for the "improvement of husbandry, manufactures and other useful arts", and the famous theatres of Smock Alley and Crow Street. Life in Dublin was not dull in the 1760's.

It was no light matter to travel from England to Ireland in the mid-eighteenth century. A land journey of anything from four to six days over execrable roads, followed by a usually unpleasant and often alarming sea-crossing (the packet from Holyhead was sometimes blown back by contrary winds when within sight of Ireland and wrecked on the Welsh coast) was sufficient to give the traveller all the exciting sensations of one visiting a foreign country, and to induce the more prudent to make their wills before setting forth. But once in Dublin there were ample compensations for the discomforts and dangers of the journey. The capital had all the brilliance which a mimic Court, a

Parliament with two houses, justly famed for the eloquence and wit of its debaters, and a vigorous social and intellectual life could bestow. Entertaining, not only at the Castle but in the private houses of the nobility and the gentry, was on a lavish scale; conversation was volatile, intelligent and daring, and though inn accommodation was poor and the streets dirty and full of drunken people and beggars, food and wine at the ridottos and other public entertainments was considered to be even better than in London.

Only the more discerning of these English visitors realised that the apparent prosperity of Dublin was no criterion of the state of the rest of the country, where deep discontent, miserable poverty and civil disorder were rampant. Why indeed should they realise it when their hosts, for the most part, seemed so sublimely unaware?

The country was in the grip of a small oligarchy who owed no responsibility to anyone but the English ministry, with the inevitable result that Irish political life was rotten with bribery, corruption and place-hunting. It was said that everyone wanted pensions not only for himself but for his sisters, aunts and cousins.

It would be an injustice to imply that all members of the Ascendancy class were privy to this state of affairs. Many of them were genuinely concerned with the welfare of the country—it was in fact from the Anglo-Irish gentry that Irish national aspirations received their first impetus —and the more enlightened among them did much to promote the interests of literature, art and agriculture. But society on the whole was unaware of the gathering storm. Reckless extravagance and high living was the order of the day.

The Viceroy Lord Townshend had taken office in 1767, at a moment when the affairs of the country were in an even greater turmoil than ever, the grievances of the rack-rented and oppressed peasants finding savage expression in the activities of the "Peep o' Day Boys", "Hearts of Steel Boys", and other secret societies which roamed the countryside at night waging war against land-lords and tithe proctors, burning, robbing, maiming and murdering.

The new Viceroy had been sent over with the mission of bringing the Irish House of Commons to heel and of breaking the power of the "undertakers", or small clique of important landowners and borough proprietors who were the real rulers of the country, and who had become so powerful that they were able to dictate terms to each new lord-lieutenant.

A soldier with convivial manners and a nature that though coarse-fibred had the qualities of frankness and courage, it seemed as though Lord Townshend might become a popular Viceroy in the best sense of the word. Unfortunately his ignorance of civil administration soon landed him in serious difficulties, while his lack of dignity and decorum made him a rare butt for the lampooners.

He dissolved Parliament in May 1768 and threw himself with his usual impetuosity into the task of breaking the "undertakers", using for this purpose their own methods —creating several new peerages, and scattering places and pensions around with a lavish hand.

It is not to be supposed that any thoughts of politics troubled the pretty heads of Dolly and Jenny Lynch as, with their mother, and a raw country girl who was to act as lady's maid, they made the journey by post-chaise from Ardnabannagh to the capital. Nor would the frightful poverty of the countryside through which they journeyed depress their spirits, or cause them the slightest qualms or uneasiness—not from any lack of human sympathy (Dorothea was to show herself capable of the most generous kindness, and Jenny's quick response to other people's joys and sorrows was one of her most notable charms) but because they were so accustomed to the sights through

51

which they were passing that these had lost, or rather had never had, any power to make an impression on them.

Tumbledown cabins, no better than hovels, their thatched roofs sprouting with weeds and (as they had no chimneys nor windows) smoking like dung-heaps from the turf fires within—were not these the usual dwelling-places of the peasantry who somehow managed to rear enormous families, to say nothing of chickens, pigs and a calf or two, inside them? Indeed the spalpeens or wandering labourers were content with temporary shelters of clay built against a high bank and roofed over with branches. One of Jonathan Lynch's favourite hunting stories had related how he had inadvertently jumped on to one of these hovels when taking a bank, to the terror and amazement of its occupants.

The children who ran, laughing and calling, out of the cabins, as the post-chaise rattled by, were always in rags, usually half naked. Dolly and Jenny probably only noticed how sweetly pretty they were with their mops of tousled hair and bright complexions. The older people were blear-eyed and sooty-faced from constant turf smoke, but all seemed cheerful, lively and friendly. Dorothea and Jenny had been brought up to believe that the poor were born needy and wretched through an inescapable decree of Providence; no doubt to serve as an object for the charity of their superiors. At the same time, in some way not clearly defined, it was supposed that their poverty was largely their own fault; they were dishonest or lazy or drank too much, the last two vices being, of course, only excusable when indulged in on a really grand scale.

Whenever the post-chaise drew up before an inn it attracted a little group of interested country people who, in the way of the Irish peasant, seemed to have endless leisure and an insatiable curiosity to hear or see something new, and who, when the two young ladies, wearing travelling cloaks, their faces framed in large calashes, stepped out of the chaise, were loud in their admiration. This was expressed so warmly and pleasantly—"God bless their lovely faces!" "Begob! wouldn't it do ye good to look at the pair of them?"—that even Dorothea, always bashful, some people said haughty, when her looks were remarked upon, could hardly be affronted. Jenny, avid for admiration of every kind, no doubt flashed her thanks with a dimpling smile and a soft look from under her lashes.

The inns of eighteenth century Ireland, judging from contemporary accounts, were far from comfortable. The wine was good and food lavish as a rule, but the service and appointments were slovenly, the servants slatternly and the beds dirty. Mrs Lynch (as Dorothea tells in a letter to her uncle Oliver) was "vastly thankful" that she had taken the precaution of bringing her own sheets with her, while Jenny "nearly split laughing" at being assured by the landlady that she could depend upon the bed being well aired for it had not been changed since the Reverend Father slept in it last week.

It is hard to say which part of the journey must have been the most disagreeable, the nights in the frowsty inns, or the days spent rattling over indifferent and lonely roads in post-chaises which seemed ready to fall to pieces at any moment, and whose interiors, from being left out in inn yards in all weathers and often used as a roosting place by fowl, had acquired a permanently musty smell.

Dorothea and Jenny however had the youthful good spirits which are proof against all such trivial discomforts. To them, who had never been further from home than Youghal and Waterford, this journey was an amusing adventure, leading to a prospect all rosy (to their girlish— or at any rate to Jenny's—imagination) with excitement and gaiety.

Dorothea, who had always been to some extent her mother's confidante, evidently realised that this visit to Dublin was a last desperate attempt on her mother's part to secure her elder daughters' futures and that, in spite of her mother's lofty assertion that every young lady was entitled to a season in Dublin, she and her sister were social privateers who (if they were not to spend the rest of their lives in rural obscurity) must wrest their fortunes from the great world with the only weapons at their command—their looks, their youth, their rustic gentility and the few best gowns packed up in the horsehair portmanteau at the back of the chaise. These reflections may have dimmed slightly Dorothea's pleasure in the excursion. Jenny living, as was her wont, from day to day enjoyed every new experience as it came and had few thoughts and no fears to spare for the future.

At this period the fashionable quarters of Dublin lay both north and south of the river, Henrietta Street, Rutland Square, Sackville Street and Arran Quay being all exclusive places of residence on the north side, while on the south side many fine houses had recently been built in Nassau, Dawson and Kildare Streets, Merrion Street and Square, Ely Place and St Stephen's Green.

Mrs Lynch, acting on the principle of not spoiling the ship for a pennyworth of tar, avoided the dowdier parts of the town where she would have found lodgings suited to her means, and fixed on Grafton Street as her headquarters.

The words, Grafton Street, suggest a luxurious and bustling shopping centre; in those days, before Carlisle Bridge was built, it was a quiet street, mainly of private houses, leading from College Green to St Stephen's Green. Such shops as there were had bow windows, with small diamond panes of glass, and painted signs projecting from the walls.

Mrs Lynch and her daughters put up for a few days at the Black Lyon Inn before taking rooms over a bookseller's and publisher's shop. Lodging in the same house was a young apothecary's assistant who "played with much taste and feeling on the flute" and who immediately fell in love with Jenny. He was very bashful and could only express his passion by love-lorn looks and by playing tender airs on his flute at daybreak and far into the night, which must have been trying to the nerves of his fellow lodgers. The unsophisticated Jenny was highly delighted with her conquest, and Dorothea shared her amusement. Not so Mrs Lynch. She had not sold the last of her jewels, and most of the family silver, to have her daughters serenaded on the flute by young apothecaries. She lost no time in paying her respects to Lady Kilrush.

How the girls' hearts must have thumped as they stood with their mother under the imposing portico of the Kilrush mansion in St Stephen's Green, listening to their mother's admonition not to be too bold (for they must remember that they were not romping now on the cliffs of Ardnabannagh) yet not too shy. Alas! her ladyship was out of town and was not expected back till next week. She would be informed that Mrs Lynch had waited upon her. Mrs Lynch took no chances and wrote a note which is still preserved in the records of the Kilrush family:

"Having brought my sweet girls to town with the object of giving them that final polish that my motherly partiality tells me is their only serious lack—for I truly believe that there is nothing amiss with their looks or dispositions—I have ventured to pay my respects to your ladyship, trusting that it will be as pleasant to you and to my dear cousin Lord Kilrush as it will be to me to renew the memories and friendship of former days. I await with impatience the opportunity of making the acquaintance of young Lord Lusk and of your daughters the Ladies Charlotte, Lucy, Blanche and Henrietta, who I hear are the most sweet and engaging girls that ever were seen."

If Mrs Lynch really yearned to see the Kilrushes' offspring as much as she said, her patience must have been sorely tried during the next few weeks. The time of Lady Kilrush's absence elapsed; the house in St Stephen's Green

55

showed signs of activity clearly indicating the return of its owners. But day after day went by and no footman in mulberry and green livery appeared at the door of the bookseller's shop in Grafton Street, with the eagerly expected invitation. A heavenly messenger could not have been awaited more fervently. Mrs Lynch could not, of course, allow her daughters to shop or go for walks abroad by themselves. She must always be in attendance, and even so her dignified and forbidding air did not prevent them being gaped at and ogled by every kind of undesirable male creature, from bucks and students to cockle-sellers and chimney-sweeps. She must have been in a fever lest some message should arrive from Lady Kilrush during her absence. What blank disappointment, and that sick sinking of the heart peculiar to hope deferred, when their landlady answered her enquiries with a shake of the head. Had the footman forgotten to give her message? Had her note miscarried? Was Lady Kilrush ill? Every possibility would be discussed and rediscussed. The November dusk fell early, the lamps on their iron brackets were lit; soon the feeble old watchman would begin his rounds. Another day was over—more money spent—nothing achieved.

To occupy the girls (who, however, were thoroughly enjoying the shops, the varied sights of the town and the promiscuous admiration which their appearance in the streets invariably attracted) Mrs Lynch arranged for them to attend classes in French, English composition and elocution every morning at Mr Whyte's well-known school in Grafton Street. This select educational establishment was primarily for boys, but Mr Whyte gave tuition to a limited number of young ladies (or visited them in their homes at a charge of three guineas for eight lessons).

Dorothea, who always felt keenly the defects of her early education, may not altogether have disliked this belated opportunity of remedying them, though it is not likely that at eighteen, and on her first visit to Dublin, she actively welcomed it. Jenny, wild for fun and excitement, and with no wish to improve her mind, idled, pouted, giggled and yawned so shamelessly that good Mr Whyte, fond as he was of his young lady pupils (especially in retrospect of those who had become peeresses), was obliged to ask her mother to remove her.

Dorothea left with her, and Mrs Lynch had to resume the fatiguing task of chaperoning her lively daughters from morning till dusk. Matters had reached this point and it looked as if the visit to Dublin was to prove a dismal and costly failure, when a trivial incident changed the course of the sisters' lives, or appeared to change them, for who can presume to unravel the skeins of an individual fate?

Dorothea and Jenny were taking their usual exercise one morning in the fashionable promenade on the north side of St Stephen's Green known as the Beaux Walk. They were accompanied only by their maid, Mrs Lynch being confined indoors by a sharp attack of rheumatism. The day was windy, and as a middle-aged and fashionably dressed lady sauntered past them, a particularly violent gust caught her large satin bonnet and swept it clean off her piled-up, powdered head. It bowled along the path, the lady's footman and pug-dog in pursuit. But Jenny and Dolly were more prompt and fleet of foot. Chasing after the errant headgear (no doubt glad of an opportunity of stretching their active young legs) they pounced on it, and laughing and triumphant, brought it back to its owner.

If Dorothea had been alone the episode would no doubt have ended with gracious thanks and an admiring look from the lady, and a shy curtsey from Dorothea. But Jenny with that spontaneity, often bordering on lack of decorum, so characteristic of her, insisted on helping the lady to put on the bonnet again, commenting enthusiastically and naïvely both on the bonnet itself and its wearer's appearance.

"La! what a sweetly handsome bonnet. I hope 'tis not crushed, ma'am, for it must have cost a fortune and becomes you vastly well."

The trivial, friendly, girlish words have come down to us through the centuries, but who can know now the sparkling merriment of the wonderful deep blue eyes, the white and rose of the flushed cheeks, the lilting voice which gave charm to even the silliest of Jenny's utterances?

Lady Moffat—this was the name of the owner of the bonnet—has recorded her astonishment, almost stupefaction, at the sight of these two young women:

"They were the handsomest pair that ever I did see. If Juno and Hebe had sprung up before me in Stephen's Green I could not have been more surprised. The elder and taller had all the majestic modesty of a young goddess and appeared to be fashioned of gold and tinted ivory. The younger nymph was more sprightly, with dark hair and brows, and a remarkable whiteness of skin, and with something so captivating, nay dazzling, in her eyes and smile that you could not take your gaze from her. Both, I perceived at once to be simple, unaffected girls, fresh from the country or the provinces. There was nothing stylish in their clothes or air, or missish in their behaviour. Their manners were free and untutored and this, which some might have considered an imperfection, added, in my eyes, to their charm."

Naturally Lady Moffat wanted to know the names of these interesting young girls. This was readily given and, inviting them to walk a little way with her, she questioned them in her imperious, benevolent manner as to their family, their place of origin and the reason for them being in Dublin. Lady Moffat noticed that Dorothea blushed and seemed inclined to reserve, but Jenny, encouraged by such kindly interest, told nearly everything. She told about their father's death in a duel, and how handsome he had been, about their dull life at Cabra House, how

58

their mother had brought them to Dublin for the season and how that, so far, they had not been to a single ball, or even a supper party or had any beaux, except a young man who played the flute and was only an apothecary's assistant.

Lady Moffat was amused by Dorothea's reproachful interruptions "Shure Jenny, the lady doesn't want to know all that." "Come, Jenny, we must go home or Mama will wonder what has become of us." To no avail. Jenny babbled on artlessly, and Lady Moffat, shrewd woman of the world that she was, soon had a clear idea of the sisters' social position and prospects or rather lack of prospects. She decided immediately—for Lady Moffat was a woman of quick and generous decisions—that she would take these young beauties under her wing and introduce them into society.

Lady Moffat was the widow of an eminent judge. Her two sons were grown up and married, and she employed her time and gratified her benevolence (which sprung from a warmly maternal heart—she had affection and energies to spare not for two but for ten children) in entertaining a vast circle of acquaintances, ranging from peers to penurious young poets, and by innumerable little acts of kindness.

The gatherings at her house in Kildare Street were celebrated—she had musical parties, fashionable parties, literary parties, scientific parties, legal parties. Sometimes, either through absent-mindedness or by design, she invited guests suitable to one kind of gathering with the guests suitable to another, with startling results. Her routs were always crowded—the house packed from ground floor to garret. Her food and wine were incomparable. Her energy and cheerfulness never flagged.

To launch two unknown, unsophisticated young girls in society was just the kind of undertaking that delighted her (particularly as, in this case, she had a hearty dislike to Lady Kilrush). She had been very personable in her own youth and was still a handsome figure. She had a generous appreciation of good looks in other women.

She lost no time in waiting upon Mrs Lynch and, with her usual frankness, unfolded to her her plans for Dolly and Jenny's social betterment. It must have taken all Mrs Lynch's Pinkerton breeding to enable her to conceal her rapturous delight at this sudden and unexpected piece of good fortune. We may be sure that she placed her daughters' welfare unreservedly in Lady Moffat's hands.

Lady Moffat would have made a successful general. She planned to open her campaign with a surprise attack on a big scale, and in a few days was able to inform Mrs Lynch that she had procured invitations for the girls to a reception and ball at the Castle, and would herself present them to the Lord Lieutenant.

The excitement into which this news threw Mrs Lynch and her daughters was almost painful. What were Dolly and Jenny to wear? That was the burning question. Mrs Lynch would gladly have had the finest dresses made for them, regardless of cost and of her dwindling resources; but Lady Moffat, with surer taste, knowing that the delicious freshness of young beauty needs no adornment, advised them to wear simple white gowns, promising to lend them each an ornament from her jewel case.

Here they are then on the eve of the Ball, waiting, tremulous and yet exhilarated, in their lodgings in Grafton Street for Lady Moffat's coach to fetch them, both in plain hooped gowns of white satin, Dorothea's dress being distinguished by blue and Jenny's by rose-coloured ribbons. On her hair Dorothea wore an ornament of turquoises, Jenny one of jargons, a rare and beautiful stone the colour of port wine. They wore no other jewellery.

How mysterious the fate of all the millions of objects of homely and domestic use of past centuries! Where are the footstools, the tea boxes, the cocked hats, the canes, the mittens, the slippers, the quill pens, the pomatum boxes, the buttons, the pots and pans? There were no salvage collections in those days and yet, except for a few choice survivors in museums, they have all been swallowed up in Time's gigantic maw, all have vanished leaving not a trace behind. What has become of the mirror that reflected those eager young faces on that momentous evening? Shattered long years ago, no doubt, and consigned to the rubbish heap; or being cracked, perhaps, banished to a maid's attic, to be broken up at last and used for firewood; or there is just a chance that it may be mouldering to this very day dusty and worm-eaten in some forgotten corner of a Dublin antique shop. However brief (comparatively speaking) its existence and forlorn its end, it had the privilege that November evening of reflecting two of the most beautiful young women in Ireland.

How pleasant it would be to see for a moment even the reflection of those sweet and radiant faces, eyes shining with expectation, cheeks softly glowing, tender lips parted, the maiden foreheads white and innocent of all mean and harassing thoughts. As it is we must do our best with the testimony left by paint on canvas, and innumerable descriptions in cold print, for perhaps this is a suitable moment to attempt a more detailed description of Dorothea's and Jenny's appearance.

The words "modest dignity", "stately", "serene", spring to the mind when writing of Dorothea. "Modest dignity" will do for the days of her brief girlhood and early married life; naïve and unsophisticated as she was at that period it is apparent that there was never anything gauche or awkward about her. She had a gentle, natural pride in her air and bearing that was impressive, and yet perhaps somehow touching. Imperceptibly, as life enriched her experience and character, this girlish dignity merged into that stateliness, "digne d'une reine" as one

61

of her foreign admirers termed it, which is the characteristic most commented upon by her contemporaries. "Serene" will best give the quality of her smooth, broad forehead and wide-set eyes; the mouth was generous with well-cut lips, the rounded chin had a hint of determination.

Those who knew her superficially thought her reserved, even disdainful. Her admirers said that she was cast in a finer mould, made of a rarer clay than the ordinary run of womankind. Those who loved her knew the deep, sound emotions and warm impulses that lay behind that tranquil and guarded face.

She was tall according to the standards of the century, amply but not heavily modelled. Her throat and shoulders were particularly admired. Her skin was remarkably fair and delicate, the white and pink being very pure and distinct. She flushed easily, and it was said that when she drank wine her throat became rosy. An exaggeration, of course, but it will serve to show the child-like texture of her complexion. There was a juvenile quality too about her hair; it was a very pale gold and had that shining sunny look that is seldom seen after childhood when it attracts the delighted gaze of grown-ups. Like her sister Jenny her features were most pleasingly set and had an air of breeding.

It is characteristic of her that the finest portrait of her is the one in the guise of a vestal virgin by Sir Joshua Reynolds. How he must have d lighted in her noble beauty and understood the depths of character behind it. The well-known portrait of her in a large feathered hat by Ramsay is a fine composition, but there is an air of indifference, even coldness about her expression which is not attractive. It is not surprising that the girlish shortening of her name was soon forgotten except by her immediate relations. To address this regal-looking creature as "Dolly" or "Doll", how absurd and incongruous! Yet to the acute observer, women of Dorothea's type, tall, fair, composed and gentle, have a kind of fundamental and rather touching simplicity not often to be found in the smaller woman, who would appear to gain in astute femininity and driving power what she lacks in inches.

The thought "A fine face—and a handsome one" is evoked by Dorothea's portraits. Jenny's portraits have a different effect. From every one of them her loveliness and her charm throw down their challenge to the startled beholder. "Admire me! Love me!" that exquisite face seems to command and to entreat. You may prefer her merry, as in the enchanting Gainsborough portrait where she is dandling a spaniel on her knee, or wistful, in the exquisite study of her by Romney where she rests her forehead pensively on her hand and gazes down at a book (Jenny who never opened anything more serious than a book of fashion prints!), but in every one of them, gay or plaintive (for the word "grave" has no connection with her), her eyes, her mouth, her whole attitude plead for adoration.

Dorothea's portraits might conceivably have been painted in our own time. Jenny could only have been painted in the eighteenth century, because only in that century could a beautiful woman command such extraordinary homage, and it was the consciousness of this homage, the daily, almost hourly incense of flattery and adulation that gave a reigning beauty like Jenny the sweetly triumphant, arch and winning expression that is peculiar to the women of that era. Jenny looks at you like a coquettish and vain child, "I am beautiful aren't I? Say that I am beautiful!" You look at her delicate features, her charming mouth, her fairy-tale colouring ("as white as snow, as red as blood and as black as ebony"), and above all at her bewitching sea-blue eyes with their long lashes, and you cannot resist smiling at her, "Yes, Jenny, you are indeed beautiful."

Mimic or representative courts are apt to be more grandiose than their originals. A Viceroy, being the symbol of a symbol, can hardly afford the little condescensions and foibles which will only add to the popularity of a real monarch. It is said that George III asked a cottage woman, in a spirit of honest enquiry, how the apple got into the dumpling. His subjects might smile at his simplicity, but on the other hand might reflect that the gods of Olympus were equally ignorant of cooking. A similar silliness on the part of the Viceroy of Ireland could only have drawn down on him the ribaldry of the lampooners.

Lord Townshend indeed, during the latter years of his viceroyalty, exposed himself to the full blast of his enemies' spite and satire by his complete lack of dignity and his taste for drink, low vices and low company, but in this year of 1768 his amiable and interesting wife was still alive, and life at the Viceregal Court was conducted with a reasonable amount of pomp and decorum.

Visitors to Dublin usually expressed their disappointment at the dismal appearance of the Castle. Inside, however, the rooms, though comparatively small, were handsomely and tastefully furnished, and could compare very favourably with the shabby state apartments of St James's.

To Dolly and Jenny Lynch, who had never seen anything more luxurious than the Assembly Rooms at Youghal, what unbelievable, almost frightening, magnificence was revealed to them on this night of the ball!

Imagine it all! Coach after coach rumbling into the "Devils' Half-Acre" (as the square beneath the state apartments was cynically nicknamed), the torches flaring in the murky November air, the footmen and lackeys helping the gorgeously dressed gentlemen and ladies to descend; and inside, soft carpets, the shimmer of countless wax candles, burning in sparkling chandeliers and in sconces on the walls, the sound of flutes and violins and harps, and a ceaseless hum and chatter of voices. How the girls must have gazed in naïve amazement at the other women, at their sophisticated painted faces, their powdered towering heads of hair, surmounted with elaborate decorations of gems, feathers and flowers (the wire frames and false locks most cunningly concealed), their costly jewellery, fluttering fans as delicate and bright as butter-flies' wings, their gowns of brocade, satin and velvet in every rainbow hue.

Bewildered at this luxury and splendour the sisters were oblivious at first of the extraordinary impression that they themselves were making. Not so Lady Moffat. With a thrill of triumphant gratification she saw the astonished and admiring stares, quizzing glasses raised, heads close together, lips whispering "Who are they?"

"Who are they?" The question ran like an electric current through the assembly. Lady Moffat, who alone knew the names of the lovely strangers, must have smiled to herself as she led them up to the Viceroy.

Everyone watched with eager curiosity and interest as the two beautiful young girls, one so dazzlingly fair, the other so brilliantly dark, made their shy and nervous curtseys. Men, then in their gay youth or in their prime, were to bore their incredulous grandchildren years later with their oft-repeated tale of how they saw the Lovely Lynchs on the night of their début. "Beautiful as angels! By Gad! you don't see women like that these days. Jenny was thought the greater beauty of the two—she had the prettiest, most alluring smile in the world and eyelashes a quarter of a yard long, but Dorothea was a damned fine girl too. They were not ten minutes in the room before wagers were being laid that they would marry into the peerage before Christmas."

It is related that Lord Townshend, while he kissed Dorothea more heartily than was consistent with viceregal etiquette, saluted the blushing Jenny on both cheeks. Whether this is true or not there is no doubt of the sisters' immediate and overwhelming success. Lady Moffat has left an enthusiastic account of it:

"The appearance in the Throne Room of these two surpassingly lovely and engaging girls struck all beholders with a kind of wonder. It is no exaggeration to say that these young women, who a few hours before were totally unknown and ignored, now attracted to their beauteous persons the gaze of all that was most elegant and considerable in Irish society. No sooner had I presented them to the Lord Lieutenant than my friends and acquaintances crowd'd round me with a curiosity almost too eager to be polite. All wished to know the names and histories of my interesting protégées, and to stare more closely at the exact proportions of their figures, the lovely bloom of their skins, which owed nothing to art, and the simple enchantment of their smiles. Some of the women admired them freely without envy. Others, who saw their own claims to beauty disputed by these prodigious rivals, pretended to find some imperfection in their appearances—Dolly was too tall and sedate, Jenny was too thin and had a silly look about her mouth—but the men, though some might prefer the fair one and some the dark one, were all of the same opinion, to wit that such a beautiful pair had not been seen within living memory."

It may be believed that the manner of the two girls, artless, spontaneous, at once timid and yet daring (for having no experience of society they could have no idea of its pitfalls), only added to their attraction. If they were as beautiful as two young goddesses they were also as fresh and unspoilt as two nymphs from Arcady.

The girls' enjoyment of this wonderful evening—of the admiration and attention they received, of the beaux (so

66

many beaux!), of the dancing, music, and delicious collation served in the long gallery, can be better imagined than described. Left to themselves they would have gone on dancing till dawn or, like the princesses in the fairy-story, till their white satin slippers were in holes. But their fairy godmother, though indulgent, was astute. She knew that nothing would fan the interest kindled by their appearance so well as their Cinderella-like disappearance from the scene of their triumph. Besides, there were signs that Jenny, flushed with unaccustomed excitement and wine, might soon do or say something foolish (Lady Moffat had been horrified to hear her giggle to Lord Moira, one of the best-bred men of the day, "Away with you, you nasty flattering fellow"). Even Dolly who had, Lady Moffat considered, more than a fair amount of good sense, was becoming rather hoydenish in her manner as the evening wore on. She must remove her young divinities before they made fools of themselves. Clearly they needed some tutelage before they could take their place in society.

Soon after midnight, regardless of Jenny's pleadings, she carried them away with her, telling them that they had occasioned enough fracas for one evening, and would soon have their fill of balls if all went well.

"It was my intention," she says, "to point out to them the defects in their behaviour, trivial in themselves, yet unbefitting to the lofty plans that I had conceived for them, but no sooner were we seated in my coach than Jenny threw her arms round me and, smothering me with kisses, thanked me a thousand times for all I had done for her and her sister, while Dolly, with tears in her eyes, thanked me more soberly but no less sincerely. And so my excellent resolution was forgotten."

CHAPTER V

ESCAPE INTO THE GREAT WORLD

I

To us, fated to experience the gigantic and hideous convulsions of a second World War, the stir caused in Dublin in that year 1768 by two young girls, who though very lovely were also very ignorant and sometimes rather foolish, seems fantastic, something almost beyond the reach of our comprehension. Even considering it from a closer view-point it seems extraordinary that reasonable, responsible people can have concerned themselves over the most trivial doings of the Lovely Lynchs (as Dolly and Jenny were soon nicknamed) at a time when Ireland was stricken with want and seething with disaffection.

Yet so it was. A modern parallel may be found in the hysterical mob-worship accorded in recent times to visiting film stars, but whereas in that case the excitement was to a great extent artificially stimulated by publicity, in the case of the Lynch girls it sprang up spontaneously in a night, a genuine, if exaggerated, homage paid by a cultured, sophisticated society to the beauty of the female form.

Lady Moffat had nothing to do but to produce her protégées, and to protect them from the results of their own inexperience. Next morning, before Dorothea and Jenny were awake, she drove up in her carriage to their lodgings in Grafton Street, and offered to remove them and their mother at once to her Kildare Street house. Mrs Lynch did not hesitate to accept this hospitable offer. She was ready to fall in with any plans which this imperious but generous benefactor might have for her daughters. The girls were bundled, yawning, out of bed, their clothes packed, the reckoning paid (by Lady Moffat), and before noon Mrs Lynch and her daughters were installed in Lady Moffat's handsome and spacious residence.

Lady Moffat had two reasons for this sudden removal. First, she had no intention of allowing Lady Kilrush to snatch her new-found treasures from her. Lady Kilrush had been at the ball. As soon as she had realised that the two new beauties were her young cousins from Ardna-bannagh (her son, Lord Lusk, a volatile and giddy youth had half an hour's start of her) she had sailed up to them, expressing her excessive delight at seeing them and vowing that she had intended to send them an invitation the very next day to a supper party. Secondly, Lady Moffat did not consider that the girls were safe in lodgings in Grafton Street. Their mother, though obviously a woman of family and of some common sense, had rusticated too long in the wilds of Waterford to be an adequate guide and guardian for two young girls who (although they did not realise it) had become, overnight, the talk of the town.

Lady Moffat must have them under her wing; she must fit them out with clothes of a stylish and deceptive simplicity, have their hair dressed by her maid, try to moderate their brogue, teach them to curtsey like ladies instead of milkmaids and to receive a compliment without giggling and blushing, instruct them in the art of handling a fan; above all she must frighten off unsuitable admirers and encourage with delicacy and tact any eligible suitors. They must appear enough in society to keep alive the interest in them, yet not enough to render them common-place.

Accordingly, for a day or two, though the road in front of Lady Moffat's house was congested with the coaches and chairs of her visitors, the Lovely Lynchs remained inaccessible. They were fatigued after the excitement of

69

the ball and were resting in their room, so Lady Moffat
excused them. They were quite unused to society, having
been brought up in perfect retirement and innocence on a
remote headland in Waterford. Dorothea was excessively
content, as long as she had a book in her hand, and asked
for no other distractions; as for Jenny, sweet girl! she was
occupied at present in arranging her collection of sea-shells.
All of which must have been very tantalising to the gentlemen who had called in the hope of receiving one of
Dorothea's sweet smiles, or one of those captivating
glances from beneath Jenny's incredible lashes.

After a few days of these stratagems Lady Moffat gave a
small and select rout in honour of her two young guests.
Those who were privileged to attend it reported to their
envious friends that the Miss Lynchs were every whit as
lovely as they had appeared at the Viceregal Ball. The
most nice examination of their features could not disclose
any serious imperfections, while their figures appeared to
be formed with the most admirable and (in Jenny's case)
most delicate proportions. Dorothea's air of modest
sweetness was much admired, also her vast quantity of fine
fair hair, while it was agreed that Jenny's eyes had ten
thousand charms that touched the soul.

In short, the sisters were a success. They were more
than a success, they were a fashion, a rage. Lady Moffat,
who had no wish to see her protégées vulgarised, endeavoured to keep the flood-tide of their popularity within
bounds by only accepting for them invitations to the most
aristocratic houses, to Moira House and Leinster House,
to the town residence of the Vesey family in Molesworth
Street, Lord Lanesborough's house in Dawson Street, and
to the receptions given by Lady Drogheda, Lady Clan-
william, Lady Dungannon, Lady Louisa Connolly and
other prominent hostesses.

But in vain. Dublin at large claimed the Lovely Lynchs
as its own. Whenever they appeared in the street they

were so thronged with admirers and sightseers of every class that they were obliged to rise at seven o'clock and take their exercise in St Stephen's Green in the dark under the protection of a lady's maid and two footmen. Their portraits appeared in every print shop, on snuff boxes, and were made into "watch papers", little vignettes which could be carried inside the watches of their admirers. Their profiles were snipped out in black paper and modelled in wax.

When they entered Lady Moffat's box at Smock Alley Theatre, they were greeted with such tumultuous applause that the performance was held up for a quarter of an hour, while outside the theatre a free fight took place among the linkboys and footmen, said to have been caused by a dispute over the relative attractions of Dorothea and Jenny. When Mrs Lynch took the girls shopping at the Hibernian Silk Warehouse in Parliament Street, the other customers climbed on the chairs and counters to get a better view of the beauties, and in the subsequent crush a child narrowly escaped being trampled to death. Dorothea relates that when Jenny heard of the accident she insisted on visiting the little invalid (who happily had escaped with nothing worse than a broken rib), taking with her gingerbreads and a doll.

Although, as has already been indicated, the rich had little real sympathy with the sufferings of the poor, charity was all the fashion, and it was customary to have charity sermons in aid of various philanthropic causes, after which ladies distinguished for their rank and good looks (or more dully for their virtue and piety) made a collection from the congregation.

The Miss Lynchs were among the ladies who acted as collectors, after a charity sermon preached in aid of the Rotunda Hospital in St Werburgh's church, in the presence of the Lord Lieutenant and his lady and a fashionable gathering. The church was packed, and when

Dorothea and Jenny dressed, according to the *Dublin Courier*, in gowns of biscuit-coloured taffetas enriched with small silver flowers, went round the pews with silver plates in their hands, preceded by gentlemen bearing wands, only the sacred nature of the building no doubt prevented the congregation from jumping up like the customers at the Warehouse to get a better view. The Lying In Hospital benefited exceedingly from the Lovely Lynchs' fame. Who could refuse to give generously to the tall and golden Dolly, or resist Jenny's beguiling smile? Their plates were soon so laden with money and even jewellery that they had to be emptied twice before the sisters could finish their collection.

At the concert held by the Mecklenburgh Musical Society for the benefit of poor confined debtors, the arrival of the Miss Lynchs caused the usual commotion. The presence of Lord and Lady Townshend kept the excitement within genteel bounds, but the whispers and turning of heads and stretching of necks must have been somewhat distracting to the performers as they warbled their way through glees and odes.

What a change had come over the lives of Dolly and Jenny Lynch! Forgotten were the winds and waves and screaming seagulls of desolate Ardnabannagh, the shabby house, the constant money worries, the slovenly servants, Uncle Oliver's snores and poor Tishie's mumblings, the long dragging hours filled with tedious domestic tasks. We see them now living that strenuous existence known as a life of pleasure, every moment, except for meals and sleep, given up to enjoyment, to recovering from one gaiety or preparing for the next. They are surrounded with flattery, compliments, kindness, with elegance and luxury.

You may imagine them at their toilets, candles burning on their dressing-table, making a little profane shrine for the radiant faces reflected in the mirror, admiring waiting-maids hovering behind them. Lady Moffat (sumptuous, one may feel certain, in mulberry brocade or black velvet or some gown of similar richness) appears at their bedroom door, examines, approves, warns ("Dorothea my child, remember that over-shyness is often mistaken for pride. Think twice before *you* speak, Jenny my love"). Their spreading satin gowns billow around them as they are lighted into the coach. ("May the gates of Paradise be ever open to receive you" whines the beggar in the gutter.) There is the drive through the murky streets, then more links and the brilliant soft candlelight and the music of some aristocratic house; a house that has wainscoted walls with carved panels and stucco ceilings, or is perhaps hung with golden-coloured damask from Italy, or papered with fantastic Chinese paper; almost certainly it will have carved marble mantelpieces of great beauty; perhaps it has curtains of yellow or crimson silk damask with chairs to match. Worthy setting for the guests who crowd up the broad staircase and into the reception rooms— men and women no better looking than ourselves but garbed with the flaunting beauty of exotic birds and flowers—worthy setting for the two young girls who were acclaimed by those who beheld them as the nonpareil of the age.

It is clear that Dorothea and Jenny had only a vague idea of what had befallen them, or what had caused this extraordinary transformation of their lives. They were aware, of course, that they were exceptionally handsome, but of the incalculable and perilous power of their beauty they, in their simplicity and inexperience, could have no conception. A few weeks before everything had been uncertain, dull and drab; now everything was gay, amusing and cheerful. Everyone seemed to like them, everyone was kind to them—it was all very delightful and in the best fairy-story tradition.

A letter of Jenny's to her nurse Kathie has survived and will show something of the naïveté of her outlook. It is badly written, worse spelt and (like most of Jenny's letters) undated, but it seems to have been written shortly after Christmas.

"KILDARE STREET

"Bid Uncle Noll to read this to you.

"MY DEAREST SWEET KATHIE,

How I wish my dear nurs could see her Doll and Jenny now and here all the pretty things that are said about us whic would give you great joy, for they say we are a sweet pare. To be sure we have all the fine clos (clothes) in the world and everyone is fighting to see us and we have all the beaus we coud wish for and are at all the publicker diversions. Dolly and me are to play act at Carton. Dolly studis her part very earnstly but I am the stupites cretur and cant say the tragikal parts for laughing.

My lady Moffat gave dolly a lace fan and me a lace cloak, and Doll and me gave her a satin pincushion with flours and seaquins we had made oursefs.

Dear Mama is in perfect health and so are your dear children who will never forget to love you. Kiss Tishie for me. I hope she receivd the dolls tea pot I sent her. I must bid a due.

Your affec.

J. LYNCH "

2

Lady Moffat made no secret, in her written recollections, of the fact that she was anxious to marry Dorothea and Jenny off as advantageously and as quickly as possible. No doubt she emphasised the same point in her private conversations with Mrs Lynch, who certainly saw eye-to-eye with her. Lady Moffat was particularly anxious to see Jenny settled with that eighteenth-century ideal of

74

connubial bliss, "a good husband and a handsome and convenient house".

Dorothea, though less generally fascinating to the opposite sex, had, Lady Moffat suspected, reserves of strength and good sense, which would help her through life. But lovely, foolish Jenny—what would happen to her if she was not settled in her early youth? Her lack of discretion alarmed Lady Moffat. Any fool—any *well-disposed* fool that is to say—could see that Jenny at present was as innocent as a child. Her indiscretion arose from that impulsiveness and enjoyment of life that was so great a part of her charm. But Lady Moffat was well aware that Dorothea's and Jenny's meteoric success had stirred up much jealousy and even hostility. Rival beauties, mothers of marriageable daughters, elderly or unattractive admirers who fancied themselves ignored or slighted—all these people must be reckoned as enemies. Even many who genuinely admired and liked the Lovely Lynchs might not be displeased to see their triumphant career checked. Only the truly generous can stomach the overwhelming success of others, especially when it is completely undeserved.

Dorothea—as one lady wrote caustically to a friend—was hardly less ignorant and ill-informed than her sister, "but at least she has the sense to keep her mouth shut, and with her beauty, which is indeed of a noble order, may pass as a very Goddess of Wisdom with her adorers, for all they care."

Jenny had a certain natural wit, a great deal of gaiety, and a droll way of saying things which charmed her admirers, but unfortunately she never paused to consider before she spoke. Her thoughts tumbled helter-skelter out of her mouth as soon as they were conceived, often with startling and unlucky results. The malicious seized with delight on her habit of making malaprops. What joy at one party when she was heard telling her hostess's schoolboy

75

son that he could not attend holy communion till he had been circumcised. Poor Jenny, during the laughter that ensued, protested that of course she knew the difference between confirmation and circumcision—it had just slipped her mind—shure, didn't they both begin with a "c" anyhow? The story sped round the Dublin salons. Nor were her attempts to grace her conversation with French phrases very fortunate. "That will give him the coup de grass", she was heard saying gaily.

These gaffes in the matter of speech were not, however, in Lady Moffat's opinion, the worst of Jenny's defects. Far more serious was her vanity, which made her swallow everything that any flatterer told her, and the levity and indiscretion of her conduct.

Lady Kilrush regarded with evident alarm and disapproval the infatuation of her son, giddy Lord Lusk, for his lovely cousin. One night at a ball it was found that Jenny was missing. Could she have been taken ill suddenly? Lady Moffat, in some alarm, hurried home, to find a laughing Jenny awaiting her, drinking syllabub with Lord Lusk and another young man, who had persuaded her to get into a chair and to allow them to act as her chairmen. The passage through the streets of two hilarious and inebriated young bucks in embroidered coats, carrying a chair with one of the celebrated Miss Lynchs inside, had attracted a good deal of attention even at that hour of the night.

Lady Kilrush knew about it with her early morning cup of chocolate, and by noon had engaged in battle with Lady Moffat. Lady Moffat defended her protégée with a glorious disregard of veracity and logic. The poor child had been overcome by the vapours, she had not wished to spoil Lady Moffat's or Dorothea's enjoyment so, in her perfect simplicity and innocence, she had accepted her cousin's offer to convey her home; an act of folly for which the blame must surely rest upon Lord Lusk who, at the

76

age of nineteen and a half, might be supposed to have some knowledge of the world and its conventions, rather than upon this angelic child.

The outraged Lady Kilrush was routed, but neither convinced nor appeased. Lady Moffat gave Jenny a severe scolding, which soon reduced her to tears of contrition—too soon, for Jenny weeping was almost as appealing a sight as Jenny laughing, and Lady Moffat had to comfort and pet her before she had time to expound to her the full enormity of her conduct.

This and other incidents were danger signals. To the ideas of that period there was nothing incongruous in wishing to marry off a girl because she was young and foolish, though her very youth and folly clearly unsuited her for the responsibilities of wifehood and motherhood.

Jenny like, and even more than, her sister, had a host of admirers and a good number of suitors. One of the most eligible, the most devoted and, in the opinion of Lady Moffat and Mrs Lynch, the most eminently desirable, was Horace Minton, fourth Earl of Aintry.

Lord Aintry, who was staying at the Castle as the guest of the Viceroy, had been greatly struck with Jenny's beauty the night of her début. Since then his admiration had increased till it could without exaggeration be endowed with the romantic name of love. Yes, Lord Aintry, a man of thirty-four, a man of fashion and of parts, was ardently and sentimentally in love, perhaps for the first time in his life. He had declared in a letter to an intimate friend that Miss Jane Lynch (the Christian name sounds unfamiliar and odd, but Lord Aintry was a man of some dignity and formality) had few equals in beauty and grace. Later he says "she has a beauty and sweetness that forces adoration".

The phrase "forces adoration" is significant. Lord Aintry was not a man, one would imagine, to rush headlong into an imprudent and unsuitable marriage. A man of wealth and the owner of large estates in Staffordshire (said to be the best managed and farmed in the county), he was well known at Court, had a certain reputation for eloquence in the House of Lords, was a prominent member of the Jockey Club, and an enthusiastic collector of medals, bronzes and other antiquities.

His face as depicted in his portraits is that of a man of breeding and intelligence. His cynical eyes and the satirical curl of his lips do not suggest a person who would give in to a sudden impulse, yet his infatuation for Jenny must be so described. That she was penniless and of no particular family could be overlooked—it was in fact all to his credit, in those days of arrant snobbishness, that he did overlook it—but her extreme youth, her ignorance, her flippancy, and passionate love of admiration and pleasure, might have given a man of his fastidious and difficult temperament legitimate cause for hesitation.

He could not help himself. His better judgment and his intelligence were powerless before Jenny's fascination. Her very indifference to him (Dorothea relates that when he proposed to Jenny she burst into tears of astonishment and confusion) no doubt added to her attraction. The gossips were writing in February 1769: "My lord Aintry's head is so completely turned by the prodigious eyelashes of the younger Lynch beauty that you would suppose him a love-sick boy of eighteen rather than a man of sense and judgment. If matters run on as they do we may expect our lovely Jenny to be coronated before long." "Let us hope", the writer adds spitefully, "that my lord will never find himself cornuted."

Though Jenny wept when Lord Aintry declared himself, we need not suppose that she entertained even for a moment the idea of rejecting him. To be proposed to by this great man, this fashionable, elegant, clever and titled man, what an astounding honour, what a fairy-tale fulfilment of her girlish dreams!

Dorothea relates that Jenny announced the news to her by throwing herself into her arms with the words, "Dolly! I am to be a countess. And so shall you be too, sister. My lord Aintry shall find you a husband as grand as himself."

The vulgarity of this outburst is only to some extent redeemed by its naïveté, its frankness and her own youth. She had been brought up by her mother to worship her own beauty and to believe that a fine marriage was the height of earthly happiness; her unawakened heart was untouched by any deep emotion. These are, perhaps, the best excuses that can be offered for her. But let us not forget that Lord Aintry, though not handsome, was a man of a striking and elegant appearance, "perfectly agreeable and genteel looking, and a fine figure of a man", Dolly describes him. He had visited all the principal Courts and cities of Europe, his conversation, though inclined to be argumentative, was cultured and witty. Altogether he must have been a sufficiently dazzling figure to a raw girl of seventeen, apart from his title, wealth and possessions, to explain her jubilation at having captured him and at having secured his fond devotion.

After all, why should she doubt her good fortune? Lady Moffat and Mrs Lynch were in raptures. Dorothea admits that she was no less delighted. Her singularly unenvious and generous nature rejoiced at her sister's good luck, while, from a less altruistic point of view, this marriage opened a brilliant social vista for herself. Jenny had vowed that she would not be parted from her Dolly, not for Lord Aintry nor any man in the world. And Lord Aintry, who would have agreed to any of his lovely Jenny's demands at that time, was very willing to offer a home to her sister.

While Jenny paraded her noble suitor round Dublin ("wild with triumph and excitement and lovely beyond words", one observer describes her) Lady Moffat and Mrs Lynch busied themselves with arrangements for the wedding.

It would have hurt Mrs Lynch's pride not to be able to give her daughter a wedding outfit worthy of this splendid match, nor did she feel justified in taking further advantage of Lady Moffat's ever-ready generosity. Lady Kilrush, rendered unusually amiable by her relief at Lord Lusk's escape, came to the rescue by procuring for Mrs Lynch a grant of £200 on the Irish Establishment. Mrs Lynch's claim to a grant from public funds may seem to our modern ideas rather flimsy, but no doubt Mrs Lynch, as the mother of two beautiful Irishwomen, considered herself at least as much entitled to benefit from the Irish Establishment as the German mistresses of George I and George II.

With this grant, and many handsome presents from Lady Moffat, the bride was suitably equipped, and on March 16th Jenny Lynch and the Earl of Aintry were married privately at the Castle in the presence of the Lord Lieutenant and his lady and a few distinguished witnesses. She wore a white and silver gown and a white hat—"very saucy"—(bridal veils and wreaths were out of fashion at that period) and was "in extraordinary beauty". Dorothea's looks were also much praised, and it was predicted that it would not be long before she followed her sister to the altar.

Outside the Castle the usual astonishing scenes were enacted. A huge crowd collected to see the bride. People screamed, cheered, fought, trampled on each other, were carried fainting and with broken limbs out of the press, and finally the military had to be called out to control the mob.

"You would have imagined a riot or battle in process outside the Castle while the younger Lynch was being made into countess", wrote one spectator. "It is said that my new Lady Aintry carries Miss Dorothea to London with her, so we may hope that this *folie de Lynch* may die down, and that there may be an end to these scenes which exceed in absurdity and indecorum anything that you can imagine."

The Lord Lieutenant lent his yacht to the newly-married couple, who thus made the crossing in style if not in great comfort. It blew a gale. Lord Aintry was much disordered, Dolly very uneasy, while Jenny, in the best of spirits and health, amused herself, while the storm was at its height, by singing Irish airs to her own accompaniment on her new harpsichord (which must have added considerably to the sufferings of her prostrate lord).

Mrs Lynch did not accompany her daughters. She must return to Cabra House, to take up the burden of caring for Tishie, and before her brother-in-law Oliver succeeded in emptying the cellar.

Later she might hope to see her daughters in all the splendour of their new lives in England. For the present she must return to the bleak and windy cliffs of Ardna-bannagh, to the endless sighing of the ground-swell, the unutterable loneliness and stillness of Cabra House, bereft of those two bright young presences.

As mothers go, Mrs Lynch cannot be accounted a particularly wise or far-seeing mother, but to nearly every mother, Providence in its wisdom has accorded quite extraordinary opportunities for exercising self-denial and self-control.

CHAPTER VI

"PASTURES NEW"—WING MAGNA

IT MUST have been a proud and pleasant moment for Lord Aintry when he introduced his bride and his family place to one another—the beautiful girl whom he had discovered (in a manner of speaking) and wooed and won in Ireland, the fine house that he had inherited from his ancestors and beautified and improved upon with such loving care.

Wing Magna is situated in Staffordshire, near the town (in those days the village) of Tutton. The original house, which was built on the site of an ancient abbey, passed into the hands of the Minton family in the early seventeenth century, to be destroyed by fire in the year 1699. The house was rebuilt in the reigns of Queen Anne, George I and George II, the original design by an unknown architect having been superseded by that of Kent, the most talented of the band of architects who gathered round that munificent patron of the arts, Richard Boyle, Earl of Burlington.

The cult of the Palladian style was flowing strongly when the restoration of Wing Magna was finally completed. The house is considered one of the most successful of Kent's achievements, and shows none of the "clumsy bleakness"—as one writer has described it—that sometimes mars the work of the English Palladians. The house is imposing and graceful, with a central block connected by two curving passages with side pavilions. The north or entrance front, with its Corinthian pillars, is approached by a fine terrace and a great Avenue of splendid beech and elm trees. The south side has a striking if not very cheerful vista down a wide ornamental canal bordered by tall thickly-growing trees, with a Garden Temple at the far end. To modern ideas it seems a pity that the view from the sunnier side of the house should thus be partially obscured, but it must be remembered that the eighteenth-century householder did not share our welcoming attitude towards the sun.

Wing Magna is set in a flat countryside which, to the stranger, seems featureless and uninteresting, though no doubt to the local inhabitants its familiarities have their charms. But it is not likely that young Lady Aintry viewed it in any critical spirit as she drove through it for the first time in her lord's fine travelling coach. Jenny had had her fill of picturesqueness, of the "savage, wild and melancholy" scenes, that were to be so much admired as the century wore on. Cliffs, Atlantic breakers, wind-tormented trees, seagulls—she exchanged them all gladly for these flat well-tilled fields, trim cottages (Lord Aintry was a careful landlord) and comfortable woods.

Besides, what did the surrounding countryside matter? The handsome wrought-iron entrance gates of Wing Magna, bearing the coat of arms of the Minton family, with their gate piers surmounted by heraldic leopards, set well back from the road in a grove of beech trees, afforded the passing traveller a tantalising glimpse of the beautiful park within. For fortunate Jenny the gates were flung open wide, with much bowing and bobbing and smiling from the lodge-keeper's family—magic portals opening on to a magic world. The gates clanged-to behind her, shutting out poverty, dullness, insecurity. The coach rumbled magnificently up the Great Avenue, between wide borders of grass scythed smooth as a lawn, beneath lofty trees hardly feathered yet with the spring foliage. The Park closed in around Jenny—in the distance (the Avenue is a mile and a half long) the austere yet gracious mansion awaited its new mistress.

Lord Aintry was a man with a strong sense of possession. What a feeling of triumph must have been his as he led his bride up the terrace steps and over the threshold of his home, marked the looks of startled admiration as the sight of her dazzling young beauty broke on his correct house-hold, saw her childish, unfeigned delight and awe at the magnificence of his house.

What a terrestrial paradise it all seemed to Jenny—the lofty hall with its doorways carved in marble and flanked by columns supporting cornices and pediments with reclining figures of nymphs; the flamboyant plaster decorations of fruit, flowers and birds on the walls, which had been carried out by craftsmen specially imported from Italy, the ceiling with its riot of sportive amorini; the cool, stately rooms opening one upon another with folding doors, the picture-gallery and the sculpture-gallery with its statuary brought from Italy by Lord Aintry, and his cherished collection of antique medals; the salon hung with pale blue damask; the library with its panelled walls, and rows and rows of calf-bound books, and its rich, dim smell; the dining-room which, in spite of its domed ceiling and alcoves and busts in niches and altar-like mantelpiece, had an unmistakable air of English dignity. To think that all these rooms, and many others, were Jenny's now—to walk about in and sit down in, to eat and play cards and dance in—each one a shrine for her beauty. For this was the delightful part of it all. Lord Aintry said openly that Jenny was the most beautiful thing in Wing Magna, his rarest treasure, his most cherished possession.

The splendours of her new home had such a catastrophic effect on Jenny's spelling and writing that the letters written during her honeymoon to her mother are barely readable. The beauties of the "patare" (parterre) at the side of the house, the quantity of indoor servants, Lord Aintry's pedigree cattle, the luxurious fact that Wing Magna possessed no less than two closets and a bathroom with hot water pumped up from the basement, are jumbled up with childish boasts of my lord's devotion—"he posatify dotes upon me and lavshes on me a 1000 tendrnesses. I can hardly exprs a wish before he has indulged it."

Dorothea's more restrained rhapsodies give us a clearer picture of those halcyon days. It is significant in her letters home that she begins with an account of Lord Aintry's fondness for her sister. Though she too was greatly impressed with Wing Magna, her thoughtful blue eyes, undazzled by marble mantelpieces and brocade hangings, watched the newly-wedded pair with anxious affection, for, with her instinctive sense of the essential things of life, she realised that Jenny's happiness, if it was to be durable, must spring from something more substantial than the gratification of being called "milady" by a host of obsequious servants, and of being the possessor of a Chinese boudoir. What she saw pleased, one might almost say reassured, her:

"I do believe, dear Mama, that Lord Aintry loves our sweet Jenny almost as much as she deserves, for I don't think the pretty thing could be loved enough! You would be highly delighted to see all the attentions he pays her. Nothing could be more tender and considerate than his manner towards her, and though she is as playful with him as with you or me he takes it in very good part. As long as he made Jenny happy I ought not to care how indifferent he was towards me, but on the contrary he is everything that is polite and amiable and declares that he would like to stand me in an empty niche in his sculpture-gallery! Perhaps you will laugh at my vanity in telling you this compliment but it will shew you that he is by no means as haughty and formal as people said, and indeed I think it very kind of him to be able to notice a sister at all, for he is quite ravished with Jenny's beauty, and no wonder for she looks handsomer and merrier every day.

"'Tis impossible for me to describe to you the fineness and elegance of this house, everything about it is most convenient and in the best of taste, or so I imagine for I have never seen anything so fine before in the way of a country mansion. I believe that I made myself ridiculous the first day by curtseying to Mrs Hoggard the housekeeper, who from her rich dress and air of gentility I took to be some aunt or grandmother of my lord's that I had not been warned of. We are occupied the hole day looking at Lord Aintry's medals, pictures, busts etc. (to tell you the truth I find the medals mighty dull and so does Jenny and says so, but he is so wrapp'd up in them that 'tis only civil to

85

try and shew some interest) and either riding or driving about the grounds and estate in a pretty little chariot. Indeed 'tis very pleasant to see how surprised and admiring all the tenants and people about here are at Jenny's looks. In the evening after a delicious collation we play at cards or Jenny and me play on the harpsichord and sing, or Lord Aintry reads to us aloud from some instructive book. We have not seen any neighbours yet, but for my part I have pleasure and entertainment enough in seeing how well Lord Aintry loves my sister."

It may be noticed that in Dorothea's fond and naïve assessment of her sister's marital happiness she takes it for granted that the devotion should all be on Lord Aintry's side. There is no word of Jenny's feelings for her husband. She is "playful", "merry", growing handsomer every day (no doubt expanding like some delicate flower in the warmth of petting and adulation), she is bored with his medals and says so. She accepts the romantic devotion of this clever, sophisticated, usually cool-hearted man with the gay and thoughtless complacency of a spoilt child.

Jenny never learnt, Dorothea was only to learn by hard experience, that what men really seek in women is not beauty nor wit nor virtue, but the ability to make them feel contented and at ease with themselves.

None of Lord Aintry's neighbours, with one exception, was permitted to have a glimpse of his bride during their brief honeymoon. It was almost as though he foresaw that this was to be his one taste of tranquil domestic life. The exception was his great-aunt Lady Hannah Martindale, his maternal grandfather's sister, who lived within three miles of Wing Magna in the dower-house of Hokeham Manor.

Most old ladies can be divided into two categories— "dear old ladies", who are vague and amiable, and "wonderful old ladies", who may or may not be amiable but are imperious, energetic and awe-inspiring.

86

Lady Hannah Martindale was certainly a wonderful old lady of a type familiar to students of eighteenth century social history, being both aristocratic and eccentric to a degree. She was the only daughter of the seventh Duke of Leominster, and had startled the fashionable world by eloping at the age of sixteen with Octavius Finch (youngest son of Sir Henry Finch, Bt.), one of the handsomest men of his day and already, at the age of twenty-two, a noted buck and gambler. The fury of her ducal father (her mother had been laid to rest in the family vault many years previously) was beyond description, and alarming to behold. But as the marriage had been consummated by the time that her elopement was discovered, there was really nothing much that he could do about it, as Lady Hannah pointed out to him in a letter which is a model of impertinence disguising itself beneath filial piety and respect.

In a year's time, after Lady Hannah had given birth to a daughter, the Duke decided to pardon her. Lady Hannah accepted his forgiveness dutifully, but informed him that she would never forgive herself for the folly of her marriage. The next day she left Mr Finch for ever, taking her infant daughter with her. No one ever knew exactly why she forsook her husband—whether on account of his mistresses, his gaming or his drinking, or, as she maintained flippantly, because she had heard all his best stories and could not endure a lifetime of repetition. She resumed her maiden name and settled down at Hokeham Manor, which her father had handed over to her.

To the astonishment of society this young, very pretty and lively woman now lived in retirement, devoting herself entirely to her daughter's upbringing. She maintained a correspondence with Pope, Addison, and other men of letters, had visitors to stay at Hokeham, but seldom stirred herself beyond the borders of the county. When her husband was killed in a brawl at a Covent

Garden bagnio, seven years after their separation, it was supposed that Lady Hannah would re-marry, but she rejected the proposals of various suitable admirers with a firmness that even the most conceited male could not attribute to coyness. It was considered most admirable that Lady Hannah should thus sacrifice her own happiness and prospects on the altar of maternal duty. Though she was known to be very attractive to the opposite sex, not so much as a breath of scandal ruffled her reputation. The older people of her circle held her up to the younger generation as an example of female propriety and devotion. But she had a few surprises in store for them.

When her daughter Frances was eighteen (she herself being only thirty-five and at the height of her good looks) she married her off to Lord Frenton, an amiable and estimable young man. The young couple had been attached to one another for several years. Lady Hannah was satisfied that the marriage would be a success. The day after the wedding she ordered her coach and, without saying farewell to anyone, drove to Dover, and embarked for the Continent, taking with her a few confidential servants, her spinet and a pet parrot.

She remained abroad for ten years, during which time she communicated with no one, though her daughter received costly presents from her from time to time, and the sums that she drew from her banker (and that were forwarded to a banker in Vienna) assured her indignant relations that she was still alive. Travellers brought back news of her. She had been seen in Paris, in Madrid, at the Court of the Elector of Bavaria, in Venice, in Vienna; after that, although it was known that she had embarked, coach and parrot and all, on a barge and sailed down the Danube, all was wild surmise. It was rumoured amongst other things that she was living with a pasha at Belgrade, that she had joined some obscure sect and entered a nunnery on the slopes of Mount Lebanon, and, most persistent rumour of all, that she was living in Constantinople as the favourite wife of either the Grand Vizier or the Sultan himself.

When ten years had elapsed she returned home, unannounced, with a new set of servants, which included a Moorish slave, her spinet and a pet ape. She was in the best of spirits and (allowing for the passage of time) in the most becoming of looks. Few people dared to ask her where she had been all this time, and those who asked her did not ask a second time, for she had a stinging tongue and was complete mistress of the art of discouraging undue familiarity.

Her acquaintances, wild with curiosity, would gladly have forgotten their breeding and stooped to question her servants, but it appeared that none of them (except the Moor) had been engaged further afield than Turin, some as near home as Paris. The Moorish slave might have provided a more fruitful subject for research, but unfortunately he was both deaf and dumb.

It was clear to them, however, that she had been in the Orient. She sometimes received the visitors, who flocked to her drawing-room, in a Turkish costume consisting of drawers, smock, waistcoat and caftan of the finest material embroidered with silver and jewels, and smoking a hookah. She divulged that her parrot had been buried near the Castle of Abydos. She distributed gifts of a rare and exotic nature among her friends—porcelain jars filled with perfume, embroidered slippers, vests of fine sables, pearl tassels and so on, and presented her daughter with some emeralds and diamonds of fabulous size. With such crumbs of information or speculation her acquaintances had to be content. It was also clear to them, from the sprightly look in her eye and her air of sleek contentment, that wherever she had been and whatever she had done, whether she had been the favourite wife of the Sultan or the mistress (as the malicious suggested) of the entire Divan, she had thoroughly enjoyed herself.

Perhaps the most astonishing part of her story is the fact that her daughter Lady Frenton never questioned her about those mysterious ten years. "If my mother wished to tell me about her travels she would do so," she said. "It would not become me to force her confidence."

It is not surprising that a tender devotion and friendship sprang up between these two remarkable women. To the day of Lady Hannah's death mother and daughter corresponded daily.

Lady Hannah settled down again in the country, interested herself in agriculture, tyrannised benevolently over her tenants and the entire countryside, wrote a book on practical physics (having acquired a taste for mathematics), carried on a prodigious correspondence, and produced exquisite embroidery for the delectation of her descendants.

It was to this interesting and formidable old lady (she was now 81) that Lord Aintry took his bride and her sister to pay their respects. No one could be considered an accredited member of the family till they had been inspected by Lady Hannah and received the hall-mark of her approval.

Lady Hannah's appearance often disconcerted the more timid of her young relations. On this occasion—Dorothea relates—she was enveloped in a kind of riding-cloak of dark cloth (perhaps a Turkish *ferigee*) and wore on her head a large plumed turban with an emerald in front as big as a turkey's egg. In spite of her great age she "showed little signs of decay", and inspected her young visitors with a keen and satirical eye.

Jenny and Dorothea having been brought up in Ireland were accustomed to eccentricity, and Jenny, undaunted by her new great aunt's odd appearance and still odder reputation, bounded towards her and kissed her affectionately on both cheeks. Lady Hannah held Jenny at arm's-length and gazed at her. "A goose but a charming goose," was her verdict. She added, "I never saw such a surpassingly beautiful face and figure but once before." "Who is she? What has happened to her, ma'am?" asked Jenny eagerly, anxious to know if she was likely to meet this rival in society. "Cut in four pieces, put in a sack and thrown into the Bosphorus," was the grim reply.

Lord Aintry, who had more wit than humour, evidently disliked the comparison (Dolly noticed with amusement), but, after her first shriek of shocked surprise, Jenny went into fits of laughter. "Lord, ma'am! what diverting tales you could tell us if you chose. Lord Aintry says that on no account am I to ask you if you was Sultaness of Turkey, so I won't, but please show me your treasures and your Turkish costumes."

This was not the first time, nor was it to be the last, that Lord Aintry was to be stupefied by his wife's lack of tact. He exclaimed, "Lady Aintry! pray recollect yourself!" and waited unhappily for her verbal annihilation. But the old lady merely laughed and patted Jenny's cheek, then taking the two sisters by the arm, led them round the place, showing them all her most interesting and valued possessions, chatting away to them very affably "and with much wit and a thousand extravagances of speech".

She took particular pains to explain things to Dorothea, bringing the ready blush to her cheeks with the words, "If you abstained from routs and balls, young woman, for five years, and passed the time in a good library, you would emerge from it a tolerably well informed and cultivated woman, but I fancy that your face will make nearly as much stir in the world as your sister's, in fact some people will consider you handsomer—and so I see little chance of your educating yourself."

At the same time she seemed highly diverted by Jenny's artless and often ignorant comments. When Lady Hannah, alluding to her travels in Bulgaria, mentioned Sofia, Jenny enquired, "Who is Sophia?" Worse still, on being

91

shown a manuscript poem that Mr Pope had written to her hostess, she exclaimed merrily, "Fi upon you, Lady Hannah! to have the Pope as well as the Sultan for a beau!"

Lady Hannah's only comment on this and similar gaffes was the cryptic remark, "This child is like the girl in the conte de fée. Everything that falls from her mouth is a pearl or a rose."

Lord Aintry probably felt that enough pearls and roses had fallen from his wife's lips for one day. Shortly after this they took their leave. The old lady presented Jenny with a jewelled girdle and Dorothea with a kerchief of finest gauze sewn with silver and pearls. To Lord Aintry she said, "I did not think, Horace, that you would be such a fool as to marry this girl. 'Pon my word, I declare that I like you all the better for it."

CHAPTER VII

"PASTURES NEW"—LONDON

IN LONDON, that spring of 1769, when the Earl and Countess of Aintry and Miss Dorothea Lynch took up residence in Berkeley Square, there were old people living who were born before the last Stuart King fled from England, and there were babies being born who, in their old age, would watch the young Victoria drive to her Coronation. In the populous city there were timbered houses with overhanging gables that dated from Tudor and even mediaeval times, and houses were being built in the fashionable quarters of the town that, surviving the onslaught of the speculative builder and the German bomber, may delight the eyes of generations to come.

So, as we wander in imagination through this London of the mid-eighteenth century, we find ourselves between the old and the modern world. We are not so much strangers as exiles come home from a far country. For beneath our gigantic London of to-day, the London of the eighteenth century still survives, an elegant, forlorn, rapidly vanishing ghost, purged by time of its squalor, its clamour and its smells. We are inclined to remember the sound of the spinet floating out through the windows of a house in Berkeley Square more readily than the cry of the rat-trap seller, the gilded coaches than the filth of the kennel, the paint and powder of the gay ladies than the sore faces of the beggars, the Chinese House at Ranelagh than the stews of Whitechapel, the unsteady figures of bucks leaving Brooks's or White's after a night of deep drinking and deep play than those of more plebeian topers. For the eighteenth century represents to us an escape from the monstrous realities of our own times. Yet no era had a lustier life of its own. We do not speak its language but we can understand it, better, it may be, than that of our grandparents.

It is spring 1769, and so the aristocratic patrons of Boodle's and the St James's Coffee House may be discussing the Wilkes affair and deploring the weakness of the Duke of Grafton's ministry, or with equal vigour and heat debating the prospects for the next Newmarket meeting or their last evening's sport at the cockpit.

It is an age of heavy eating and heavy drinking; faces become alarmingly rubicund with temper or excitement; voices are loud and imperious; personal dignity is very touchy, a careless word or joke may flare into a deadly encounter at dawn in Hyde Park. Yet in the drawing-rooms of Mrs Montague, Mrs Boscowan and other intellectual hostesses, conversation is urbane, cultured, free from cant, at once refined and vigorous.

London, though rapidly expanding, is still comparatively

small. A walk of twenty minutes or so will bring the citizen into the country. Cows graze in the fashionable purlieus of St James's Park; you may buy their milk for a penny a mug. There are thickets of gorse and broom at Brompton; snipe can be shot in the desolate marshes of Belgravia known as the Five Fields; Kensington and Chelsea are country villages. The tide of fashion is flowing westward. May Fair, "a vile and riotous assemblage", has been abolished for some years, and the district is favoured by the aristocracy. But St George's Hospital still stands among fields; there is a turnpike at Hyde Park Corner, an apple stall and a one-storied inn at the entrance to the Park; Park Lane is known as Tyburn Lane.

We need not become too nostalgic over the rural amenities enjoyed by these eighteenth century Londoners. The immediate outskirts of London at this time are anything but attractive, consisting in fact mainly of dung-hills, ash-heaps and patches of waste ground, which in turn give place to useful but prosaic market-gardens, while the heaths of Hampstead, Finchley and Putney are uncomfortably full of highwaymen and footpads.

In the city the old gates of Aldgate, Cripplegate and Ludgate have been taken down and sold; street signs, always liable to be blown down on the heads of the passers-by in a gale, are becoming a thing of the past; houses are numbered; in parts of the town cobbles are being replaced by granite pavements, but rubbish and ordure is still lightheartedly thrown out into the streets; visiting foreigners run the risk of being hooted at and pelted; executions, sometimes of children in their early teens, wend their way up the "heavy hill" to Tyburn.

Society is compact and intimate. Hyde Park is thrown open on Sundays to the "vulgars", but during the week a gentlewoman, in search of adventure, may walk there masked and feel assured that anyone she meets will be (at any rate in theory) of her own class. Ranelagh and

Vauxhall are frequented by all classes, but the "ton" takes care not to arrive till midnight.

At St James's Palace the respectable King and dowdy little Queen hold their weekly drawing-rooms. The guests may laugh at the King's fussy "What! What!", and his preoccupation with domestic matters, such as the refusal of the royal cooks to wear wigs, and the iniquity of the custom of "vails" by which a man can not dine with his own father without tipping the servants, but the Court is still the centre of the social system. The darkness of insanity has not descended on the King, the Prince of Wales is a child, the day of the great Whig hostesses has yet to come.

It was to this London which, stilled by time, has for us the miniature charm and interest of an eighteenth-century print, but that, to its contemporaries, was a vast, bustling, noisy, crowded metropolis, that Dorothea and Jenny came in that spring of 1769, fresh from their conquest of Dublin, their feelings, no doubt, a mixture of expectation and apprehension.

Warm-hearted Dublin had acclaimed them as her reigning beauties, but London was a different, more formidable matter. In Dublin they had only to compete with local belles; now they were entering a critical society that was accustomed not only to some of the most lovely and accomplished women in the British Isles, but to beauties of cosmopolitan repute. They had taken Dublin by surprise, breaking in on it in all the exuberance of their rustic simplicity. Now the quill pens of the gossip writers had been busy, and rumours of the two Irish beauties, who were said to be the handsomest pair that had ever come out of that island famed for its pretty women, had preceded them across the Channel. Moreover they had no kind and worldly-wise Lady Moffat to display and direct them; it soon became evident, at any rate to Dorothea, that Lord Aintry was of an extremely jealous

95

disposition and would prefer to keep his wife's charms as much as possible to himself.

It is unlikely that these anxieties took definite shape in the sisters' thoughts, but they must have lurked in the background of their minds. Dorothea was unusually free from personal vanity—one of her friends records that Dorothea was one of the few handsome women she knew who could pass a mirror without glancing into it—but she was shrewd enough to know that her future must depend upon her success in London. What could life hold for her but three alternatives—a dreary and ignominious return to the solitudes of Ardnabannagh, continued dependence on her brother-in-law's bounty, or marriage? Can it be wondered that she hoped, with the bland optimism of girlhood, that this marriage would be at once stylish and happy, thus satisfying both her family's ambitions and her own sentiments. As for Jenny, her vanity and love of admiration were insatiable and unabashed, growing apace like some unpruned and too luxuriant plant.

It is as tedious to record unbroken success as it is to record unmitigated misfortune. But there it is—"the Lovely Lynchs" took London by storm. The report of their beauty was declared to have fallen far short of the reality. The election at Brentford with Wilkes as one of the candidates, the notorious Miss Chudleigh's marriage to the Duke of Kingston, the Duke of Grafton's divorce and his Duchess's remarriage, even these juicy topics had to take second place for a short time to the advent of the "Hibernian goddesses".

They went everywhere, and everywhere they went they were acclaimed as the wonder of the age. The *folie de Lynch*, in spite of the pious wish of the letter-writer already quoted, had not died out but merely transferred itself across the water.

They were presented at Court; even in these august precincts the other guests thronged them so outrageously

96

that Jenny fainted away. Queen Charlotte, not given, one imagines, to enthusiasm over the attractions of others of her own sex, invited them to a private audience a few days later at Windsor, that she might have an undisturbed view of their celebrated persons. The Queen no doubt approved of Dorothea's air of sweet composure, her rather constricted heart was evidently touched by Jenny's sprightly and child-like gaiety, for (according to Dorothea's letter to her mother) "Her Majesty was most affable and condescending to us. She is a little runt of a thing. I'll engage that you would never take her to be a queen, but she is perfectly genteel, and I am sure has a very good character. She told Lady Hertford that Jenny had a very engaging manner and was kind enough to say that she also found me agreeable. She had us taken to the nurseries where we saw the youngest child, a very fine little girl. Jenny snatched her up in her arms exclaiming, 'Oh, the pretty baby!' whereupon the royal nurse bridled and said, 'Baby indeed! I think your ladyship means *princess*' which made Jenny and me laugh. We was presented to His Majesty too, and he asked me most minutely about the effect of the climate upon conditions in farming in the south part of Ireland and what the labourers subsisted on, and other questions which I was puzzled to answer."

Queen Charlotte was not alone in being disarmed by the simplicity and artlessness of the two young Irishwomen, qualities which to some extent warded off the antagonism that their great beauty by itself would have provoked. It must have been difficult to be critical of two young creatures who were so anxious to be liked and so entranced by their new surroundings. Indeed their brogues, their naïve remarks, even Jenny's laughable gaffes, having the charm of novelty, seemed to add to their fascination.

No fashionable gathering was complete without the presence of young Lady Aintry and her sister Miss

Dorothea Lynch. Horace Walpole gave a supper-party in their honour at Strawberry Hill. They were the principal guests at an open-air (and very damp) fête at Stowe. At a masquerade at Richmond House, Dorothea as a Muscovite Czarina and Jenny as a Patagonian Venus with her little Cupid (Master Charles Featherstone)—one sees Lord Aintry's taste in this—were the acknowledged queens of the ball. As they drove up to Richmond House the mob stopped the coach and, holding up torches to the windows, demanded to see the Irish beauties. Lord Aintry, in whom the spirit of equality was imperfectly developed, would have ordered the coachman to drive on, and Dorothea, though impressed by the good-humour and civility of the crowd, felt embarrassed at this public inspection of her charms, but Jenny, pulling off her mask, said, "Why by all means take a look at me, my friends. It won't do me any harm and won't cost you anything," addressing the people in such a droll and merry manner that they were enchanted, and with three cheers for Lady Aintry and her sister and husband, let the coach pass on. Lord Aintry's displeasure can be easily imagined. He chided Jenny; she only laughed.

A distinction, as coveted as that of being presented at Court, and even harder to attain, was bestowed on the Lovely Lynchs when they were admitted to the member-ship of Almack's. This exclusive club was run by a group of fashionable men and women, the men candidates for election being elected by a committee of ladies, and the women candidates by a committee of men. To be elected to Almack's was a token of social, if not moral, impec-cability. Even peers and peeresses had been rejected and there was no appeal against the committee's decision. No wonder that Jenny and Dorothea, when their names went up for election, waited in some trepidation to hear the verdict. The Countess of Aintry sounded well enough, but would their squireen Lynch descent pass muster?

Jenny vowed that she would never enter Almack's without Dolly. It must be both the Lovely Lynchs or neither. "If Dolly and me is not elected to Almack's I shall dye of mortifikation" she declared in a letter to Lady Moffat, who must have smiled at the writer's naïveté. How likely that a committee of men would vote against admitting to their company two of the most beautiful young women of the age! Sure enough Lady Aintry and Miss Lynch were granted the coveted privilege of dining, playing cards, and dancing in this social Elysium.

The two sisters, during this first season in London, led a life which was a constant succession of entertainments and gaieties. Jenny, in particular, threw herself with ardour into the routine of a woman of fashion. Seldom out of bed before midday (for she and Dolly were seldom in bed before four or even five in the morning), Jenny held a kind of reception in her bedroom, while her hair-dresser or maid dressed her hair and she sipped her cup of chocolate. Her husband's relations and friends came to pay their compliments to her, quantities of hangers-on sought by flattery to impose on her good nature and secure some financial or other benefit, needy poets and authors presented her with poems written in her praise or asked to be allowed to dedicate their books to her. Milliners, mantua makers and jewellers hovered in the background, also flower-girls bringing daily bouquets for Lady Aintry and her sister from admirers. And Jenny, the centre of it all, her eyes still languorous with sleep, her cheeks soft with its bloom, chatted, gossiped, giggled, laughed, promised (her benevolence was sincere, spontaneous and quite unreflecting), as happy as a lark, "hardly ever saying a word of sense and yet with something in her every look and syllable that diverted the mind and ravished the heart."

Many of Lady Aintry's visitors would dearly have liked to have witnessed the maiden toilet of her sister Miss

Dorothea, who sat with a book (recommended by Lord Aintry) in her hand—for every time she went out in society she was startled and pained by some fresh realisation of her own ignorance—while her maid brushed and perfumed her profusion of silky golden locks. But, propriety apart, Dorothea liked to be alone at such moments. No one, except her maid, set eyes on her till she left her room, fully dressed, looking (as one very minor poet put it) like the young Diana emerging from an Attic grove.

The sisters then drove to the City for an hour's shopping, to examine the silks, brocades and velvets of the mercers in Gracechurch Street and Cheapside—"This, Madam, is such a diverting lutestring. It suits your ladyship's face to perfection"—to admire the exquisite model furniture and tiny silver tea and coffee sets and other nicknacks in the toy shops, to stroll through the book-shops, where Dolly, gazing round in awe and bewilderment, wondered how she would ever find time to read all the books that Lord Aintry assured her should be familiar to every educated woman, while Jenny amused herself by throwing some young bookseller into rapturous confusion with a smile.

Jenny's purchases were indiscriminate and beyond count. The elegant and tasteful house in Berkeley Square was soon cluttered up with them, so that Lord Aintry complained that it looked like Brook Green Fair. For the first time in her life she found herself in possession of large sums of money, and able to give rein to the fancies and impulses of a vain, extravagant and generous nature. She bought clothes and hats and satin bonnets and shoes and jewels and fans for herself and Dorothea, wine and china tea and muffs and silver plate and Chelsea Porcelain for her mother, toys and dolls and ribbons and odds and ends of lace for Tishie, enough shawls for Kathie to "keep her decent from now to the end of eternity" (Kathie's own words), and snuff-boxes and books for Lord Aintry who rarely took snuff and already possessed one of the finest private libraries in the country, and embroidered screens and pieces of Battersea enamel for Lady Moffat, and pastries from the confectioner's shop of Domenicus Negri (later Negri and Gunters) in Berkeley Square for any beggar child who happened to be standing by.

Or the sisters might drive or ride in the Park, where their appearance always excited much interest and attention. So the morning passed till dinner at two or often three o'clock—for Jenny, to her husband's exasperation, was very unpunctual. The afternoons would be spent in paying visits or in sitting for their portraits, or at some exhibition of paintings or prints or Etruscan vases, to which they were escorted by Lord Aintry, indefatigable in his efforts to educate his butterfly bride.

Then it was time to return home for the long elaborate toilet before the theatre party or the ball, the evening spent at Mrs Cornely's Assembly Rooms, or the alfresco entertainment at Ranelagh or Vauxhall. Another frivolous day and glittering night was over. Jenny's kneeling maid removed the shoes (perhaps of mouse-coloured silk or pale pink satin with rosettes) from her mistress' tired, pretty feet. Dorothea, who insisted on having her hair dressed fresh each morning—one of her few vanities—would lean back with sleepy, drooping eyes, while her attendant pulled down the towering edifice of her coiffure and brushed the powder out of the fine blonde tresses.

No wonder that Dorothea wrote to her mother, "I assure you we live like Queens."

CHAPTER VIII

MARRIAGE À LA MODE—DOROTHEA (1)

THERE ARE some women who never develop mentally far beyond girlhood. This quality, whose disadvantages become increasingly apparent as middle-age approaches, may give them an elusive charm while youth and good looks endure. It is clear that Jenny was one of these women. Marriage, and later motherhood, left her the same sprightly, frivolous, essentially simple-hearted creature that she had been in adolescence, so that she was totally unequipped to withstand the adult passion which was to break into her life with devastating force.

Thus she was evidently unaware of the fact that the interest aroused by the Lovely Lynchs in London differed, thought subtly, from that of which they had been the centre in Dublin. Then they had been two marriageable girls whose futures lay as blank and dazzling as untrodden snow. Anything might happen to them. Speculation could run riot around their destinies. Now Dorothea, whose tall blonde beauty received as much admiration, though of a more impersonal kind, as her sister's provocative loveliness, alone retained the mysterious, almost sacrificial allure of virginity. Jenny was married, "settled", if the word could be applied to such a flibbertigibbet. She had done very well for herself and, beyond producing an heir for the Aintry family, could hardly be expected to do better. The malicious would guess how long it would be before she took a lover; many of her admirers would ask themselves the same question with a more personal interest; rival beauties would watch her person for a sign that childbearing was going to impair her figure and her social activities; the merely curious or good-natured would observe her gowns, her looks, and laugh over her absurd turns of speech.

It was Dorothea who provoked the questions, "Who will she marry?", "Will she do as well as her sister?" over countless feminine tea- and card-tables, and whose matrimonial future was made the subject of wagers at Boodle's and White's, her youthful dignity and reserve adding piquancy to these speculations. Jenny neither realised this nor, if she had realised, would she have cared, for she had a naïve and well-merited confidence in her powers of fascination, while the relationship between the two sisters was of a deep tenderness that left no room for jealousy.

For Jenny it was always "Dolly and me" or sometimes "Me and Dolly" (for her hasty, ill-considered letters were as careless in style as they were in spelling) as though they were still the Lovely Lynchs, standing hand-in-hand on the threshold of their unknown destinies. It is proof of Lord Aintry's failure to impress himself on Jenny's heart that, almost to the end of her life, she was waiting eagerly for something to happen, waiting for a nebulous, rare felicity which would transform her existence and fulfil the promise of her wondrous beauty.

At the same time Jenny's chief preoccupation at this time was to marry Dolly off as successfully and as contentedly (for she believed herself to be very fortunate in the possession of Lord Aintry's devotion) as herself. Her efforts to bring about this happy state of affairs were embarrassing to Dorothea, who was nearly as anxious to marry as Jenny was to see her married, but who was burdened with a pride that was no part of Jenny's nature.

Jenny's parties for Ranelagh, Vauxhall and other places of entertainment at this time usually consisted of some half-a-dozen eligible young men, with herself and Dorothea as the only women, which did not make for popularity among her own sex. If any of the guests, as often happened, paid court to Dorothea, Jenny adopted the most obvious methods of throwing them together, arranging for them to occupy the same coach, which on a gala night at Ranelagh or Vauxhall might mean a prolonged tête-à-tête as the mass of coaches crawled forward, or, having led her party to the concert room, would express a sudden wish to see the fireworks—"But pray do not move, Dolly. I would not spoil your pleasure in the harpist for the world. My sister dotes on music, Lord So and So, and you may keep her company." All this regardless of whether Dorothea fancied the young man or no, for Jenny's idea was that if Dolly could not accept every eligible beau she should at least have the opportunity of refusing them.

Though Jenny was by no means averse to receiving homage herself, if any young man whom she had earmarked for Dolly ventured to transfer his attentions to herself, she discouraged him with a severity which contrasted ludicrously with her usual coquettish manner.

In vain Lord Aintry pointed out to her that these foolish manœuvres would injure rather than promote Dorothea's matrimonial prospects, and would make Jenny herself an object of ridicule. In vain Dorothea, touched as she was by the fond solicitude which prompted them, begged her sister to leave matters to take their own course. Jenny fancied herself as a matchmaker; she would not be satisfied till Dorothea had made a splendid marriage. She was indignant to hear that Miss Wrottesley, a niece of the Duchess of Bedford, who had not a quarter of Dolly's air, was to become the Duchess of Grafton—that made one Duke less available for Dolly—though Dorothea assured her that she had no ambition to marry a man who had already divorced a wife. Another Duke (his Grace of Kingston) had been snatched by the notorious Miss Chudleigh, who was reliably reported to be married already. It was said that the Duke of Gloucester was secretly married to Horace Walpole's niece, Maria, the Dowager Countess of Waldegrave. If royal dukes were to marry commoners, why what a magnificent royal duchess Dolly would have made! "It is a crying sham (shame) to see all these old married women" (wrote Jenny to her mother with a fine disregard of facts) "carrying off the beaus. I think they do very ill. I wonder they do not blush at themselfs. It is a real Rape of the Sabins." (Lord Aintry had evidently been giving Jenny a course of ancient history.)

Unfortunately she voiced her indignation in public as well as in her letters to Ardnabannagh, which drew down on her the derision which Lord Aintry had foreseen. The kindly-disposed gave her credit for her sisterly devotion, and thought it mattered little what such a lovely, silly creature said; the less charitable asked—What could you expect of a young person raised to the peerage from her native bogs?

Lord Aintry, always sensitive to his own personal dignity, and pained at this evidence of his lovely nymph's folly and lack of taste, was thankful when the Season drew to its close and the time approached for him to remove his wife and sister-in-law to Wing Magna. During those last few weeks of June, Jenny redoubled her efforts to arrange a brilliant match for Dolly. At last, when Lord Aintry had actually given orders for their departure from Berkeley Square, it seemed as if her efforts were to be rewarded. A young man had joined their circle who not only appeared to be very much attracted to Dorothea, but who, if Dorothea's radiant air could be trusted, had engaged her shy affections. His name was Charles Chessel, fifth Marquis of Mandlesham.

One look at the portraits of Lord Mandlesham will be sufficient explanation of his swift and decisive capture of

Dorothea's heart. They have the manly beauty (so admirably set off by the fashions of the period), the air of distinction and good breeding, too unconscious to be described as hauteur, that when we see its counterpart in a modern face draws the admiring comment, "He is like an eighteenth century portrait." The features are finely cut and regular without being insipid, the ruddy colouring and hair of a warm brown (he never used powder) are very comely; the expression in the indolent dark blue eyes is sweet and humorous; about the whole countenance there is an air of careless and debonair charm that is irresistibly pleasing.

Charles Mandlesham was fortune's child. His father and mother had died of smallpox when he was an infant, but a bevy of doating aunts and several conscientious uncles had endeavoured to supply him with the affection and care of which this loss had deprived him. They had been successful, almost too successful. In their anxiety to compensate "poor sweet little Charles" for his orphaned state (so an aunt, Lady Elizabeth Nash, alludes to him when announcing regretfully in a letter that "Our pretty little Love" had bitten a small cousin's ear) they ended by spoiling him. True, his naturally amiable disposition was not soured nor his warm heart chilled by the harsh educational methods prevalent in some homes at that period. To the end of his days he remained responsive to affection, ready to enjoy life and anxious that everyone else should enjoy life too.

Though naturally lazy he could show considerable energy and perseverance when engaged in some enterprise that interested him. His taste though less austere than that of Lord Aintry was wider, and certainly more productive of entertainment for himself and others. He indulged it with the lavishness, tinged by eccentricity, typical of that aristocratic age. Everything that he did, he did easily and well. He rode, he boxed, he fenced like a professional; he had a pleasing tenor voice, he spoke French, Italian and Spanish, and of course Latin, with ease; his sketches and architectural designs show that he had a very fair artistic talent; his knowledge of horses and dogs was said to be unequalled by any man in his sphere of life, while he had the finest private collection of Raphaels and Domenichinos in England.

With all these advantages he had one serious lack. He was unable to look unpleasant facts in the face. He had not been brought up to do so, and his naturally pleasure-loving nature inclined him to avoid unpleasantness—especially of an emotional nature—like the devil.

His principles were excellent (an uncle, the Bishop of Glossop, had written a treatise especially for his benefit entitled, "Letters intended for the Instruction of a Young Nobleman in Exemplary Living and Holy Dying") and he remained constant to them in his political and public life and in his general dealings with his fellow-men, but when it came to his emotional life they were apt to prove a frail support. He tried to please everyone, especially women, and was bewildered and distressed at the unpleasantness in which he often found himself involved in consequence. He had three ways of dealing with an awkward situation—to laugh it off, to promise amendment (without pausing to consider if the promise could be kept), and to hand out money. When all three methods failed he was at a loss. On the whole, however, he found life smooth sailing. His generosity and bonhomie made him as popular with men as other qualities, easier to imagine than to describe, made him with women.

He grew up to find himself the possessor not only of great wealth and estates but of a great name. The Chessels, the Cavendishs, the Russels, the Bentincks, the Keppels, these and a few other powerful families had virtually ruled England since the time when they had summoned the House of Hanover to the English throne.

Now George III, the first of the Hanoverian kings to feel himself an Englishman, was endeavouring to break loose from the Whig yoke, and to rally round him a Court party of Tories and Scotch nobles. The Whigs were obliged in consequence to reconsider their traditional policy, and the party had split into three groups—those such as the Bedfords and Grenvilles, who believed in maintaining the present position, another powerful group led by the Dukes of Richmond and Portland who, under Lord Rockingham's leadership, stood for the Constitution of 1688, and thirdly, the Whigs who, led by Lord Chatham and his able but unpopular disciple Lord Shelburne, saw in reform a chance to infuse new vitality into the party.

At twenty-two, Charles Mandlesham's age when he first met Dorothea, politics took second place with him to sport (he was one of the most enthusiastic members of the Jockey Club), travelling, gambling and every form of amusement. But he was not entirely unaware of his responsibilities, and already inclined towards the more progressive elements in the Whig party. This is not to suggest that he was in any way a democrat in the modern sense of the word. His outlook and his behaviour was patrician in the extreme—independent, impulsive, and strongly personal. His manner towards all classes, high and low, had an easy geniality and simplicity which came from his naturally amiable temper, and a sense of his own position so deep rooted that he had never had to consider it (except possibly during his schooldays at Harrow where he was always beaten twice over, once for the offence and once for being the Marquis of Mandlesham). Like other of the younger and more enlightened Whigs of his day he was vaguely aware of the "Mob" (as he would have called them) as a potential political force, but the idea that power might eventually pass from the hands of the aristocracy to that of the people would have seemed to him as improbable as it would be undesirable.

108

This, briefly, was the man who was to enthral Dorothea's heart and who, in his insouciance, was to teach her all that she needed to know about love and about herself.

As soon as it was observed that Lord Mandlesham was in constant attendance upon Lady Aintry and her sister, the indefatigable quill pens got busy. Estimates of Dorothea's chances of capturing the gay young man sped by post to every part of England, and even to the Continent. The columns of the more scandalous magazines were full of hints and sly innuendoes.

That Dorothea had fallen in love was obvious to everyone who saw her. There was a glow of happiness about her that put the final touch to her beauty. "Dolly looks as bewtiful as a Rose these days", wrote Jenny excitedly, "I hop to tell you the swete bewitching cauze in a few days." Lord Mandlesham showed a strong partiality to Dorothea; that was also clear. But there was a reason, known to anyone who knew anything, why it was highly unlikely that he would marry at present. It was to be hoped that the affair would fade out with the end of the London season, and before poor Miss Lynch's affections were too deeply engaged.

So matters stood when Lady Aintry gave a small select party for a *ridotto al fresco* at Ranelagh. The weather had been abominable but had cleared, and the night was fine and warm. The place was packed, there was music, and a beflagged gondola on the canal, the garden was hung with coloured lights and decorated with festoons of flowers. Jenny who, in spite of her fragile appearance, had a hearty country appetite, had brought her own refreshments (for the meagreness of the "regale" provided at Ranelagh was notorious). The party supped on salmon, fried smelts, ham, roast chickens, and pigeon pie, a gooseberry tart, strawberries, a melon, and no doubt partook freely of Lord Aintry's excellent wine.

The conversation, which was very merry, happened to be on the subject of marriage. Someone turned to Charles Mandlesham, who was, it appears, in the liveliest of spirits, and asked him teasingly why he did not marry, upon which the rest of the company entered into the joke, declaring that his reputation was such that there was not a respectable woman in London who would have him. Upon which Lord Mandlesham, much amused, but also one suspects a trifle piqued and probably a trifle tipsy, turned to Dorothea, who was sitting by looking "like a goddess in white and silver lutestring", and said, "Miss Lynch, will you have me?" After a moment's hesitation she said, "Yes, to be sure."

We may imagine the sudden silence that fell on the noisy party, as they heard the emotion in Dorothea's voice, saw her face flush with astonishment and joy, saw her, forgetful of all around her, gaze with ecstatic eyes at the man she loved.

Lord Mandlesham, not quite sure what he had done or what had happened, took her hand in his and called out to the company to drink their health. This they did, feeling that it was the best way to cover up an unaccountable and perhaps embarrassing situation, concluding that the whole thing was an elaborate joke, and yet not sure of that either, for Jenny was bubbling with exultation, while Dorothea sat by in "a kind of happy maze".

So the evening came to an end and, as they got into their coaches, the departing guests murmured eagerly to each other, "And pray what will Tessy Bellingham say to this?"

CHAPTER IX

MARRIAGE À LA MODE—DOROTHEA (2)

I

How IRREVOCABLY lost in time is the genius of the actor and actress! Paintings, sculpture, writings, endure; the tradition of the great ballerinas is handed down through generations of dancers. Every pirouette at Sadlers Wells is a tribute to Melle Heinel of Stuttgart, who first performed it in Paris in 1766. Even Elizabeth Lindley's angelic voice, though it charmed audiences in Bath long before the age of mechanical recording, evokes a plaintive echo in our imaginations, because we know that the essentials of a good singing voice are the same to-day as they were in ages past.

But the actor's or actress's art is intensely individual, their personality its subtle instrument, composed of a myriad looks, gestures, inflections of the voice, ways of moving. When this has vanished what remains? Nothing but the record of their effect on an audience far removed from us in time and taste.

We know that the audience groaned, wailed and cried during the stage death-scene of such and such a popular actor. We are not convinced that we should have been equally affected, especially as it was customary at that time to lay down a carpet on the stage upon which the hero of the play could comfortably expire. It would have been exciting certainly to have witnessed the set-to between Peg Woffington (playing Roxana) and George Ann Bellamy (as Statira), when Peg in an access of jealous fury drove the younger actress off the stage and stabbed her almost in view of the audience. But would the mannerisms of these celebrated ladies have enthralled us as they did their contemporaries? It is impossible to say. They delighted their audiences and left names behind them that will always provoke interest and curiosity. That is immortality enough.

Teresa (Tessy) Bellingham was not, even in her own day, considered one of the great exponents of her art, but her immense popularity as an actress and her notoriety as a woman give her an assured place in any history of the eighteenth century stage. Critics praised her "unaffected gaiety and vivacity in comedy". She had "infinite spirit and wit", "a prodigious fund of humour and audacity", and a way of singing and making pleasantries peculiar to herself and that sent her audience wild with pleasure. Moreover, she had what was called "a good breeches figure", with a remarkably shapely leg, and wore men's attire with a pretty pertness that won applause from box and gallery alike. When she simulated love on the stage she did so with "a liveliness and gusto that made every man in the audience wish himself in the hero's shoes". As she was not beautiful, indeed hardly more than tolerably pretty, it is evident that Tessy Bellingham, whatever her histrionic powers, was highly endowed with sex-attraction.

Her private history was extraordinary. She was the illegitimate child of an Irish peer and the daughter of a Quaker woollen merchant. Her father, Lord Kilmallock, driving through the town of Clonmel, caught sight of Deborah Savery as she came out of the Friends' Meeting House, followed her to her father's house, bribed a servant to arrange a rendezvous and within a few days had persuaded the lovely Quakeress to abandon her family and place herself under his protection.

She lived with him for a year in Dublin, at the end of which time she died in childbirth. Lord Kilmallock, however attached he may have been to his Quaker mistress (it is said that after her death he would not look at another woman for six months), evidently had no wish to burden himself with the upbringing of their bastard child. He took the infant Teresa with him to France and left her in a convent at Rouen. The nuns were entrusted with a sum of money sufficient to cover the expenses of her upbringing, and it was understood that at a suitable age she should take the veil or, if she had no vocation for a religious life, be trained as a governess.

Lord Kilmallock no doubt thought that he had made a very decent and adequate provision for his daughter's future, and stepped into the travelling coach, which was to bear him across the Alps, with a sense of a tedious duty conscientiously performed. He cannot be blamed for not foreseeing the wild unsuitability of the alternative careers which he had selected for young Tessy.

The good nuns must have had qualms on the subject before many years had passed. Tessy, in her fragmentary and racy memoirs, declares that even in the cloistered surroundings of the convent she soon became aware that by far the most interesting part of the human race went about in breeches.

Any doubts that the nuns may have had were finally resolved when Teresa, at the age of fourteen, fled from the convent and joined a troupe of strolling mountebanks who were passing through the town. She travelled in their company through the length of France till they reached Nice during carnival week. Here, as she and her companions performed their antics in a public square, she was observed by a young English gentleman of good family, Mr Edward Falconer, only son of Sir Joshua Falconer, Bt., who was doing the Grand Tour in charge of a tutor. The precocious youth (he was only eighteen) was instantly captivated by the fifteen-year-old waif. He sought her out and—to quote Tessy herself—"besought me to enter into a tender engagement with him." Tessy, who throughout her life was a woman of quick decisions, accepted his offer, and travelled again through France, this time in a northerly direction, in a coach instead of a cart, and dressed not in cast off garments but in a variety of elegant and expensive gowns.

It may well be asked, what was young Mr Falconer's tutor doing all this time? The regrettable answer is that the tutor, who seems to have been as much affected by the festive atmosphere of Nice as his pupil, had so far forgotten his duty as to elope with a married woman, thus leaving Mr Falconer free to enjoy the society of his charming Tessy.

The young couple, blissful in each other's love and ignoring the parental letters which followed in Mr Falconer's wake, travelled in a leisurely way to Paris, and after a brief sojourn in the capital crossed to England, where Mr Falconer installed his youthful mistress in a house in Park Lane. But alas for love's young dream! it vanished, as Tessy poetically put it, "as swiftly as morning dew". In more prosaic language, Mr Falconer's parents, discovering his whereabouts and his entanglement, brought him to heel by the simple method of cutting off his allowance. Regardless of his pleas they informed him that when he was twenty-one they intended him to marry a neighbouring heiress; in the meantime they banished him to a Scotch university.

The distracted youth wept, swooned, blasphemed, fell into a high fever—so he informed his abandoned flame in a letter in which he assured her that he loved her to adoration, and enclosed a £10 note, which was all the money that he could procure. This £10 and her natural endowments which, as has been indicated, were considerable, were the only weapons with which the fifteen-year-old Tessy, friendless and nameless, faced an indifferent world. She was then and always undaunted.

For a time she passed through considerable hardship and even misery. She joined a band of strolling players and was thrown into jail with the rest of the company by a zealous magistrate when an informer denounced them as "rogues and vagabonds". She performed in a booth at Bartholomew's Fair, she sold oranges at the Haymarket; she was one of the girl attendants at a side-show at Cuper's Gardens who, for a small fee, kissed grinning apprentices and clerks fastened by their necks in a pillory. Finally she was reduced to taking a place as a serving-maid in a Covent Garden gaming-house.

It happened that opposite the gaming-house was a club of more savoury reputation frequented mostly by sporting gentlemen. Early one morning Tessy was scrubbing the steps of the gaming-house, singing to herself as she scrubbed with all the exuberance of her sixteen years. The delicious gaiety of her voice attracted the attention of the club members opposite who, yawning and heavy-eyed, were concluding a night of cards and wine. They crowded to the windows, loud in their appreciation of the sprightly voice and roguish singer.

Among them was Francis Hibbett, an actor of some note, celebrated especially for his performance of tragic roles. Mr Hibbett was a good-looking, agreeable young man; he was much caressed, as the expression went, by the aristocracy, and prided himself upon being a sportsman and a beau as well as a well-known tragedian. As soon as he set eyes on Tessy he recognised her possibilities both as an actress and a woman. He offered to train her for the stage, introduced her to Beard, the Manager of Covent Garden Theatre, and completed his benevolence towards her by becoming her lover.

Tessy's fortunes were now in the ascendant. Up till now she seems to have dispensed with a surname. For her stage début she borrowed the name of an Irish village, and in June 1762, Mrs Teresa Bellingham was billed to appear at Covent Garden as Cordelia to Mr Hibbett's Lear.

Tessy's saucy personality can hardly have appeared to advantage in this role, even though she wore a bodice and train of pink satin over a petticoat of pale green tiffany, with a wreath of rosebuds in her hair and, totally inexperienced as she was, it was a tribute to her charms that the rowdy audience did not boo her from the stage. No doubt as a result of her lover's influence most of the parts that she filled during that season were tragic ones, unsuited to her gifts and quite beyond the range of her undeveloped powers, so it is hardly surprising that she was only a moderate success.

The green-room of Covent Garden Theatre, however, must have seemed to her a dazzling contrast to the malodorous back-quarters of the Covent Garden gaming hell, and Tessy could have no complaints of her lover's generosity or style of living. They had a house in King Street, St James's, kept a phaeton and horses, and entertained lavishly. So lavishly, in fact, that within a year of the beginning of their liaison Mr Hibbett was arrested for debt, and confined in the Marshalsea Prison.

It is impossible not to admire Tessy during this crisis. She accompanied her lover to prison, acted by night, and cooked, washed and scrubbed for him by day. Her good spirits and extraordinary vitality never flagged amid the dismal surroundings of the prison. Hibbett must have felt completely assured of her devotion. But those who consorted with Tessy were liable to receive shocks. No sooner had he obtained his discharge, through the good offices of an uncle, than she left him. It seems that she had begun to tire of him some time ago; only his misfortune had continued to attach her to him. Now that he was comparatively affluent again she had no further use for him. Francis Hibbett, who was as captivated by Tessy as ever, threatened suicide in vain. She declared her resolution of not listening in future to any but honourable proposals. It must be marriage and a coach for her, or nothing.

This mood of calculating prudence, so alien to Tessy's nature, may have decided her to accept an invitation from Barry to appear under his management at the Crow Street Theatre in Dublin. Dublin would provide her with a fresh field for her professional and social activities. Moreover, though her father Lord Kilmallock was dead, she had several influential connections on his side of the family who, if carefully approached, might be disposed to show kindness to their illegitimate young relation.

Tessy was fortunate. She made the crossing from Park Gate, near Chester, to Dublin in the company of a widowed lady, Mrs Curry, who happened to be the companion and close friend of Lady Sibella Vane, the late Lord Kilmallock's spinster sister. Mrs Curry was much taken with the young actress's engaging manners, and naturally struck with the interesting circumstances of her birth. We may be sure that Tessy, in recounting the history of her life, suppressed the more lurid aspects of her career, only retaining those which would diffuse a haze of pathos and romance around her person.

Proof of Mrs Curry's good-will became apparent, a few days after Tessy's arrival in Dublin, in the form of a summons to wait upon Lady Sibella Vane at her house in Kildare Street. Lady Sibella greeted her unacknowledged niece with the well-bred insolence in which eighteenth-century ladies of rank could indulge at pleasure. "Well, young woman, let me have a look at you. 'Pon my word, you have not inherited much of your poor wretched mother's beauty. So much the better for you. However, your person is tolerable enough, and I will allow that you dress with more simplicity and taste than I would have expected from a player. I am heartily glad to see you in chintz. Nothing is more vulgar for a young person of your station than silk of a morning. Always dress plain except when you are upon the stage, and your acquaintances may recollect that by birth you are a lady as well as a bastard."

Tessy was hot-tempered enough on occasion, but luckily her sense of the ridiculous overcame every other feeling now, and enabled her to accept these remarks with a deceptive and winning air of meekness. Lady Sibella promised to promote her welfare, also to take a box for her opening performance as Angelica in *Love for Love*.

Tessy was now launched on a season of unqualified theatrical and social success. Irish acting has always been distinguished for its vitality and brilliance; the rivalry at that time between the Crow Street and Smock Alley Theatres was intense, and the audiences at both theatres, though no less disorderly than those at the London play-houses, were perhaps more genuinely critical and appreciative. Tessy's talents blossomed in this stimulating atmosphere and, in her own words, she soon became "the favourite child of the Dublin public".

Her private life went swimmingly too. Lady Sibella, gratified at her protégée's success, introduced her to "many females of the first rank", who invited the sprightly young actress to their receptions, and treated her with marked kindness and patronage.

Tessy seems at this point in her career to have been positively intoxicated with the idea of respectability. She records with satisfaction the elegant parties at which she sang ballads and played the harpsichord, and her own decorum of behaviour, speech and dress, as though unaware that decorum and Tessy Bellingham could never be permanent bedfellows. Perhaps after her haphazard and raffish existence she enjoyed playing the part of an unfortunate, hardworking but refined young lady in the fashionable drawing-rooms of St Stephen's Green, and Kildare and Molesworth Streets, and derived a malicious amusement from acting the role with her tongue in her cheek. Perhaps she really imagined that a substantial marriage would provide a sufficient outlet for her tempestuous nature.

In either case a disastrous event soon put an end to her aspirations in this direction. A disgraceful feature of life in eighteenth-century Ireland was the Abduction Clubs, whose members, rascally young buckeens, banded together to carry off wealthy heiresses. By some extraordinary mischance Tessy Bellingham, who had no social standing beyond that gained for her by her talents, no family, and no money except her stage earnings, was fixed upon by one of these gangs as its victim. A wild young ruffian called Lucius Fitzpatrick was to be her "husband" (for needless to say these forced marriages were illegal) with some half-dozen of his friends to assist him.

Whether in their ignorance (they had but lately come to Dublin from the wilds of Kerry) they were misled by Tessy's fashionable appearance and acquaintances into supposing that she was the legitimate daughter of the late Earl of Kilmallock, or whether they confused her identity with that of a Miss Bellington, the daughter of a wealthy Dublin wine merchant, was never clearly explained. At any rate, as she left the theatre one night they stopped her chair, dragged her out of it, killing one of her chairmen, forced her into a coach and drove furiously out into the country.

Tessy always had plenty of spirit. She relates that Lucius Fitzpatrick's face was streaming with blood from the scratches she inflicted on it. But her struggles, cries for help and protests did not avail her. She was carried to a remote spot in the Wicklow mountains where a defrocked priest "married" her to Fitzpatrick.

For the next few weeks she was dragged through the south of Ireland, the officers of the law in close pursuit. She had convinced Fitzpatrick by now that she was not the prize he had imagined her to be, but he could not release her, for her evidence would put a rope round his neck. It appears, too, that he was not insensible to those attractions that were later to make her celebrated, for he swore that "he would not let go of her even if she was heiress to nothing but her shift".

She was finally rescued by excise men from a disused lighthouse off the Kerry coast, where her captors had concealed her during their absence on a drinking carousal. A few weeks later Lucius Fitzpatrick and two of his accomplices were arrested as they attempted to escape to France on a smuggler's boat, and were brought to trial at Limerick assizes. Tessy was, of course, the chief witness against them, and her evidence brought them to their death.

Her feelings must have been painful. Brutal as the outrage had been, there seems no doubt that Fitzpatrick had a certain wild and ruffianly charm, and he protested, perhaps with sincerity, that though he had committed the crime on the assumption that Tessy was an heiress, he had become "totally enchanted with the delightful Bellingham".

Tessy was unscrupulous but not hard-hearted. When sentence of death was passed upon Lucius Fitzpatrick and his accomplices she swooned, swooning again (according to her account) when she received a lock of her abductor's hair which he sent her with his hearty regards and apologies upon the morning of his execution.

The trial had brought Tessy a great deal of publicity of a disagreeable and unprofitable kind. Lady Sibella Vane and her friends seemed to consider the abduction more her fault than her misfortune, and Tessy, shaken in spirits and health for the first time in her life, was thankful to take refuge with her mother's Quaker relations who came forward to help her in this extremity.

They were "wet" Quakers, which meant that Tessy could wear her laces, gauzes and other fripperies, in their house without offending their susceptibilities. The solid comfort of their establishment, the abundance of their table, the orderly serenity of their life, must have been soothing at first to Tessy's jangled nerves. But it can be easily imagined that the routine of devotion and good works (which included the distribution to the poor of religious tracts written by Tessy's hostess and aunt, Mrs Savery) soon palled. Tessy admits that her teasing humour got the better of her gratitude; she offended her relations by ridiculing their pious opinions and habits, shocked them by her flighty talk and audacious stories, and ogled her cousin William Savery, who fell a helpless victim to her wiles. The Saverys, in fact, soon discovered that they had given shelter not to a wounded dove but to a mocking-bird, and when Mrs Savery surprised her son and niece together in a compromising situation she bundled Tessy out of the house without any ceremony.

Tessy returned to Dublin by the next coach, convinced now that neither the role of fashionable gentility nor sober respectability was suited to her talents. She returned with delight to the stage which was her true setting.

Unfortunately she reckoned without that loathing of informers which is so deep-rooted a characteristic of the Irish people. This trait, understandable as it is in the light of Irish history, and though it springs from motives that are not in themselves ignoble, is sometimes carried to an excess that ignores fairness and hinders law and order. In this case, it had gathered itself into a hostility, totally unreasoning, against Tessy. The fact that she had been barbarously wronged by Fitzpatrick was ignored; it was only remembered that she had been the means of bringing him and two of his accomplices to the gallows. Fitzpatrick was transformed in the eyes of the mob from a dastardly scoundrel to a dashing hero of romance. With cruel fickleness, and possibly incited by enemies of Barry's, they turned against their favourite, and the night of her reappearance at Crow Street in the role of Lady Easy in

The Careless Husband was the occasion of one of the worst riots in the history of the Irish stage.

No sooner had Tessy made her preliminary curtsey, than the cry—dreaded by actors and actresses—of "Out with the ladies and down with the house!" was raised by a group of buckeens (cronies no doubt of Fitzpatrick), while from the gallery howls of "Informer!" "Who killed Lucius Fitzpatrick?" and "Down with the treacherous whore!" were hurled at the astounded Tessy.

She had her defenders, however, and these fell on her opponents with swords and fists, so that soon free fights were raging in every part of the house. Tessy, with her usual courage, had tried at first to stand her ground, and even to say her opening lines, but the turmoil was indescribable, and when rotten eggs and harder missiles were hurled at her she fled from the stage and took refuge in her dressing-room. The rioters, swarming on to the stage and behind the scenes, began to search the back of the theatre, and things were looking serious for Tessy, when a young Englishman, who had been watching the performance from the stage itself, came to her rescue. Pushing his way through the frightened players and stage hands, he rushed into Tessy's dressing-room, wrapped her in his cloak and, forcing his way at the point of his sword through the mob, bore her into the safety of a coach.

When Tessy had recovered her breath she learnt that her protector was Mr Harry Ogley, a member of a well-known banking family, who was visiting Dublin on business. He was thirty years old, unattached and, though not handsome and somewhat swarthy in complexion, had a pleasing person and an affluent and stylish air. In a very short time Tessy became his mistress, returned with him to London and set up house with him in Soho Square.

Soon after her return to London she made her début at Drury Lane, under the management of the great Garrick, in the role of Araminta in *The School for Lovers*. Her unhappy experiences in Ireland, whatever they may have done to her character, had not impaired her talents. On the contrary she brought to her acting a new zest and a wicked gaiety that her audiences found irresistible. As far as her profession was concerned she had found herself, showing the ability of the true artist to transmute disappointment, unhappiness and even failure into the gold of creative achievement.

Besides being possessed of immense vitality she was a hard worker, and as long as she was under the benevolent discipline of David Garrick she managed to subordinate the vagaries of her temperament to the demands of her profession. She had to compete with actresses of the stature of Mrs Clive, Mrs Abington and Mrs Yates. She was too busy establishing her own position to indulge in those tantrums which later made a manager swear that he would sooner see his theatre in flames and the Bellingham in the midst of them than ever consent to her being part of his company.

Her popularity with the public increased rapidly. It was the custom in those days for the young blades to crowd the wings and even the stage during the performances, commenting audibly on the players' appearance and acting. Garrick strongly discouraged this practice during his management of Drury Lane, but when Mrs Bellingham was billed to appear the boxes were filled with her admirers, who expressed their devotion to her in the loud and familiar manner usual among eighteenth-century playgoers, and her dressing-room was besieged when the play was over. In private life she was no less sought-after, one fashionable young man offering her £10,000 to be admitted to her favour.

All this was highly displeasing to Mr Ogley, who was of a jealous disposition. His irritation at last broke bounds at a supper-party at his house over which Tessy was presiding as hostess. In a playful mood she had made mention of the fact that she had twice been in prison, once in a country jail and once in the Marshalsea, whereupon Mr Ogley, exasperated beyond endurance, one must suppose, at some provocative look or gesture on her part, burst out that next time she would find herself in Bridewell, and that she might rot there before he would lift a finger to release her.

Tessy turned pale at this brutal insult. All the guests looked embarrassed. One of them with a cry of "Shame!" struck his host on the cheek. At dawn the two men fought a duel in Leicester Fields. Mr Ogley was wounded. When he was conveyed home he found that Tessy had left him. She had no mind to play the role of ministering and pardoning angel. No one could cut her sentimental cables quicker than Teresa Bellingham.

The chivalrous and impulsive young man who had championed her sought her out in her lodgings in Tavistock Street to convey to her his sympathy and respect. These sentiments soon gave place to something warmer. Before long Tessy Bellingham was the acknowledged mistress of Charles Chessel, fifth Marquis of Mandlesham.

2

This was the formidable rival against whom Dorothea had unknowingly matched herself. Formidable, because Tessy's fascination depended neither on her looks nor on her character. Her figure was good, her face, with its pert nose, large mouth and mischievous eyes, could hardly be described as pretty, though some beauty might be granted to the colouring of her pale, mat skin and russet hair. Those men who associated with Tessy usually had cause to regret it for, though neither calculating nor cruel, she was amoral, living only (apart from her profession) for the gratification of her wayward impulses and desires. She made no pretence to virtue or good principles; those who loved her did so at their own risk. She tired of them, but they did not tire of her, because she never bored them either as a companion or as a lover.

How pathetically ill-matched these two antagonists were —Dorothea with her unruffled golden beauty, her nature candid as a child's, the rustic gentility and pretentiousness of her upbringing, and Tessy, "that seductive piece of mischief" as one admirer described her, who had fought a lone battle since childhood, who had no illusions, few scruples and a large and varied experience of the male sex.

Tessy had a temper and a tongue. It is related that Mr Ogley, goaded beyond endurance by her taunts during one of their quarrels, rushed out into the street and falling on an inoffensive scavenger tossed the man into his own cart. Having thus relieved his feelings he ran back into the house and, throwing himself at Tessy's feet, implored her forgiveness.

There is no doubt that Charles Mandlesham had captured Tessy's variable affections to a greater extent than any of her other lovers had succeeded in doing. His charm, the essential kindliness and generosity of his nature, his high rank and the air of careless ease and confidence which it had given him, all combined to make him a very desirable lover even to the experienced Tessy. It may be that she even played with the idea of giving up the stage and endeavouring to "elevate herself not only to his bed but to his title", as one gossip writer expressed it. At any rate she had every inducement to please and cherish him, and for some months they lived together "in the most tender and harmonious connection of successful love".

It was impossible, however, for Tessy to control her moods and caprices, and shortly before Lord Mandlesham met Dorothea he and Tessy had had a series of disagreements, culminating in their first serious quarrel. Charles Mandlesham was easy-going to the point of weakness, but even his indulgent good-nature had its limits, and he had a horror of unpleasant scenes. He left Tessy, vowing not to see her again till she had apologised for her outrageous words and behaviour which, as Tessy was not in the habit of apologising, seemed to make the rupture final. At the same time, and this was characteristic of him, he continued to make her a handsome allowance, to send her presents of hothouse fruit and flowers from Crome, and even to exchange notes with her, beneath whose phrases of reproach and teasing sarcasm can be discerned clear signs of unassuaged desire.

This then was the position when Charles Mandlesham became engaged to Dorothea. It would be more creditable to him to be able to say that he honestly believed that he had broken with Tessy for ever. Perhaps he did believe it on the surface of his mind. It is more probable that he did not consider the problem at all.

He must have had some qualms, because it appears that he woke up the morning after the ridotto at Ranelagh with a splitting headache, and the resolve to call on Dorothea and confess to her that he had entered into the engagement in a spirit of reprehensible levity, and was neither free nor worthy to become her husband. His courage held firm till he reached the morning-room of the Aintry's house in Berkeley Square, though it must have been painfully shaken by the sisterly warmth of Jenny's greeting. She ran out of the room to fetch Dolly. He waited in a state of profound mental discomfort easy to imagine, wishing, no doubt, that he could change places with the most miserable beggar in the square outside.

Dorothea came in, shy, dignified, glowing, her face transformed by happiness. He could no more have spoken the words that would shatter her hopes than he could have picked up one of Lord Aintry's antique daggers off the table and stabbed her to the heart. He was irretrievably snared by her simple trustfulness and his own good-hearted weakness. How flattering, too, to his masculine vanity to have this goddess-like creature blushing before him, disarmed by love.

Next Lord Aintry was on the scene to lend Dolly his brotherly support. He admired Dorothea's appearance and poise and respected her good sense—that was as much affection as he could feel for any woman who was not Jenny—and was pleased that she was to make such a fine match. She would be a handsome young peeress, and in every way would be a credit to her exalted station. Perhaps her example would even have a salutary effect on his own adorable but so foolish Jenny. He knew about Tessy Bellingham of course but, in the manner of his class and age, considered that a man's illicit love-affairs had no bearing whatever on his matrimonial plans.

The few close friends to whom Lord Mandlesham confided his predicament urged him to continue the engagement, pointing out to him the necessity for him to settle down sooner or later, and the merits of Dorothea's person and disposition.

Sir Timothy Wakely wrote: "The lady in question, though admittedly not your equal in rank, is not only beautiful to a degree, with a symmetry not often seen in this degenerate age, but has a strong natural understanding though uncultivated. The time must come when you will have to part with your frail fair one—if indeed you have not done so already? I confess that I am not very clear on this subject. What better opportunity, my dear Charles, could present itself than this, when the only alternative is cruelly to mortify a beautiful and deserving young female?"

It seems unkind to suggest that this sage advice was not entirely disinterested, but it must be recorded that the scandalmongers said that Sir Timothy Wakely had designs on the "frail fair one" himself, and that after Tessy's break with Lord Mandlesham the baronet's coach was to be seen most nights outside the actress's house.

Charles Mandlesham's relations naturally approved of a marriage which would proclaim his release from the Bellingham's snares. If Miss Lynch of Cabra House was scarcely a suitable consort for the Marquis of Mandlesham, she was at least a lady, chaste, and of an ennobling beauty.

So amid the congratulations of their respective families, Charles Mandlesham and Dorothea Lynch were married at Wing Magna on August 19th, 1769.

In September Dorothea wrote to her mother from Crome, "I am the most fortunate woman in the world".

She penned these conventional words in all sincerity. Life seemed to stretch before her with the hazy sunlit beauty of a fine spring morning. She was married to the man she loved and, as if this was not happiness enough, honour, wealth and security, and all the importance and interest attached to a dazzling social position, were laid at her feet. It was a fairy-tale existence, but would have meant little to her without the presence of the fairy prince himself. She moved through the brief weeks of her honeymoon as though in a happy dream. This was evidently the impression that she made on one visitor, Lady Mary Thain—

"The new Marchioness has a fine figure and a fine head. She is perfectly agreeable, unaffected and simple, and by no means overcome by the fearful magnificence of Crome. Yet she has a rapturous air as though she had but recently descended from Elysium. This must be attributed I suppose to his lordship of whom she is passionately enamoured. She cannot take her beautiful eyes off him and he, in his turn, shows her every gallantry and attention."

Such exalted happiness cannot endure in an imperfect and mutable world. It must descend to less rarefied levels in order to breathe. But the descent need not have been so cruelly swift. Like Icarus, Dorothea soared too high; her wings, like his, were only fastened by wax which, melting in reality's sun, plunged her headlong into an ocean of disillusionment.

Prolonged honeymoons were not the custom in fashionable eighteenth-century circles. Innumerable social duties and pleasures called the Mandleshams back to town in the early autumn. Mandlesham House, the private palace which Charles's grandfather, the third Marquis of Mandlesham, had built for himself in Mayfair, was hurriedly prepared, and even in part redecorated, to receive its new mistress.

The household accounts, still preserved in the Muniment Room at Crome, give a vivid picture of the bustle and excitement at the great London house. We can see the groom of the chambers—a person of terrifying hauteur who never accepted anything but gold as a "vail"— pacing up and down the beautiful ballroom while hordes of lesser domestics dusted the great chandeliers and the swags of carved flowers over the doorways, bees-waxed the expanse of polished floor and hung up the new curtains of crimson silk damask embroidered with golden wheat ears. Under the housekeeper's supervision a regiment of maids, in mob-caps and aprons, shook out the bed curtains and mattresses stuffed with "superfine seasoned swan feathers", and cleaned out cavernous wardrobes for the reception of her ladyship's gowns, which in due course would become the perquisite of the upper waiting-maids and be sold by them at exorbitant prices. Below-stairs Monsieur Périgord, the French chef, in a frenzy of culinary inspiration, which must have been trying for the scullions and turnspits under his command, evolved a "Potage à la Marquise" composed, among other ingredients, of six chickens, three pints of cream and twenty eggs. The footmen were to have new liveries of mulberry and silver, the hall-porter was to have a new high-winged chair, Lady Mandlesham's little negro page a suit of yellow satin.

Soon after their return to London the Mandleshams gave a ball which the ubiquitous Horace Walpole described as "the most magnificent entertainment of its kind since the feast of Ahasuerus".

Dorothea was "in extraordinary beauty", in a gown of pale green moiré embroidered with silver sea-weeds and shells. It was remarked that she looked happy beyond measure. The "sweetness and obligingness" of her aspect was commented upon. Jenny, her sister-goddess, was of course by her side; her appearance in a dress of rosy gauze glittering with silver spangles "exceeded for beauty anything that was ever beheld". Certainly the *folie de Lynch* had not yet abated.

This was the apogee of the Lovely Lynchs' triumph. Never again would they both appear together so radiant, so carefree, so sure of their destinies. Let them enjoy themselves while they may to the sound of violins and harps and gay, chattering voices and laughter, in the glitter of the iridescent chandeliers and of jewels, in an atmosphere perfumed with late roses and eau de luce and bergamot. The golden hour will soon pass, will soon be buried deep beneath the dust of Time.

3

A few days after this ball Lord and Lady Mandlesham entertained a party of friends in their box at Drury Lane. The play was *The Provoked Husband*, with Mrs Tessy Bellingham in the role of Lady Townley.

It is difficult to imagine why Charles Mandlesham chose to put his resolution to the test in this embarrassing manner so early in his married life. That he was actuated by a callous disregard either for his young wife's or for his discarded mistress's feelings is out of keeping with the amiability of his nature. The simple probability is that someone in the party—perhaps the unsuspecting Dorothea herself—wished to see the play and, as usual, he took the line of least resistance.

To Tessy his presence there with his bride at her own first stage appearance of the season seemed an audacious challenge. Tessy never let a challenge pass unanswered. This was the kind of risky, provocative situation in which she revelled. She was too clever a woman and an actress to commit the vulgarity of making an obvious set at her former lover. Rather she seemed by her subtle glances, smiles and inflections of the voice, to remind him that they shared a delectable secret. The audience, tingling with excitement, knew that Tessy was out for reconquest yet, with consummate skill, she did not allow the situation to become out of hand or to affront Lord Mandlesham's fastidiousness.

Never had the remarkable fascination which seemed to emanate from her been more in evidence than it was that evening. Every man in the audience was at liberty to imagine that it was displayed for him; everyone knew that Lord Mandlesham was its particular object.

"The little devil Bellingham surpassed herself last night at Drury Lane", runs one cynical comment. "Like the great Cæsar she may proclaim 'Veni, vidi, vici.' Alas! for the noble Marquess's good resolutions. They were quaking during the first act, crumbling during the second, and in ruins before the fall of the curtain."

This malicious comment was not far off the truth. Before the play was over Charles Mandlesham realised with consternation that he was still in love with Tessy. Moreover her figure—no longer boyishly slim, but flaunting a not yet unbecoming rotundity—announced to him quite plainly his approaching paternity. (For it was Tessy's boast that she never had more than one lover at a time.)

Everything appeared to him now in a totally different light. All the circumstances pleaded on her behalf. Her tantrums and tempers could be attributed to her physical condition. How ill he had used her, how inconsiderately and impatiently, failing her at the moment of all others when she needed his kindness and attention. What an enchanting wretch she was when all was said and done, full of spirit and devilry, no mere "sprightly girl in genteel comedy" but the most seductive actress that ever trod the stage, and as seductive off the stage as she was on it. Good feeling, nay honour, demanded that he should be reconciled to her and offer his protection to her and to his unborn child. What was more, he wanted so much to be with her again.

So his thoughts must have run, till with a horrid jolt he realised that the beautiful young woman by his side was his loving and confiding bride. What an intolerable position for a man to be in! Whatever he did he must injure one of these charming women. How could he have known that one look at Tessy would undo all his firmness? No wonder that one of the party in his box recorded that "pleasure and confusion were mingled in his countenance to an extraordinary degree".

Dorothea was to write to her daughter the words, "Sometimes in life you may experience in a few moments the emotions of many years." When she wrote these words was she thinking of that evening at Drury Lane when she learnt in a flash of cruel enlightenment that her husband loved not her but another woman, that he had never loved her, that her happiness was built on nothing but self-deception? This, not her wedding night, was the end of her girlhood.

Dorothea, though unsophisticated, was not a fool. Tessy's triumphant demeanour, the scarcely concealed curiosity, malicious or pitying, of her acquaintances, the tense, excited atmosphere in the theatre, above all Charles's face, told her everything.

Like someone bleeding from an internal wound she

rallied all her pride and courage to conceal her desperate hurt. "Lady Mandlesham displayed a superb tranquillity which did more credit to her sense than her sensibility", commented one observer. Another one wrote more charitably: "I pitied the poor young woman from my heart. She was as white as her gown, but conducted herself with an admirable composure and dignity which would have made me love her had I been a man."

If Dorothea had had any doubts as to the relationship between her husband and Tessy Bellingham, or the paternity of Tessy's child, they would have been brutally dissipated by a copy of the *Town and Country Magazine*, sent her by an anonymous hand, which gave an easily recognisable and salacious account of Tessy's career, her amour with Lord Mandlesham and his ill-considered marriage to Dorothea. Society, the writer said, was waiting eagerly to see who would win the struggle for the noble lord's accommodating heart—his beautiful Hibernian spouse or the inimitable Mrs T——y B——m.

Dorothea was no good at making scenes. This trait which made her extremely agreeable to live with over a number of years was to stand her in bad stead now. If she had wept and pleaded with Charles, or gone into the hysterics that were a recognised part in those days of a refined female's armoury, he would no doubt have made a determined effort to keep away from Tessy. He was fond of Dorothea, he respected and admired her. ("When Miss Dolly Lynch comes into a room she makes all the fine ladies look like milliners' girls", he told a friend.) Moreover she had the advantage of having easy access to him—an important consideration where he was concerned.

If this crisis had occurred later in their married life Dorothea would have known better how to deal with it. But the blow had fallen too suddenly and too soon. She had been cast down from too lofty a state of happiness not to be stunned by the fall. Her nature being what it was she took refuge in proud reserve and silence. What she suffered behind the serene and beautiful mask that she presented to the world can only be guessed. Out of the depths of bitter experience she gave her daughter this advice: "Never flatter yourself that you are impervious to the baser emotions—spite, malice and above all, jealousy —till you have had the opportunity of experiencing and the chance of overcoming them. You may think you know yourself better than you know your dearest friend. Beware! one day you may find that you have had a stranger slumbering in your soul."

Charles, who had waited unhappily for some kind of an outburst from his young wife and was prepared to admit that he was a scoundrel and a brute, was amazed, rather hurt and greatly relieved at her non-committal attitude. If she was not going to drag the unpleasant subject to the light *he* was certainly not going to do so. Perhaps she did not care so much after all. Perhaps she was satisfied with her title, her position and his regard. Perhaps she was one of those lovely but unemotional women whose ardour was quenched by their first experience of sexual life. These suppositions, though not flattering to his vanity, were soothing to his conscience.

Very soon Lord Mandlesham's coach was to be seen again outside the door of Mrs Teresa Bellingham's house in Jermyn Street. The *Town and Country Magazine* recorded for its readers' edification that the actress had won the day.

CHAPTER X

CROME

FOR THE first time in her life Dorothea felt not only bitterly unhappy but also very unwell. Soon she knew that she also was bearing Charles Mandlesham's child. This knowledge, which should have filled her with joy, now seemed to put the final touch to her humiliation. She had some experience by this time of the "beau monde" and its ways. They would lay bets at White's and Boodle's as to the outcome of her and Tessy's pregnancy. Would the wife or the mistress, or both, present Mandlesham with a son? Well, she would not be there to be stared at, discussed and joked about. Her health gave her an excuse to retire to Crome. It was a retreat and she knew it. By leaving London, she left the field clear to the brazen Tessy who went about everywhere with her lover, had his initials, surrounded with a wreath of forget-me-nots, blazoned on her carriage and appeared on the stage (in the insouciant manner of eighteenth-century actresses) till within a week or so of her confinement. But Dorothea, sick in soul and body, was in no shape to challenge her triumphant rival. For perhaps the only time in her life she hauled down her colours. Another inducement to leave London was the embarrassment which Jenny's championship of her cause entailed.

It had been almost as great a shock to Jenny as to Dorothea to learn the true state of Dorothea's matrimonial affairs. But unlike Dorothea the discovery did not stun her into silence. She expressed her indignation and anger freely and to anyone who would listen, heaping all the blame upon Tessy (for she had a weakness for her handsome brother-in-law), comparing her, with her usual inaccuracy, to Messalina, Jezebel and Lady Macbeth. When they met face to face at a reception at Mrs Cornelys' Assembly Rooms, Jenny said loudly, "Pah, this place stinks of grease paint", and left, remarking as she walked away, "I was told that women of the town had been seen here on the staircase. I did not think that they would admit them upstairs."

Tessy revenged herself for this insult in her own fashion, giving an impromptu imitation of Lady Aintry at a supper-party at Vauxhall, in which she took off Jenny's airs and graces and ridiculous turns of speech to the life.

Jenny could think of no better retort to this than to attend a performance of *Romeo and Juliet*, with Tessy in the role of Juliet, and to laugh loudly as Tessy stabbed herself and sank on Romeo's body.

Dorothea pleaded with her sister in a letter:

"I am most sensible, dear sweet Jenny, of the warm sisterly partiality which makes you hate Mrs Bellingham, as you say, but I beg you a thousand times not to embroil yourself with her on my behalf, or even let the thought of her disturb your own happiness. And for heaven's sake do not spit in her face, as you threaten to do! You cannot hope to have the quickness of retort of a Mrs Bellingham, and in endeavouring to challenge her in that way you will only expose yourself to mortification and injure yourself and me. Good breeding and decorum are our only weapons. They are poor ones I agree against the audacity of a Mrs B. but we cannot be different from what we are. Pray do not distress yourself on my account, dearest sister. This would only add greatly to my melancholy. I have no wish to play the part of injured innocence. I should have reflected before rushing into a marriage in which all the advantages were clearly on my side, for I see now that good looks in themselves are not sufficient to gain ascendency over a man's heart. You have often told me, in your fond way, that I am not vain. I begin to believe that lack of vanity can be in itself a form of conceit! I have quitted London willingly for I am too sick at the moment to enjoy a bustle, and by putting these months between me and what has occurred I hope to regain my calm of mind. I believe I shall like this place very well when I can find my way about it! The other day I was lost in the grounds and had to be recovered by a search party of two footmen and a page!

Your loving sister,

DOLLY."

She added in a postscript the writing of which betrays her agitation:

"Pray do not think that my lord neglects me. He is kindness itself and has made every arrangement for my comfort. I wish I did not like him so well."

The "fearful magnificence" of Crome cannot have been a cheerful refuge for a bruised spirit. Dorothea went there in preference to the six other houses of which she was mistress, because it was the only one that she knew, and perhaps for the unacknowledged reason that it was her husband's principal residence.

This vast mansion in Buckinghamshire had been built on the site of a smaller house by Charles's father from designs by the architect Henry Flitcroft. Two small villages had been removed to make the park, which was twelve miles in circumference; the avenue to the entrance front of the house was two miles long. The house itself, with its lofty portico flanked by Ionic pillars, was intimidating. One flippant visitor, indeed, declared that he always felt like a sacrificial lamb being borne to the altar when he ascended the broad sweep of steps to the front door. This suggestion of antiquity was continued in the marble hall modelled on the form of a Roman basilica, with a mosaic pavement which had, in fact, been brought from Rome. The view from the other side of the house was calculated to reduce the beholder to a gasp of admiration, sweeping as it did, placidly and majestically, down an immensely long avenue to a large artificial lake, and beyond it to a vista of more wooded avenues and plantations.

The park itself was covered with a bewildering variety of temples, pavilions, obelisks, urns and other monuments. It seemed that whenever the late Lord Mandlesham had had nothing better to do he had erected a Garden Temple in honour of Psyche, or Female Chastity, or Venus, or of the Protestant Martyrs and Reformers. A hundred-foot obelisk commemorated the Duke of Monmouth; there was also a Shakespeare monument, a Mausoleum, on a knoll above the lake, in which no one was buried, a Rotunda with nothing noteworthy about it except an air of grandiose failure, a rather gloomy Orangery, and a charming and elegant Dairy with fountains, marble floor and utensils of finest porcelain.

In contrast to all this grandeur the kitchen and back quarters were at some distance from the house and connected with it by an underground tunnel, so that the hordes of menials who were needed for the maintenance of the great house should not intrude their vulgar presences on its immediate surroundings. Dorothea, sitting in state with her waiting gentlewoman, Miss Honora Pim, through the splendidly served but tepid meals, must often have thought with longing of the days when she could run into the smoky kitchen of Cabra House and help herself to a potato roasted on the ashes, or a slice of wheaten bread and honey.

Association casts a curious charm over places and people. Dorothea's letters to her mother at this period unconsciously betray her state of mind by their nostalgic allusions to her home. "I think constantly of you, dearest mother, and of dear Ardnabannagh. It seems years since I heard a seagull's cry."

Anything less cosy than the haunted, desolate house on that bleak headland can hardly be imagined. Yet to Dolly the remembrance of it brought a melancholy solace as she wandered forlornly about the fine park at Crome, along damp, seemingly endless paths littered (despite the labours of innumerable gardeners) with fallen leaves. In her profound disillusionment and depression she longed for the wild cliffs of Ardnabannagh, for the harsh voices of the seagulls, the smell of seaweed, the clean, fierce breath of the Atlantic gales. Here in this huge English palace she was a stranger—a stranger, too, in the heart of the man she loved.

Her melancholy, however, was not entirely unrelieved. Charles Mandlesham was an unfaithful husband, he could not be an unkind or neglectful one. He sincerely wished to see everyone belonging to him cheerful and comfortable. He had not the resolution to break with Tessy—indeed he was more madly in love with her than ever—but he could at least salve his conscience by sparing Dorothea unnecessary mortification. He not only sent her many presents—a new harp, a pet monkey, a book on Greek sculpture (with a note "For a statue of Lady Mandlesham see page 17, but your neck is more beautiful"), an ivory etui-case of exquisite workmanship, a paining by Canaletto, a piece of tapestry in silk and wool which, with its mandarins, Chinese ladies, parrots and flowering trees, is typical of the "chinoiserie" in which the eighteenth century delighted, he also came frequently to Crome, bringing with him small parties of friends whom he knew would be congenial to Dorothea (for a tête-à-tête could only be embarrassing to them both).

These intimate house-parties were agreeable; as

Dorothea emerged from the nausea of the early months and felt well again, she could not help looking forward to them, and to the moment when Charles rode or drove up to the door, filling the great solitary house, it seemed, with his gay and vital presence. It was all very well telling herself that she was a betrayed and injured wife, that pride and morality demanded that she should remain aloof from him till he renounced Tessy. Reason told her that such an attitude would probably condemn her to years of loneliness, that in a society where conjugal fidelity was derided as a stuffy bourgeois prejudice, her position was by no means unique. The remedy was in her hands—the worldlings would tell her: let her stop moping and take a lover. They could not know to what helplessness she had been reduced by her love for Charles.

With what anguish of tenderness and regret, with what a mingling of the keenest pleasure and pain, she must have watched Charles during those winter evenings as they sat with a few friends in the "Little Drawing Room", a delightful room with wainscoted walls and narrow oaken doors, dating from early Georgian times and a survival of the older house. The curtains would be drawn, shutting out the wind and rain and the park with its absurd temples, the candles lit in the silver candlesticks, a fire burning between the wrought-iron fire-dogs. Perhaps Charles would be leaning against the chimney-piece in something like the indolent, debonair attitude in which he is depicted in one of his portraits, one hand caressing his spaniel's satin ears, the firelight throwing its fitful light on his charming, pleasant face, his vivid colouring, his wine-coloured velvet coat. The conversation would be of politics, sport, literature, farming, science, philosophy, art —for Charles Mandlesham was interested in everything and was far better informed than one might have imagined from his dilettante air. He would recount for Dorothea's benefit the gossip of the town, amusingly but without malice. ("He is most indulgent to everyone—including himself!" a friend notes with affectionate exasperation.) One topic only had to be avoided—the stage and the latest triumphs of Mrs Tessy Bellingham.

Or perhaps they would play at cards and Charles would tease his wife on her "infernal good luck", declaring that it was a good thing that he had already bestowed all his possessions on her ("but not your heart", Dorothea might have added to herself), as otherwise she would have him beggared quite.

Or he would bring out his plans for altering the lay-out of the park and garden at Crome, for his father's and grandfather's building mania had descended to him in a more horticultural form. He was an enthusiast for the work of the celebrated landscape gardener, "Capability" Brown. With his assistance he intended to transform the park, to do away with all formality and petty detail, to have everything as "natural" as possible.

The kindliness of his nature made him somewhat ahead of his time, for "benevolence" was not yet the vogue that it was to become later in the century. He also had designs for a model village to be built for his tenants, and for a charity school to accommodate ten female orphans from the ages of two to fifteen years who, "giving promise of talent in singing, drawing and modelling are to be trained to earn their living at the same".

Dorothea was dubious about this—would there be sufficient orphaned talent in the neighbourhood?—and in the end persuaded him to endow an orphanage of the more orthodox kind—but the gardening plans interested her, for she had a strong bent that way herself.

Then, in a day or two, he would ride away again, promising to send her five small volumes in quarto of the Letters of the Great Painters, and silence and loneliness would descend again upon Crome.

On March 5th Dorothea's private journal contained the entry: "Dreamt last night that Mrs B. had given birth to a Leprechaun. My lord was displeased. I was glad. She only laughed. Have been in deep melancholy all day and ashamed."

The coincidence is curious. On the night of Dorothea's dream her rival was indeed delivered, not however of any abnormality but of a healthy son. More interesting, however, is the light which it throws on Dorothea's state of mind at that time. The train of ideas is easily discernible— the disturbance in her mind produced by the conflict between her jealousy and her natural magnanimity and scorn for "the baser emotions", expressing itself in an image borrowed from her Irish childhood, her dread of Tessy's triumphant maternity, her subconscious acknowledgment that Tessy, audacious and without scruple, held all the winning cards. "She only laughed."

Tessy took motherhood in her stride. Three weeks after her confinement she appeared again on the stage in "better looks and spirits than ever she was". No wonder. By giving birth to Lord Mandlesham's child she had greatly tightened her hold upon him. Moreover she had robbed her rival of that great moment in a woman's life when she shows her husband his first-born son.

It is significant that Charles's gifts to Dorothea at this time were more numerous than ever. His efforts to console her can only have added to her bitterness. What woman wants such sedulous and laboured kindness from the man she loves? She must have been aware, with an uncontrollable pang, of a new air of elation in Charles's expression and manner. His sophisticated existence had not made him cynical or even blasé. He felt a simple pride and pleasure in his son (as indeed he was to do in all his children), more suited, his friends would have considered had they suspected it, to one of his ploughmen than to a man of rank and fashion.

Something of Dorothea's soreness of spirit slipped past her usual good taste and reserve on one occasion soon after the birth of Tessy's child. The Mandleshams were showing a party of friends over the grounds; one of them suggested (surely jokingly!) that Lord Mandlesham ought to build another temple. "To whom should it be dedicated?" someone asked. "Why, to the Goddess of Fertility, of course," Dorothea said unkindly. It was observed that Lord Mandlesham flushed and looked "somewhat pained" at this unexpected thrust.

On May 25th Dorothea gave birth to a daughter. Everyone was very sorry for her, and predicted that by her failure to produce an heir her position would be considerably worsened. In actual fact Charles was delighted with his daughter. He had had no sisters himself, or girl cousins. A baby girl to him was an irresistible novelty. The child, who was christened Carolina Jane, was as pretty as a doll, with a look, even in her cradle, of her aunt Jenny. "She certainly has a degree of elegance in her appearance (if not her manners) which I would not have supposed possible in so young an infant", Lord Mandlesham reported, apparently quite seriously, to a great-aunt.

Dorothea was passionately devoted to the child from the moment that she first took it in her arms. Her life, which had seemed aimless and desolate, now took on a new purpose. She resolved to live in retirement at Crome and, putting every hope and regret behind her as far as Charles was concerned, to devote herself to her daughter's upbringing.

She was in advance of her time on the subject of infant hygiene. She insisted on nursing the child herself, refused to allow it to be wrapped in swaddling clothes, and kept it in the open-air as much as possible. (She thanked Lady Moffat, however, in all sincerity for sending her Dr Anodynes's necklace, and promised to hang it round the baby's neck when it was teething.) Contrary to the prognostications of various family dowagers, Carolina did not die but thrived.

So the summer passed. In September a visitor came to Crome who was to alter the whole trend of Dorothea's life. This was Jenny's great-aunt by marriage, Lady Hannah Martindale. Jenny wrote from Wing Magna in some excitement: "My great ant Martindale bids me tell you she is comming to you next weak. Lord Aintry says this is a progedy. She had not been known to stire from her house for 10 years. Pray remember she does not ate meat or any fleshe. Pray write *imediately* and tell me the object of her vist. I shall be dyeing of curosity."

The manner of Lady Hannah's arrival was in accordance with her usual eccentricity. First of all a running footman appeared, requesting the Marchioness of Mandlesham to have a crowdie ready for Lady Hannah. It was to be made of vegetable water or milk, and thickened with oatmeal and frumenty. Next, Lady Hannah's travelling coach arrived. Out of it emerged (in charge of an attendant) not Lady Hannah but her pets—a very old dog, a young fox and a tortoise. The usual retinue of servants followed behind, and Lady Hannah, who detested travelling in a closed vehicle, brought up the rear, wrapped in a burnous, and riding a Syrian ass.

Dorothea in a considerable flutter was waiting for her in front of the house. The old lady embraced her, then took a look at the imposing façade of Crome. "It will make a notable ruin", she commented acidly.

Some of Lady Hannah's sayings during her stay are recorded in Dorothea's journal:

"Jenny's husband is a fool because he loves her too much; yours is a fool because he does not love you enough."

"I dote on Jenny. But her bright charms are as dangerous as a lighted candle carried about by a child walking in its sleep."

"I could have married old Lord Mandlesham had I chose. He was mad for love of me when I was fifteen and less of a fright than I am now! If I had been that young scamp Charles' grandmother, I would have brought him up better than those old fools of aunts I promise you!"

"The Bellingham ought to be sewn in a sack and thrown into the Thames. But if she were, half the men in London would jump in after her."

A final entry on the eve of Lady Hannah's departure reads:

"Lady H. talked to me till 2 oclock of the morning. In the end I promised to do as she directed me."

No one will ever know now what Lady Hannah said to Dorothea as they sat together over the fire in the Little Drawing Room. Whatever it was, it made Dorothea leave her country retreat soon afterwards, and take up residence again at Mandlesham House. What is more, the manner of her re-entry into society showed the world that she was no longer prepared to be relegated to the position of a forlorn and forsaken wife.

The bustle which heralded her return equalled that which had preceded her arrival at Mandlesham House as a bride. Mantua-makers, milliners and jewellers were told to hold themselves in readiness. An entire wing was redecorated and refurnished for young Lady Cara and her nurses. The whole house was filled with white roses—Dorothea's favourite flower.

Dorothea's journey up from Crome was almost in the nature of a royal progress. News that one of the Lovely Lynchs was travelling to town spread rapidly. At an inn at Chesham no less than six hundred people sat up all night to see Lady Mandlesham step into her coach. At the sight of her with her pretty babe in her arms (for she would not trust it even to its nurse on the journey) they broke into loud cheering.

Those who were privileged to see Dorothea in the privacy of her nurseries at Mandlesham House agreed that Lady Mandlesham holding her baby was "the finest sight conceivable", and put one in mind of a painting by Correggio.

In fact she made motherhood quite fashionable that season, and several titled young mothers took to walking about in the Park carrying their infants and wearing a soulful expression on their faces—but none of them enjoyed Lady Mandlesham's success in this line, and they soon returned with relief to their card-tables.

Dorothea, however, did not intend to remain cloistered in her nurseries, absorbing though she found her maternal duties. Not long after her return to town she presided over one of those brilliant entertainments for which Mandlesham House was to be celebrated. She was in a gown of white satin over a petticoat of silver brocade. The Mandlesham diamonds adorned her lovely throat and arms, a sparkling tiara crowned her piled-up mass of fair, shining hair. (It was reported that Lord Mandlesham had made her promise, when she married him, never to use powder.) Her appearance was acclaimed as splendid and queenly to a degree. Yet there was a sweetness and candour in her smile which was very pleasing. Some inner excitement had lent unusual animation to her face and heightened her delicate complexion to a wonderful brilliance. Lord Mandlesham was by her side as she received her guests at the head of the great staircase, and seemed to join in the general admiration of his wife.

Jenny was absent that night, in bed with a feverish cold, and this was almost Dorothea's first appearance alone at an important social function. As a rule the eyes of the beholders, after paying their tribute of admiration to the handsome elder sister, rested in a kind of fascination on the volatile Jenny. Now that general attention was concentrated on Dorothea it was agreed, with considerable relish, that the Bellingham had better look to herself.

In modern military language, it might be said that though Dorothea was not able to launch a counter-attack against her foe, her withdrawal had come to an end, and she was using every means in her power to consolidate her position. She could not hope to be the object of Charles's passion, but she could still play an important role in his life. As his wife, as the mother of his legitimate child, and the mistress of his great houses and vast estates, she had an undisputed position and, what was more, she meant to lay claim to it. In the portraits of Dolly painted at this time, her expression, though amiable, has a hint of determination not apparent in the earlier portraits.

Perhaps the instincts inherited from her far-off, tough, fighting Lynch ancestors had come to her aid; perhaps it was just the tenacity of a woman in love.

CHAPTER XI

MARRIAGE À LA MODE—JENNY

IT WAS not long before Dorothea had something else to worry about besides her own domestic troubles. Jenny and Lord Aintry had been married now for over a year and a half, and it was becoming obvious to their friends that the marriage was not going well. For a fashionable husband and wife to be politely indifferent to each other was nothing extraordinary. Examples of conjugal harmony in high circles were not in fact as rare as the cynics liked to suppose but, on the whole, it was not considered modish to be in love with your own husband or wife. Or if you must be in love, then you could at least

147

have the good breeding not to show it. It was true that the late Duke of Richmond had sat by his wife's side all night at a ball kissing her hand, but a duke could infringe the conventions in a way not permitted to lesser men.

The Aintry marriage, however, presented some unusual features. Lord Aintry, that cool, sardonic and elegant man, had undoubtedly married for love, displaying in his wooing the impetuosity of a love-sick boy. Nor had his devotion to Jenny foundered during the early months of their married life. It had been sorely tried in many ways. Jenny's sweet and playful manner barely veiled her profound if unconscious indifference to him. She was equally charming to her servants, her pet animals, the cottagers at Wing Magna, the link boy who lighted her to her chair. It was as natural to Jenny to try to charm people as it was for a bird to sing. She believed herself to be very fond of her husband, but seldom considered his feelings or his wishes. As her confidence in her powers of fascination increased, stimulated to a dangerous degree by the immoderate flattery and adulation she received, she began to flout him with the gay insolence of a spoilt child. At first she had been overawed by his superior culture and manners, and grateful to him for the worldly benefits that he had bestowed upon her. Now she began insensibly to feel that if he had not married her someone else equally grand and distinguished would have been glad to have done so. Gratitude turned imperceptibly into complacence—a childish complacence it is true, but exasperating all the same to her husband.

At first with pain and then with resentment, Lord Aintry watched his young wife, whom he had adored with a romantic fervour, drift away from his influence, or rather whirl away in an eddy of racketing pleasures and gaieties.

Her foolish sayings, which were so diverting to her acquaintances, offended his good taste. Her vanity was pathetically transparent and expressed itself in remarks

148

that were eagerly snatched up by the malicious and repeated round the town. "Lord Aintry says Dolly and me is *hors de combat*", she said proudly, leaving her astonished hearers to guess that her husband had used the phrase *"hors concours"* to affirm the supremacy of the Lovely Lynchs' good looks.

"Now I have seen the new beauty I shall be quite easy", she was reported to have said after her first sight of a rival. At a masquerade at Chesterfield House, a little boy, who was staying there, ran up to her and staring earnestly in her face said, "They told me you were very beautiful but you are even more beautiful than they said." "You pretty little love!" cried Jenny snatching him up and covering him with kisses, "have you never seen me before?"

Such naïve delight in her own attractions might seem disarming. Lord Aintry only saw the ridicule which it brought upon her—and himself.

Her gaffes, though generally considered amusing, sometimes made her enemies. A titled lady, renowned for her gallantries, dealt for Lady Aintry at a card-party while the latter went out of the room for a few minutes. On her return Jenny said agreeably, "Ah, I see a virgin angel has been dealing for me." Naturally no one, least of all the infuriated woman, believed that Jenny had not been guilty of a provocative piece of malice. In vain Jenny protested that she had just said the first thing that came into her head. The name was too piquantly incongruous not to stick. The lady was henceforth known as "The Virgin Angel" and hated Jenny accordingly.

The worst of it was that Jenny had not the least wish or intention of cultivating her mind and improving her understanding. Why should she, when nearly everyone told her that she was perfect as she was (for unmalicious herself she never suspected that she was laughed at behind her back)? Let Dolly have French and Italian lessons in the morning, or devote so many hours a day to serious reading, or attend the Belle Assemblée, where a number of ladies debated on abstract subjects before an attentive audience. Jenny was not going to waste one precious moment of her youth on such frumpy pursuits. It was Jenny's delight to burst in on her sister during her hours of study and entice her away to a shopping expedition or a drive in the Park. "Shure, Dolly, now you are a Marchioness you don't need to improve your mind", she teased her.

Probably Dorothea did not admit even to her sister that her pursuit of knowledge was not as detached as it seemed. She realised that if she wished to shine in Charles's eyes as a hostess, and interest him as a companion, she must educate herself, for good-looks alone would not enable her to hold her own in the brilliant and cultured society in which she moved. Such arguments would not have appealed to Jenny, who, confident in her possession of Lord Aintry's love, made not the least effort to retain it.

With deep concern Dorothea watched the growing estrangement between her sister and brother-in-law. Fair-minded as a rule, she did not pretend to be impartial where her adored Jenny was concerned. Though she realised how exasperating Jenny's behaviour must be to her husband, she could not help feeling that with his greater knowledge of the world and intelligence—to say nothing of his seventeen years' seniority—he was also to blame. Jenny, whatever her faults, was so good-natured and responsive to affection, still so fresh and tender underneath her flighty manner. But there was something unbending and haughty in Lord Aintry's disposition, and irascible in his temper that made him as deeply resentful now as before he had been deeply in love. Never before in his life had he loved any creature as he had loved this ignorant Irish girl, whose wonderful eyes and sylph-like grace had bewitched him into a marriage in which he gave everything and received very little in return.

His love died slowly, almost imperceptibly, with many a rally, in which his passion for Jenny struggled with his disillusionment; and Jenny, blissfully unconscious of the hurt that she had inflicted on him, for her own heart was as yet unawakened by suffering, danced and gambled and laughed and chatted her way through the crowded puerile days and the hectic gaiety of the nights.

"Young Lady Aintry is the queen of the gay, fluttering, unthinking young people of fashion", one letter-writer reported. Later she is described as surrounded by the "gay and dissolute and committing a thousand extravagances, though with a wild innocence in her air which makes me believe her to be nothing worse than giddy and indiscreet, whatever her enemies may say to the contrary."

At first her "extravagances" were of a more childish than adult nature. It may seem laughable, at this distance in time, to record that one of the chief causes of dispute between her and Lord Aintry was the lateness of the hours she kept. Jenny had had enough of early bedtime during her girlhood at Cabra House. Now she seemed to grudge every moment lost in the unconsciousness of sleep. When the ball or masquerade was over there would be a supper-party, and over this the merry company lingered for hours with song and music, talk and laughter. The guttering candles would be replaced, the wine-glasses refilled; voices became low and confidential. Lady Aintry's eyes glistened beneath her lashes that lay on her cheek like a black bird's wings, her exquisite face glowed as she listened to the gallantries and compliments murmured into her ear by her latest beau. It would be dawn, sometimes broad daylight, before her chairmen carried her home to Berkeley Square.

Dorothea had the embarrassment of being present at a quarrel between husband and wife on this very subject.

Lord Aintry told Jenny that in his opinion eleven o'clock was a reasonable time to go to bed, except when some gala occasion should warrant a later hour. "Eleven o'clock!" Jenny exclaimed. "Why that is the very time when I begin to enjoy myself." "So much the worse, Madam, for your health and looks," retorted Lord Aintry. "You will destroy them both if you persist in these ruinous habits." "What would you say if I did not come home till four o'clock to-morrow?" said Jenny mischievously. "I would order the doors to be locked at midnight." "And if I should not come home till to-morrow night?" "You would never come home again, Madam," was Lord Aintry's stern reply.

There must have been something behind this trivial bickering which made Dorothea record it with such minuteness in her journal. What impressed it so painfully on her mind—some flash of defiance in Jenny's brilliant eyes, some hardening of her mouth, or was there a new note in Lord Aintry's voice that sounded a warning to Dorothea's anxious ears? Did she see husband and wife face each other with the sudden, surprised hostility of strangers, aware, for all the familiarity of their bodies, of the deep separation of their souls?

As time went on Lord Aintry had more serious cause for complaint. In her search for excitement, Jenny fell a victim to the fashionable vice of gambling. At first she played in her friends' houses; later she became an habituée of several of the better-class gambling-houses. In the eighteenth century any member of the peerage had the right to run a gaming house, and some of them were not above using their town houses for this purpose. These semi-private gambling-houses were conducted with a strict regard for decorum and etiquette. Swords were left at the door, and upstairs attendants stood round the rooms to keep order and watch out for card sharpers.

There were two tables. At the silver table, where the

stakes ranged from the modest sum of one shilling upwards, might be seen the "cits"—apprentices, lawyers, clerks, students and the like. At the gold table, where the lowest stake was half a guinea, Jenny, accompanied by some admiring beau, could be sure of meeting people of her own circle (though there might also be a country squire or two and even a highwayman in the company)—friends like Lord Stavordale, not yet twenty-one, who had lost £11,000 in a night at Almack's, but recovered it by one great hand at hazard, and his cousin, that fat, ugly, fascinating young man Charles Fox, who was considered one of the best speakers in the House of Commons and one of the most fashionably-dressed young men in London, and who had already incurred gambling debts to the tune of thousands of pounds.

Though the company might be good, the effect of this atmosphere on Jenny was bad. Jenny was never meant to be a plunger. Unlike Dorothea, who had phenomenally good luck at cards and a cool and steady head, Jenny was both a wild and an unlucky player. No one less calculating or level-headed ever sat down at a card-table. She played deep because it was fashionable and exciting and, as her losses mounted up alarmingly, she played still deeper in a kind of panic.

Unlike many ladies of quality Jenny was scrupulously honest about paying her gambling debts. She paid up, and by paying plunged further into financial difficulties till she was driven to resort to the money-lenders.

It was now that she realised that, at heart, she was afraid of her husband. On the surface she might defy and tease him with a lively impertinence, but in this crisis she dared not go to him for help. Instead she turned to her sister. Dorothea, who had noticed with concern the dark rings under Jenny's eyes and the feverish brightness of her cheeks, was perhaps relieved to find that her troubles were only financial. Her own private allowance, handsome though it was, would not suffice to clear Jenny of her load of debt, and so she asked Charles for help. That she did so is proof both of her devotion to Jenny and of the urgency of the situation. It must have mortified her intensely to have to ask her husband for a favour which she could not feel came within her legitimate rights as a wife, and to confess to him Jenny's folly. Perhaps, too, she reflected sadly how these last two years, though apparently so full of success, had tarnished the bright prospects of the Lovely Lynchs, she herself an unloved wife, Jenny in the money-lenders' toils.

She need not have fretted. Charles was an accomplished giver. He did not blink an eyelid when Dorothea disclosed to him the amount of her sister's debts and, before she had time to make her faltering request for aid, said, "Poor Jenny. She will never pluck up courage to confess this to that cold fish Aintry. Had we not better help her?" The next day he sent his wife the money in an inlaid satinwood box.

Dorothea, her heart overflowing with gratitude and relief (and perhaps cherishing the unacknowledged hope, "He would not have done this if he had not cared for me"), hastened to Berkeley Square. She could not say that Lord Mandlesham had given the money on condition that Jenny would refrain from high play in future. This would have been quite foreign to Charles's easy-going nature, and he had no particular liking for promises of reform either from himself or others. Dorothea, on her own account however, begged Jenny to give up gambling before it ruined her happiness and peace of mind. Jenny, thoroughly scared, promised readily enough, and kept her promise to the extent that she never again landed herself in such serious difficulties, though entries in Dorothea's private account book seem to prove that on several subsequent occasions Jenny had to enlist her sister's help to pay her debts.

This particular crisis was over, but Jenny's way of life was still unsatisfactory. She flitted from pleasure to pleasure—the word "dissipation" would be too harsh—in a way that testified to her inner restlessness and discontent. Though few, curiously enough, threw serious doubts on her virtue, her conduct was considered indiscreet to the point of scandal. It was reported, to give an instance, that she had been seen driving in her coach along the Piazza at Covent Garden. This was a well-known rendezvous frequented by ladies in search of an evening's mild adventure. A young beau would order his coachman to drive alongside the coach of some lady who had caught his fancy. The coachmen would swear at one another, the lady would lower her window to see what was the matter and would encounter her admirer's ogling glance. For an hour or more the coachmen, who were adept at this kind of game and well paid to do it, would contrive to bring the coaches alongside each other, and the beau and the lady would exchange languishing, coy, rallying, bold or bashful glances. It was a harmless pastime but hardly a dignified one for the young Countess of Aintry.

Then there was the episode of the highwayman. Lady Aintry's chariot was stopped by one of these robbers as she returned from an entertainment at Kensington. Instead of handing over her valuables with a dignified protest, she put her head out of the window and talked to the ruffian with such engaging familiarity that he ended by only keeping the contents of her purse and handed her back her watch and rings (she had managed to conceal the rest of her jewellery in her bodice) for the sake, he told her, of her "beautiful Irish eyes". Jenny was delighted. Lord Aintry was not.

Jenny's flirtatiousness was innocuous enough as a rule, but on one occasion it nearly cost a man his life, when Sir Harry Hewes and Mr Ned Temple quarrelled over her at the Star and Garter Tavern (both maintaining themselves to be her favoured partner at a recent ball), and fought a duel on the spot. Before they had finished, the walls of the room were bespattered with blood and Mr Temple was seriously wounded. Jenny, in a flutter of pity and compunction, had herself conveyed to his house, only to be confronted with his dragon of a mother, who refused to allow this dangerous charmer near her son's sick-bed.

This was more than Lord Aintry could stand. He threatened to lock Jenny up if she did not behave herself. Jenny wept, went into hysterics and screamed for Dolly. Lord Aintry, distracted, sent for his sister-in-law. After a disagreeable scene, it was a relief to everyone when Dorothea discovered that Jenny was with child. Dorothea implored Lord Aintry to be patient and considerate; Lord Aintry, alarmed for the health of his wife (whom he could not help loving still in a kind of infuriated way) and of the unborn child, was anxious and compliant; Jenny, sobbing piteously, promised amendment, and agreed to go down to Wing Magna with her husband. "For if I am to look a fright, shure I might as well hide myself in the country."

There is no record of Jenny's life at Wing Magna during her pregnancy, except the rather startling statement from Dorothea (in a letter to Lady Moffat) that "Jenny, who is in fine health and looks, diverts herself and indulges her good heart by teaching her charity children herself every Thursday". One wonders whether the subjects that Jenny taught included spelling!

On January 3rd 1772 Jenny was brought to bed of a son, Horace Augustus Jonathan.

It seemed as if this auspicious event might mark the beginning of a better relationship between Jenny and her husband. Lord Aintry's gratification at having a son and heir overflowed into renewed tenderness towards the child's mother.

Bonfires were lit round the estate, and the tenants treated to a roasted ox.

Jenny was very proud of herself. She wrote in high feather to her mother: "If only dear Dolly could have a son now I shd sing the Nunk Dimity."

Her affectionate wish was granted on July 12th when Dorothea gave birth to a son who was named Charles Henry. Fortune seemed to smile again upon her favoured daughters, the Lovely Lynchs.

CHAPTER XII

HALCYON DAYS

I

MRS LYNCH, during her first visit to her daughters in England in the spring of 1773, wrote to Lady Moffat:

"I take the opportunity of a courier to Ireland to fulfil my promise to your ladyship and to assure you that I find my lovely daughters in as fortunate a situation as my maternal tenderness or your ladyship's excessive goodness of heart and amiable interest in their welfare could desire. I need not describe to you the joy of my reunion with my beloved children—your mother's heart will depict those sacred moments better than I could do. I was also prodigiously well received by my sons-in-law. There is a warmth and frankness about Lord Mandlesham's manners which is instantly pleasing, but Lord Aintry, though more reserved, is all that is civil, rational, and correct.

"Knowing your partiality for Jenny, I may venture to tell you that she is still the most graceful figure in the world, her eyes and mouth as bewitching as ever, though she is a trifle thin and troubled with a little cough from the life of gaiety she leads, for I need not tell your ladyship that though she dotes on her little son, motherhood has not sobered her sprightly spirit and, as she says herself, she can frisk and gallop at a ball with the best of them.

"I believe however that your ladyship would be astonished at the improvement in Dolly. She fills the part of a great lady to perfection and with no air of conscious effort. Her beauties and good nature make her the admiration of society. I need hardly tell you that her husband shares in the general approbation of her. In this connection I had the pleasure of overhearing the following remark which Lord Mandlesham made to her in a low tone when she was inviting him to admire an engraving of a Grecian statue, 'I declare Dolly, you are goddess enough for me'.

"When I see my daughters in the enjoyment of rank, beauty and fortune and consider how much of their present elevation is due to your ladyship's benevolence, I am sensible that I am under a perpetual debt of gratitude to you."

It was natural that Dorothea and Jenny should endeavour to present their mother with as favourable a picture as possible of their married lives, and that her sons-in-law, in their different ways, should further this amiable deception. Lord Aintry, so "civil, rational, and correct", would refrain from sharing with Mrs Lynch his bleak conviction that in marrying her daughter he had married a lovely goose. Lord Mandlesham's good-nature would exercise a restraining influence on his frankness where the subject of Mrs Bellingham was concerned.

Yet Mrs Lynch's paean of praise for her daughters' good fortune, pathetic as it may seem to us in its maternal fatuosity and obtuseness, was not founded entirely on delusion. Though, beneath the surface, the forces that were influencing their destinies flowed on unchecked, superficially their lives seemed to be passing through a halcyon spell.

The birth of Jenny's son had relieved, if only for a time, the growing tension in the relationship between her and her husband. The youthful radiance of looks and spirits that was so great a part of her charm had flowered anew in the atmosphere of commendation and solicitude that surrounded her after her baby's arrival. Like a child who rejoices in adult favour without quite knowing why it is bestowed, she responded readily to Lord Aintry's approval, glad that she had been able to please him so easily, for what were a few hours of pain compared to all this praise and petting? She had no notion that it was necessary for her to make a sustained effort to regain her husband's love. Her grave, dark-eyed little boy she regarded as a plaything, and motherhood itself as an amusing joke. After the birth of Dorothea's baby she wrote comic little notes to her sister in which the infant Lord Marchington presented his compliments to his cousin Lord Fulmer, and invited him to a mouse-hunt, or some similar social event, in the nurseries at Wing Magna. She was glad that she had had a son for this was what Lord Aintry and everyone else wanted, but would not a pretty little girl, whom she could have dressed in muslins and sashes like a big doll, have been charming too?

After a few anxious months of measuring and tight-lacing she found, to her intense relief, that maternity had not added so much as an inch to her slender waist. This was a matter for rejoicing hardly less ecstatic than that of her safe delivery. She disregarded the troublesome little cough which her mother had remarked, and plunged once more into the life of pleasure which attracted her as irresistibly as a candle-flame attracts a moth.

Dorothea's situation was different. She was keenly aware of all that was unsatisfactory in her position, though no doubt less sensitive to its humiliation than a modern woman would be. For a nobleman to have a kept mistress as well as a wife was a commonplace of eighteenth-century life. For his wife to continue to live with him in spite of it and bear him children was considered not only good sense but good breeding, for the interests of the family and society must be placed above the vagaries of the individual's private life. The nurseries of a great house might shelter the man's but not the woman's bastards, as lovely warm-hearted Georgina Duchess of Devonshire was to learn in the years to come; but outward decorum must be maintained and the family name remain at least officially unsullied.

With Dorothea love, that plays havoc with theoretical emotions, delighting in knocking over pride, dignity and reason as though they were so many ninepins, powerfully reinforced this tradition of wifely complaisance. The thought of Tessy Bellingham was like an unhealed wound, but she could not have hated Charles even if she had tried, and there is no evidence that she ever did try. Instead, she bent all the energies of her gentle but resolute nature to creating a seemly life for herself and her children inside the distorted setting of her married life.

She must accept Tessy's influence, however galling and mortifying this might be, because by refusing to accept it she would cut herself off from everything that made her days worth living, but this did not mean that she was of no significance in Charles's life. On the contrary, she might flatter herself that if it had not been for Tessy's baleful fascination she might have been in a fair way to possessing Charles's heart.

There was a part of his life—when he was with Tessy—from which she was as utterly debarred as though he and she were strangers. She could not follow him there except in jealous thoughts which, had she indulged them, would have turned her life into a nightmare.

Her path and Tessy's seldom crossed, though there were a few occasions when they did, with embarrassment to all concerned. There was the evening, for instance, when

Lady Mandlesham entertained a party of friends in her box at Drury Lane, having ascertained, of course, that Mrs Bellingham would not be appearing. An actress was taken ill at the last moment, and Tessy stepped into her part. To make matters worse she borrowed the actress's gown, not realising that it was one which Dorothea had worn at the Birthday Ball, and in which she had been very generally admired. It had been sold by her maid and thus acquired by the other actress (the part was that of "Cleopatra" and the episode illustrates the haphazard way in which theatrical wardrobes were replenished at that time). Dorothea changed colour at seeing her "superb suit of silver tissue" make this unexpected appearance on her rival's unexpected person (probably she did not even know that the dress had been sold), but she quickly recovered herself and watched the performance with an unruffled brow. Unfortunately someone in the gallery called out: "My lady Marchioness looked handsomer in that gown than you do", and there was some laughter and booing. Tessy played on till the end of the act but afterwards, in her dressing-room, went into a paroxysm of rage that surpassed anything that had been seen in that theatre in living memory. By the time that she had been cajoled on to the stage again, Lady Mandlesham had pleaded a headache and retired.

It is significant that immediately after this scene Lord Mandlesham found it necessary to visit his estates in Northumberland.

There were of course certain spheres in which Dorothea reigned supreme. As the head of one of the great Whig families, and a young man of considerable personal popularity and ability, Lord Mandlesham was a notable addition to that section of the Whig party which was led by Lord Rockingham, and supported by the Duke of Richmond and Portland. Mandlesham House was a natural meeting-place for all those Whigs who, like the great Burke, strove to find a formula by which respect for tradition and love of liberty might be united. As Charles's wife Dorothea was one of London's leading political hostesses. It was a role that needed intelligence and tact, and her success in this capacity must have given her a keener sense of confidence and satisfaction than all the triumphs won by her beauty alone. Her physique and temperament fitted her for the task. As a contemporary put it, "Those who see her for the first time are, as it were, subdued by her proud beauty, telling themselves that they never saw so glorious a figure, but they are soon put at their ease by a perception of her many excellent qualities and natural good disposition, and charmed by something singularly artless and candid in her manner."

There seems, in fact, to have been an attractive contrast between her stately appearance and this spontaneousness, due in part perhaps to her Irish upbringing, which broke every now and then through her reserve and gave a freshness to her personality that never deserted her.

She had been reared in a tradition of lavish if crude hospitality. Now she was able to express it in a more splendid and refined form. Her parties at Crome soon became celebrated and invitations to them were eagerly sought-after. The conversation would be of serious matters; questions of the day such as the iniquitous folly of imposing taxes on the American colonists would be hotly debated, decisions of far-reaching importance to the state would be made, in the apparently casual manner of the eighteenth-century oligarchy. Dorothea, who since her childhood had heard politics discussed with excitement and even violence, listened, encouraged, questioned with interest and discretion. But when the discussion was over, tempers subsided and antagonisms were smoothed out under the influence of Lord Mandlesham's pleasant wit and excellent wine and Lady Mandlesham's handsome looks and lilting Irish voice.

Politics alone would have been an arid meeting-ground for husband and wife. Dorothea had reason to bless her roistering father who had brought her up to ride almost as soon as she could walk. A true Irishwoman in her passion for horses, she was able to participate in Charles's hunting and racing pursuits in a way that Tessy, with her convent and strolling-player background, could never do. No doubt Dorothea first took to hunting in Leicestershire (where Lord Mandlesham had a hunting lodge) for the love of the sport, and with no particular object except to distract her mind from sad thoughts. But when she saw her husband's eyes rest on her in marked admiration as they rode home together after a memorable two hours' hunt ("her golden hair all tumbled about her shoulders in the prettiest way imaginable"), can it be doubted that she realised with a thrill of entirely feminine triumph that a new weapon had been placed in her hands? After that she hunted regularly, indifferent to the fact that many people still considered it an unfeminine sport, and also accompanied Charles to all the more important meetings at Newmarket. Lady Mandlesham, in her sky-blue habit and riding her favourite chestnut, became a familiar figure on the Heath.

Next to their children, their gardens were the strongest bond between Charles and Dorothea. Charles at this time was enthusiastically transforming the demesne at Crome to the plans of "Capability" Brown. The formal gardens and avenues, the geometrically-shaped flower-beds, the sedate paths, the carefully tended topiary-work —birds, beasts and pyramids—were swept away. In their stead there were to be clumps of trees, meandering paths, and stretches of grass, imitating as far as possible a "natural wilderness". Straight lines became as abhorrent to Lord Mandlesham as they were to his mentor, Lancelot Brown. He sat for hours in his library examining and sometimes altering the plans that were to give the groun s that much desired uncultivated effect. But though enthusiastic he was open to suggestion. When Dorothea pointed out to him that by destroying the fine avenues of beech and elm he would virtually leave the place treeless for years, he agreed to spare them. Their correspondence to each other on the subject survives. Dorothea writes in her restrained rather formal way:

"Your lordship was good enough to say when you was here last week that you would spare the Great Avenue etc. for my sake. I am satisfied that you will not have cause to regret your kindness. Consider, my dear lord, that it takes a tree some fifty to a hundred years to come to perfection, which hardly affords us any reasonable expectation of wandering in the shade of Mr Brown's groves—except possibly as spirits!"

Charles writes back cheerfully:

"You are entirely in the right about the trees. I must have been asleep when my tutors taught me botany. A hundred years or fifty—'tis all the same to me. It would be no satisfaction to me either to be wheeled about in the groves in an invalid chair or to be buried in them. I am sorry that you do not like the idea of the rough grass reaching up to the windows of the house. I think this would enhance the natural effect especially with sheep grazing. You ask, 'Would it not depress you to look out at it before breakfast?' After a Jockey Club supper last night everything depresses me so damnably that I am hardly in a state to judge. I would wish you to have what pleases you. Could we not have the terraces on the south side, grass and sheep on the north; this will be considered lopsided by the purists but what matter so long as we have what pleases us? We will talk the matter over on Saturday."

In the middle of these alterations, a complication arose. Trimble, for many years head gardener at Crome, not surprisingly, had a mental breakdown. He showed suicidal tendencies, and Dorothea was much concerned lest he should be found hanging in some corner of his doomed garden. Lord Mandlesham sent several eminent physicians down to Crome to prescribe for him, but in vain. Trimble's gloom became more profound and, in a mood of religious melancholia, he prophesied woe to the Chessel family and the universe in general, evincing a tendency to confuse Crome with the Garden of Eden.

Charles and Dorothea exchanged several letters on the subject. Charles wrote ruefully: "This is a pretty kettle of fish. Are we to renounce all our fine plans for the sake of a mad gardener? Yet if the poor fellow should do himself a mischief what a horrible thing it would be to have on our consciences! I trust this is not contagious, or we shall have my valet threatening to blow his brains out because I will not wear my hair à la grecque, and your maid vowing to swallow poison if you do not leave off wearing a sacque. In all seriousness does it not seem to you that we are entirely at the mercy of poor crazy Trimble? Why do we not all go mad, my dear Lady Mandlesham?"

In the end, at Dorothea's suggestion, Trimble was offered the position of head gardener at Lord Mandlesham's Northumberland seat. Fortunately the old man regarded this proposal in the light of a direct command from heaven and went north, in comparative sanity, to supervise the hot-houses, green-houses and parterres of Highframlington Park.

The transformation of Crome went on peacefully. Jenny wrote to her sister: "I shall dye with envy when I see your fine new garden. My Lord Aintry has become such an oeconomist he will not even let me do away with the ha-ha."

2

These interests and occupations, absorbing as they were and, imperceptibly yet constantly, weaving together the fabrics of Dorothea's and Charles's lives, could not compensate her for the lack of the one thing that she most longed for—her husband's undivided confidence and love. There must always be some restraint between them, the unspoken word, the unasked question, the reminiscent smile on Charles's mouth that tortured Dorothea with jealous surmises (and yet perhaps after all he was not remembering Tessy but some joke or racing story heard at Almack's). Did he still love Tessy with the same infatuation? She could not ask and was too proud to discover by underhand means. Would Tessy relinquish her hold of him? Dorothea would look at his manly and graceful figure, his gay and distinguished face, and despair of any such easy solution to her troubles. He had been Tessy's lover since he was twenty; how subtle must be her knowledge of him, how firm her hold on him. He was still in his twenties, in the full vigour of his young manhood; what chance then that he would soon tire of Tessy's manifold seductions?

It may have been during some such mood of spiritual loneliness and discouragement that Dorothea discovered St Chidwiddin Old Hall. Her physicians ordered her to Bath in the summer of 1773 to recuperate from a low fever, and thither she repaired in August with travelling coach and six, cabriolet, running footmen, men servants and maids and all the paraphernalia of a lady of quality. Lord Mandlesham had rented a house for her in Kings Circus and, that she might not suffer unduly from "the affliction of hired furniture", had sent down a Salvator Rosa, a Poussin and a Domenichino from his collection at Crome, as well as various objects of furniture of which he knew her to be particularly fond.

But Dorothea was in a restless state of mind and not to be soothed by these attempts at appeasement. She soon tired of immersing herself in the famous baths, surrounded by floating bowls of essences and perfumes, and by other titled ladies who quizzed her person to see if she was as well-made without a hoop as she looked in one.

She wrote impatiently to Jenny: "If anything could convince me that I am perfectly restored, it would be the stupidity of the conversation in the Cross Baths, and the indignity of being swaddled in blankets and carried back to my house in a chair. The book sellers' shops are good, but you cannot pick up a book without hearing at your elbow, 'Good day your ladyship. I trust I see you well?' You will see I am not in an amiable temper! I wish you was here, Jenny, and then we would laugh at it all together."

A chance acquaintance at Bath asked Dorothea if she had ever stayed at her husband's property in Cornwall, St Chidwiddin Old Hall. At once Dorothea felt a strong wish to visit this place, and announced her intention of doing so in a letter to Charles.

He answered in surprise: "What extravagant fancy is this of visiting Chidwiddin? Yes, I believe it has a roof and even a housekeeper, but no one has been known to reside there since the days of the Gunpowder Plot. It is very deep dirty country. You will have to undergo the most barbarous inconvenience to reach it, and when you are there (if your coach is not overturned into a ditch on the way) you will have no other employment than to climb cliffs and clamber over rocks (unless indeed you have a mind to set up in business as a wrecker!) I am sorry that you are so weary of Bath, though heartily glad that you are mended enough to feel so impatient. If you are in such a violent hurry to leave why not remove yourself to Brighthelmstone? However I will not bore you by giving you advice which I know you have no intention of following. Adieu! errant lady, if you have not returned within a twelvemonth I will come and search for you."

Dorothea's journey to the West country cannot have been either speedy or comfortable, but accustomed to travelling over Irish roads, she probably found it nothing extraordinary. She loved Chidwiddin Old Hall at first sight. The little manor house which dated from mediaeval times, though its present structure was sixteenth century, was snugly situated in a valley or coombe, on the very borders of Cornwall and Devonshire (a trout stream which ran by the house, in fact marking the boundary), sheltered even in winter from the sea gales which roared up the valley. In consequence of its situation there was an extraordinary feeling of peace and seclusion about the old house. To descend into the valley by a precipitous track (it could hardly be called a road) was to leave the outside world behind.

The house itself was (and still is) a perfect specimen of a Tudor manor house in miniature, with its central courtyard, its hall panelled in linenfold, with a little musicians' gallery and an oriel window, the solar with oak beams as massive as those in the state cabin of a sailing ship, the chimney-pieces with their richly carved overmantels of heraldic design, the latticed windows and twisted chimney-stacks. Nothing could have been a more complete contrast to Crome with its pseudo-classical grandeur, its expanses of marble floors and echoing, high-ceilinged rooms. This house was intimate, a little secretive with its winding stairs, deep window embrasures, odd corners and closets, matured by centuries of use to a sturdy but gracious domesticity.

The garden would have distressed Mr Brown; it was symmetrical and formal to a degree, as dignified as a little princess dressed in a farthingale. It had a "mount" or artificial hillock, an arbour, a knot-garden with dwarf box-hedges, surrounded by a pleached alley, a tiny maze and a sundial, engraved with the words,

> "Our pleasence here is all vain glory,
> This fals world is but transitory."

With delight and amusement Dorothea surveyed her tiny domain. She wrote off to Lord Mandlesham begging him to oblige her with a history of the place and to send her any hangings that would be suitable for its walls, also a list of flowers and herbs proper to antique gardens. In reply he told her that St Chidwiddin had originally belonged to the family of Treludicks, who had lived there since the days of Richard Lion Heart, their most distinguished member being Sir Thomas Treludick, a renowned Elizabethan sea captain and explorer. Late in the seventeenth century it had passed into the possession of the Chessel family by the marriage of Charles's great-grandfather to Priscilla Treludick. He had bespoken for her a pair of virginals, and a tapestry woven in a design of "leopards of gold, falcons, swans with ladies heads, stars, birds, griffins, eagles and flowers." As for plants he was sending her down a rare edition of Thomas Tusser's *Five Hundred Points of Good Husbandry*, with a list of flowers and herbs cultivated in Tudor times.

"I regret that I have not been able to discover a single murder or ghost to add to the pleasing sense of gloom with which I am sure Chidwiddin must inspire you. The Treludicks dull dogs! had a habit of dying in their beds." He added, "It is very handsome of me to give you this help, for I perceive that Chidwiddin and its confounded buckramed garden has made you faithless to Crome and Lancelot Brown."

Beneath his bantering tone there is a trace of pique that Dorothea had found solace in a place remote from him and uninfluenced by his taste.

St Chidwiddin, by its situation, had an attraction for Dorothea which she could not impart to her husband, the country round reminding her of Ardnabannagh and of girlhood days before Charles had come into her life to fulfil, and almost simultaneously to destroy, her young illusions. In spite of the treeless, windswept appearance of the countryside, the house, hidden in its deep coombe, was well sheltered with trees. The glossy brown trout stream murmured its way beneath the overhanging boughs of small oaks and willows, and through lush meadows jewelled with lacy cows-parsley and buttercups and other late summer flowers. But as the coombe widened out, the stream tumbled over boulders, the hillside was bare and open to the wind and sun and rain, beautiful with lights and cloud shadows, and springy underfoot with wild thyme and heath.

Here Dorothea might have fancied herself at Ardnabannagh, and familiar too were the savage cliffs and the breakers at the valley's end. The stream ran across the sands towards the sea, and at high tide the waves ran up into the river, so that fresh and salt water mingled together in a rapturous reunion.

In her long solitary walks towards the sea-coast Dorothea renewed not only her physical health but something vernal and spontaneous in her nature that had been dealt a nearly mortal blow that night at Drury Lane. There was a sadness in the salty winds that blew about those cliffs, about the waves that spent themselves unceasingly against the rocks, and in the shrill cries of the seagulls as they flew up the valley before a storm, but in the sunshine the silver-crested waves raced in to the shore like a charge of wild horses, and if there was conflict here there was also infinite freedom, reminding Dorothea of how fugitive was her personal destiny in the face of the eternal things.

She could not remain away long from her children nor —though she would not perhaps admit this to herself— from Charles, and early in the autumn she returned to London and Crome. But she had found a refuge far from the world of fashion and politics, a place in whose quiet and solitude she could draw on the reserves of strength that were hidden in her soul.

Dorothea wrote from Paris to her five-year-old daughter Carolina:

"August, 1775.

"MY DARLING CHILD,

Your aunt Jenny and me came here after a horrid tossing on a boat and a long drive in a coach. This is a fine city but noisy and dirty. The French people are very polite, and a gentleman will not let a lady cross a room without giving her his hand. Aunt Jenny and me are going to see the King and Queen to-morrow. The Queen is very beautiful. The King is not so handsome but good. Aunt Jenny and me will wear tall feathers on our heads.

I have sent a pretty french doll for you. She is a fine lady and has a satin gown, a spray of flowers at her breast, a cap of blonde lace and a mother of pearl necklace. She is bringing her own little silver toilet table with mirror and brushes. But bid your other dolls not to be jealous of her, for her face is wax so she dare not sit by the fire for fear of melting. What shall you call her? Would not Angelique or Celestine be a pretty name? I have sent a musical box for your brother Charles which plays six tunes.

There is a lady here, Madame de Lapalisse, who has a little boy three years older than you. She says that when you are older I shall bring you to France to play with him.

Kiss Papa and little Charles for me. Aunt Jenny has kissed the paper here X for you. God bless you, my sweet little love.   MAMA."

Many a broadly-flowing river can be traced back to a small spring. The sources of an individual destiny, apparently so trivial and inconsequent in themselves, constitute a profound and awful mystery. Dorothea, sitting in her apartments near the Faubourg St Germain, prattling tenderly on paper to the child Cara, could not know that the first threads of her daughter's fate were already on the loom.

She may have smiled to herself as she wrote to her little girl about dolls, silver toys, and feathers, for she was in that carefree mood when every triviality can become a delight.

"Jenny and me are taking a holiday from breeding and are away to France", she had written to George Selwyn with the frankness of the age. The last twelvemonths had brought Dorothea the disappointment of a miscarriage, and to Jenny, who had set her heart on a daughter, the lesser disappointment of a second son. Lord Aintry had shown a certain amount of satisfaction—though of a restrained nature, as befitted the arrival of the second heir —when the baby, Frederick, was born, but Jenny was growing increasingly less responsive to his feeling and wishes. She caressed and played with her "poor little boy", as she alluded to the new infant, to Lord Aintry's annoyance, who saw in her chagrin about its sex a feckless lack of appreciation of her responsibilities towards the Aintry family, but her buoyancy of spirit seemed to have deserted her. Physically she remained in a low and languishing state. She was very thin, and troubled at night with a cough. Lord Aintry, who was impatient of ill-health in anyone except himself, advised the Wells or Bath. Lord Mandlesham, with a surer knowledge of feminine psychology, advised Paris.

"Do you not think that our wives deserve a holiday from us?" he asked his brother-in-law. Lord Aintry responded coldly to this banter, but could not veto the plan without seeming churlish.

Charles quoted to Dorothea the saying that Paris was a paradise for women, a purgatory for men and a hell for horses, and assured her that no woman's education was complete till she had tasted the delights of French society, adding, "But I shall follow you to Paris if you stay there too long, my dear Dolly, lest your education should become too complete!"

The sisters set off in high spirits across the Channel, Jenny declaring that her brother-in-law's suggestion had already done her more good than all Dr Hunter's nasty pills and purges.

"Oh, Dolly, shall we be as excessively admired in Paris as we was in London?" were Jenny's first words as she set foot on French soil, her naïve and overweening vanity unextinguished by an appalling crossing. No doubt Dorothea, who was a bad sailor, dismissed the question with a faint smile, but on reflection she would have to admit to herself that the Lovely Lynchs had taken the field again. They had conquered Dublin and London; it remained to be seen if they would add to their trophies the approbation of Europe's most elegant and critical society. She might have reflected, too, on the change in their circumstances which the last half-dozen years had brought about. Obscure, penniless, unsophisticated, they had had no assets but their hopes and their bright young beauty when they had arrived in Dublin. Now they were women of rank, the bearers of distinguished names, versed in the arts and graces of the fashionable world, with the bloom bestowed by six years of luxury and admiration. Yet Jenny, greedy as a child bobbing for apples, was still avid of admiration, and Dorothea, always uncritical to the point of obtuseness where her sister was concerned, smiled and envied her.

They brought with them introductions that opened wide the doors of the greatest houses in France, and everywhere they were accorded a royal welcome. "Everyone is so kind and flattering to us, I fear our poor heads will be quite overset", Dorothea wrote to her husband. That Jenny's head at least was in this condition is evident from her letters to her mother (she had at least learnt enough caution not to boast of her conquests to Lord Aintry):

"Dolly and me is quite gluted (glutted) with comppli-mants and *billy douse* (which is what the frogs call love letters) Mons de Lauzun writs to me 4 times a day. Dolly is estemed a Beauty of the 1st order, and they say I am an angell both in face and shape. They say we have put poor Lady Barymore quite in the shade but" (added Jenny with a sudden gleam of modesty) "I think this is becaus there is only one of her, for truly she is just as handsom as we."

Again the duality of the Lynch sisters' beauty and the striking contrast in their looks was to sweep them to triumph. Jenny was considered coquette beyond measure. With her vivacity, her delicate grace, her iridescent frivolity, she must have fitted into the Gallic scene as naturally as a Watteau shepherdess. Her eyes, blue as the western seas between the long black lashes, gave a hint of strangeness to her beauty which the "petits-maîtres" found inexpressibly captivating. Her charm was such that even her ludicrous French was forgiven in circles where to be ridiculous was the next thing to being damned.

On the whole Dorothea received the more profound admiration. It was agreed that, though her sister was ravishing, Milady Mandlesham had "le bon air". Her tall, well-modelled figure, her profusion of silky fair hair, and the rose-like delicacy of her complexion, conformed so exactly to the French ideal of an Englishwoman (for they neither knew nor cared that "La Belle Anglaise" was Irish) that at her entry into a ballroom or salon all conversation ceased and the beholders were (as one of them expressed it) "ébahis".

The very candour of her clear blue eyes provoked amorous speculation. It was thought impossible that such a beautiful woman could be as chaste as she looked.

It would have shocked them (for marital love was con-sidered of all things the most indecorous and absurd) had they known that she valued her experiences and triumphs mainly as material with which to entertain her husband.

Her letters to Charles give a fragmentary but vivid picture of the life around her. It seems as though in writing to Charles she is able to shed that almost imperceptible aloofness, with which her wounded love and pride endeavours to protect itself in his too dear presence. She confides in him freely, all that catches her eye or takes her fancy, confident that he will share her interest. The life of the streets engrosses her no less than that of the salons; the crowded rattling streets where the young nobles drive their cabriolets with a lofty disregard of human life and limb; the Pont Neuf where market-women, clattering by in their sabots, jostle fine gentlemen and black-robed lawyers. From the window of her apartment (which is shaded by trees and which has a salle à manger in stucco with panels of *verd antique*) Dorothea of a morning watches the wigmakers hurrying along, curling-tongs in one hand, wigs in the other, and the confectioners' boys in white jackets, bearing coffee and syrup to their clients.

She sightsees indefatigably, visiting among other things the Ecole Militaire, the Ecole de Chirurgie, the Gobelins, the State Treasures, the Botanic Gardens (where she makes a list of shrubs and flowers for Crome), the Salpêtrière Hospital and the celebrated Monsieur Buffon. No wonder that Jenny, who did not share Dorothea's urge for self-improvement, lay in bed till midday and flatly refused to do any sightseeing beyond that entailed by a daily drive along the Boulevards.

Dorothea's fine faded handwriting, the yellowed writing-paper, evoke the sultry warmth of the Paris streets in those far-away summer evenings of 1775; the gilded coaches drawn up in courtyards beneath the lighted windows of stately "hotels"—the Maréchales de Mirepoix or de Luxembourg, the Duchesse de la Vallière are entertaining to-night—the hot, crowded salons, bright with candles, where conversation has been distilled to a sparkling essence of gallantry, philosophy and wit.

175

Dorothea is amused by one of her admirers "who in his partiality for me complimented me on 'la noblesse de votre âme, Madame.' Jenny is quite vexed because no one has admired *her* soul, only her eyes!" She admits to Lord Mandlesham that she is vastly taken with the middle-aged Duc de Coigny, a man of admirable intelligence and integrity with a superb air, also with the Prince de Ligne, nicknamed "Charlot" by his intimates, who is loved by the Queen, the King, the royal family, in fact everyone, for his charming flow of good spirits and good humour. (In her journal she makes the revealing comment, "He reminds me of Lord M. though by no means so handsome.")

Dorothea and Jenny are presented at Court; in virtue of their high rank they are granted "les honneurs du Louvre", which entitles them to a "tabouret" or stool, a coach upholstered in red velvet and an embrace from the Monarch. (Mrs Lynch in far-away, windswept Ardnabannagh must have read and marvelled.) They attend the "bal paré" in celebration of the marriage of Madame Clotilde to the Prince de Piedmont. The weather is oppressive; Jenny, weighed down by her hooped Court dress and train and feathers, nearly faints during the minuet; the charming Queen, observing her distress, sends a page to her with smelling-salts, and other attendants with ices and baskets of China oranges and peaches. Marie Antoinette and the Lovely Lynchs exchange long looks of mutual admiration; the Queen, gracious and indiscreet, takes off her gloves that they may admire her singularly beautiful arms. She remarks to Comte Edward Dillon, "Milady Aintry is ravishing, but if she were my wife her fragility would frighten me," and of Dorothea, "There is a woman that I could love."

Dorothea and Jenny stay at Chanteloup, where the Duc de Choiseuil resides in splendid exile, at Chantilly, the seat of the Prince de Condé, at the Prince de Conti's

L'Isle d'Adam and at other country estates. Here amid idyllic surroundings the life of fashion continues, card-playing, music, dancing, amorous intrigues, above all sparkling conversation, with the addition of carriage drives, open-air fêtes, and hunting parties in the forest. Dorothea wears her new bottle green riding habit and lets her husband know, in a modest way, that both her appearance and her riding are admired. Jenny too gives a good account of herself in the saddle. Her fellow guests are amazed that this sylph-like creature can ride as well as a groom.

All the same there was something about French country life that did not altogether satisfy Dorothea. She recollected that Charles, for all his leisurely air, was an excellent landlord with an extensive and practical knowledge of farming, as proud of his fat cattle as of his Italian Masters.

The French countryside, from what she could observe, formed a stark, neglected background to the opulent existence of the nobility. A few years ago the contrast would not have struck her so forcibly—tumbledown hovels and barefooted peasants were a commonplace at Ardnabannagh, though there was a liveliness and humour about Irish peasant life that, to the unobservant, softened the outlines of its misery, and often a friendliness and always a mutual love of sport between landlord and peasant that disguised the deep cleavage between them. Six years of England had altered Dorothea's standards. She had a mental picture of her husband's tenants to set against her glimpses of the impoverished country that lay outside the park gates of her noble host's domains—prosperous Leicestershire farmers who, after a day with Lord Mandlesham's hounds, sat down to a gargantuan meal of mutton pies, pork, beef and ale, their trim wives who were not ashamed to invite Lady Mandlesham into their wainscoted parlours where grandfather-clocks ticked out the placid hours, the Buckinghamshire cottagers with their snug thatched cottages, and bright patches of garden and apple-cheeked children. . . .

Yet such is the power of words that, back again in the Paris salons, listening to talk of reformation, economy, philosophy and of the dawning age of reason (all of which edifying subjects were *bon ton* at the moment), Dorothea forgot these unfavourable impressions, and assured her husband that on the whole she found the French nation in a flourishing and happy state. Their King was excellent —in spite of his habit of making horrid grimaces—their Queen was charming, their statesmen were enlightened (had not M. Turgot abolished the corvée?), and their aristocracy, though somewhat light and fickle, much to be commended for the liberality of their sentiments. The vile American war, which Charles and she and their friends deplored, was loudly condemned by the French. Though she could not but agree with their disapproval of the folly and tyranny of the administration in provoking the colonies, she confessed that it piqued her to hear her country criticised. "I am evidently not fitted yet to live in the age of reason for I find that I wish to reserve to myself the privilege of abusing our King and Government, and get as crusty inside as any Tory courtier when I have to sit and listen to the Frenchies (as Jenny will call them) explain to me that if we win the war it is the end of English and American liberty, and if we lose it our commerce is ruined. Jenny, who is looking over my shoulder, says that I should forget politics when I am on holiday, and that I would do better to tell you that Melle Rosa Bertin, the Queen's modiste, is to make me a pearl grey dress spotted with gold in the Circassian style. I do not know if you will be as interested in this as Jenny supposes. You would be more entertained I think if I could give you a notion of an English Garden which a lady proudly shewed me round yesterday. I say 'shewed me around', but indeed by turning once on my heel I could survey the whole lay-out. And yet into this space of ground the size of a pocket handkerchief was crammed everything that we have at Crome; a temple, a grove, a winding river (2 feet wide), rough grass and even a sheep—nay, more for they have a mountain as well, some ten foot high, from which one may have a fine view over a cucumber frame and a dunghill. I managed to keep my face very well, and bring out one or two convincing compliments (for it was a moment when candour had to be suppressed in the interests of courtesy) and was glad that you was not there to upset my composure."

Dorothea's and Jenny's first visit to France coincided with a peculiarly brilliant period in the life of the French Court. The old King—Louis le Bien-Aimé—had died over a year ago, rotten with smallpox and vice. Court mourning was at an end, and a series of superb entertainments marked the opening of a new social era. The young King was respectable and well-meaning; the twenty-year-old Queen was intelligent, spirited and a delight to behold. It was the reign of youth. To be over thirty was to approach decrepitude. As for the withered grand-seigneurs and dowagers whom the Queen irreverently nicknamed "The Ages", there was no place for their senile counsels in the lively circle that surrounded Marie Antoinette.

No wonder that the Queen—who as Dauphiness had chafed under the power of her father-in-law's mistress the Du Barry, had been made the tool of her husband's bigoted, intriguing aunts, and had been spied on by the Austrian Ambassador and the emissaries of the Kings of England and Prussia—was intoxicated by her new freedom.

It was her ambition to be the best-dressed woman in the kingdom, and in the extravagance and elegance of her toilettes she was a Queen of Fashion as well as of France. Her love of dress was only exceeded by her passion for diamonds. Music, dancing, acting and gambling were all her pleasure. The censures of her Imperial mother on her mode of life distressed but did not deter her.

This capriciousness and restless search for excitement was the symptom of a deep-seated emotional want. It was common knowledge, not only at Court but in the streets of Paris, that after five years of marriage the King had not yet fulfilled his obligations as a husband. At the best he would have been an incongruous mate for his wife. With all his good qualities he was totally lacking in spirit and elegance. There was a grossness and lethargy about his nature that was most unkingly. He ate like a hog; hunting and locksmith's work were his favourite occupations. It was said that his antics during the royal *coucher* were embarrassing; he would scratch himself in front of the courtiers, or duck and pretend to run away when his nightgown was handed to him. Yet he greatly admired his wife; if he could have provided her with the children for whom she longed, all might have been well.

As it was, it was remarkable that the Queen had not consoled herself with the lovers attributed to her by the slanders of her enemies. Instead she plunged into this life of extravagant frivolity, surrounding herself with a crowd of young, gay and dissolute companions, and endeavouring to relieve her sense of frustration by romantic friendships with her own sex.

For several years Marie Antoinette and the Princesse de Lamballe had been inseparable; the Queen had recently appointed her friend to the post of Mistress of the Robes. Notwithstanding this honour Madame de Lamballe's star was waning; the Queen insensibly had grown weary of the Princess's simplicity, her lack of common-sense, her self-pity and her absurd attacks of nerves (she would faint at the smell of a bunch of violets or at the sight of a lobster), and above all of her inordinate devotion. Moreover the Queen was falling under the spell of the fascinating Comtesse Jules de Polignac, who looked like an angel by Raphael, witty, indolent and a woman of the world. In Madame de Polignac's salon, surrounded by clever, intriguing women and their lovers or complaisant husbands, Marie Antoinette, delighted with the easy familiarity of the atmosphere, could exclaim, "Here I am no longer the Queen. I am myself." She could not foresee that the insatiable appetite for favours of these intimates of Madame de Polignac was to undermine, not only her own peace of mind, but the foundations of the throne itself.

Susceptible as she was to good looks and charm in men or women, the Queen could not fail to be attracted to the two celebrated Irish sisters who were visiting Paris. Dorothea's and Jenny's formal appearances at Court were soon supplemented by private invitations to the Petit Trianon, the Arcadian little realm that the Queen was creating for herself as a refuge from the stifling boredom and fatigue of Court life.

Here, in an atmosphere of happy make-believe, the Queen, dressed in a simple white muslin gown with a fichu, entertained the King, members of the royal family and a few privileged friends to supper or to little parties in the Orangery. Ceremony was set aside, everything was as simple and artless as possible.

Jenny, with her spontaneous merriment and her inconsequent remarks which had an absurd charm of their own, was an ideal guest for these informal parties. Her vanity though preposterous was not odious, for it was redeemed not only by its naïveté but by her sweet and caressing manner, and her genuine wish to give as well as receive pleasure. The Queen agreed with the men that Milady Aintry was very seductive, but probably Jenny's temperament, with its emotional restlessness and love of pleasure, was too akin to her own to appeal to her. For

Dorothea, however, she felt one of those instant attractions that with her were usually the prelude to a devoted friendship.

She invited Dorothea not only to evening parties, but to sit with her in the mornings in her salon in the Petit Trianon, a room whose light and elegant furnishings seemed to symbolise her longing to escape from the cumbersome majesty of Versailles. As she stitched at her tapestry, selecting the coloured threads from baskets or taffetas bags set on low chairs around her, the young Queen confided freely in Dorothea. She may have heard rumours of Lady Mandlesham's matrimonial troubles (so different from her own since they came from having a husband only too well versed in the art of love-making) which invested Dorothea in her eyes with an aura of melancholy romance. Or she may have sensed the warm human kindness that lay beneath Dorothea's aloof demeanour.

Her confidences, at first, were on the subject of her life in general, particularly of her immense boredom at the wearisome ritual and ceremonial of Court life. This boredom was like a physical oppression; she was convinced that it was the cause of her migraines and feverish attacks. Though her days at Versailles were hemmed in by elaborate etiquette, she was denied the most ordinary privacy. Dorothea learnt with amazement that after her sister-in-law the Comtesse d'Artois' confinement, the fishwives had pursued the Queen to the very threshold of her apartments, reproaching her with her sterility. Marie Antoinette spoke of her dislike of dining in public with the King, of the presentations, the *Grand Couverts*, of the elaborate *toilettes* when, from the moment that she was handed out of her great canopied bed till the time that she was dressed ready to be escorted to Mass, she was surrounded with people, first by the ladies of her bedchamber and chambermaids, then, at the *petite entrée* by her physician, doctor, secretary and other officials, till finally at the *grande entrée* everyone poured into her bedchamber, the ladies who held high office in her suite, the King's brothers, the Princes of the Blood, the Captain of the Guard and the officers of the Crown. Dorothea had, in fact, been privileged to attend one of these ceremonies and had commented on it rather scornfully in a letter to Lord Mandlesham: "Such a pother about getting out of bed and dressed you never saw."

Now she felt a warm sympathy for the illustrious victim of all this pomp and ceremony. Had not she herself, in a much lesser degree, sometimes felt oppressed by the grandeur of Crome? Remembering St Chidwiddin Old Hall, snug and sturdy in its coombe, she found the Queen's delight in the Petit Trianon very understandable; her plans for its improvement, for having a little theatre where she could act with her friends, a model hamlet and a dairy, seemed to Dorothea not ridiculous but touching. Marie Antoinette had heard of the beauties of Crome and wanted advice about the garden of the Petit Trianon, which she wished to be a blending of the English and Chinese styles.

The Queen enquired with tender and envious interest after Dorothea's children, and soon was hinting to her new friend of the unsatisfactory condition of her married life. She spoke of the King with a curious mingling of disdain and wistful affection. "I never cease wondering at my strange position", she said with an air of deep melancholy. "I am afraid of being bored. I am afraid of myself. I must have bustle. I must have endless change."

Her mood altering, she drew Dorothea in front of a long mirror and playfully compared their looks. "Our skins and hair are so alike we might be sisters, but your features are better. My forehead is a little too high, my lower lip too prominent. I am painfully struck with the emptiness of my expression compared to yours." She sighed deeply, only shaking her head with a little smile when Dorothea said, "But your Majesty forgets that I am five years older."

Dorothea was both honoured and disturbed by these confidences—honoured not only because they were those of a Queen but of a woman whose essential goodness and sincerity she discerned under her superficial frivolity, disturbed because she knew the unhappiness that prompted them and could do nothing to relieve it. Neither her circumstances nor her temperament permitted her to give the Queen the intimate and sentimental friendship that alone would satisfy her.

She wrote in her private journal:

"I feel a sincere sympathy and admiration for the Queen. With her charms and her peculiar situation it seems to me little short of a miracle that she has preserved her virtue, and greatly to her credit. She has a most gallant bearing of the head, the loveliest neck and arms; in short she is a picture of grace whether she sits still or moves. It is most vexing that she should be married to such an insensible husband. Her capriciousness, I believe, comes more from her youth and her unsatisfied desires than from her true character which is sincere and upright. She is only 20 but has already made implacable enemies, more especially among the women. The virtuous deplore her giddiness, the licentious are enraged by her light-hearted purity. Though she never forgets her dignity as a Queen, she is thoughtless and too confiding. She is surrounded by flatterers, and chooses her friends without sufficient care. The King's brother, the Comte d'Artois, who is one of her boon companions, is handsome and engaging but a good for nothing, mischievous and futile. It was he and his cousin the Duc de Chartres who persuaded her to abandon lotto and backgammon for faro. Her debts are enormous.

"My informant on these matters is the Duchesse de

184

Lapalisse, a most amiable and intelligent woman whose friendship I am happy to have gained. Unlike most women at the Grand Court she makes no secret of her affection for her husband, who is ten years older than herself, and in every respect worthy of her, and has a fine little boy Jules, upon whom she dotes. . . ."

The entry breaks off abruptly here. Did Dorothea pause to mend her pen or, suddenly sleepy, lay it down, reflecting with pleasure on her new friend's refined face, her expressive almond-shaped eyes and humorous mouth? This was the first time that she had felt a strong impulse of friendship for a person of another nationality; there was a naïve satisfaction and wonder in finding that two minds, spiritually akin, could ignore the barriers of speech and custom.

She may have sat there dreaming at the writing-table, the candlelight illuminating her golden hair and grave, gentle face, only half-hearing the muffled night sounds of the Paris streets outside, the rumble of carriage wheels on the cobbles, the mournful cry of a nightwatchman, offering his services to late revellers—"Voici un falot!", a snatch of quarrelsome voices or of song. Her consciousness, tranquil and unaware, caught no premonitory echo of those other sounds that the future would make audible, no tramp of feet, no roll of drums, no savage, unappeasable cries. Her thoughts may have been far away in England where her child Cara slept rosily in her little crib.

4

The return home from an enjoyable trip must always bring a certain feeling of flatness. In Dorothea's and Jenny's case they had particular reasons—beside their natural regret at leaving a city where they had been fêted like queens—for feeling subdued, as their coach bore them slowly away from the gates of Paris along the

Calais road. Jenny, though she might not reflect long enough to acknowledge it, was returning to an empty and fretful marriage. Lord Mandlesham had warned Dorothea in a letter: "Aintry is in an excessively morose way at hearing of the prodigious scenes of gallantry and magnificence at which you and Jenny have been assisting. I cannot conceive why a man plagued with such a jealous disposition took one of the two foremost beauties of the age to wife."

Dorothea had no cause to complain of a grudging husband. Perhaps she would have been thankful for a display of jealousy, however unreasonable, on Charles's part. She longed to see him and her children again, but once back in England she must lose the illusion of an uninterrupted affinity which their correspondence brought her. England contained Charles; it also contained Tessy Bellingham.

As often happens, outside circumstances combined to aggravate the sisters' inward depression. The weather was bad, rain had turned the roads into a quagmire; the short November dusk was deepening into night when a wheel came off their coach, nearly overturning it into the ditch and throwing them into a heap on to the floor. Dorothea, who had a good deal of personal dignity and disliked being made to look ridiculous, would have endured the situation on her own with good-natured resignation. Jenny regarded it as a joke and went into fits of laughter as their attendants helped them out of the coach.

Even Jenny's volatile spirits, however, flagged when, after riding pillion behind their postillions for several miles in the rain, they found that the only inn in the apparently deserted neighbourhood was inconsiderable and dirty, and were told by a disobliging landlord that the best room was already engaged by another English traveller. The room allotted to them was dismal, with grubby white-washed walls hung with a piece of tapestry which, from its appearance, seemed to be the favoured breeding-ground of moths and spiders, and furnished with two curtainless beds, a board laid on cross bars for a table, and a few rickety rush-bottom chairs. The prospect of spending the night here was cheerless, especially as the efforts of a slatternly maid to kindle a fire on the hearth had only resulted in a few smouldering logs. Dorothea surveyed the damp-stains on the walls and felt the draughts from windows and door with some concern on Jenny's behalf, and hoped that it would not bring on her cough or one of her feverish colds.

There was a time when neither she nor Jenny, with only experience of Irish inns, would have felt these discomforts so acutely, but their standard of comfort was high nowadays. When they travelled, if the hospitality of some friend's country house was not available, they broke their journey only at the most well-appointed hostelry, behind whose glowing red-curtained windows could be found the solid comforts which made good English inns the admiration of foreigners.

Both Dorothea and Jenny were pleasantly surprised when the landlord appeared and said that the English gentleman, hearing of his countrywomen's plight, begged them to favour him with the honour of their company for supper.

"I would sup with the devil himself if he had a fire," was Jenny's reply.

The chivalrous stranger had not only a fire in his room but a table already laid for supper. As the ladies entered he rose with smiling alacrity to greet them. He murmured some polite phrase, then stopped in apparent, and to Dorothea (who has left an account in her journal of the scene), unaccountable confusion. After six years of unprecedented adulation and flattery it really seems that she was unconscious of the effect that the sudden appearance of the Lovely Lynchs was likely to have on an

187

ordinarily susceptible young man. Not so Jenny, we may be sure.

The young man, no doubt congratulating himself on the dazzling reward of his politeness, recovered himself and introduced himself as Desmond Kyle, a Captain in the "57th Foot" rejoining his regiment in England after a visit to relations.

Dorothea was civilly returning the introduction, when Jenny broke out impulsively, "Kyle! Why, sister, wasn't that the name of people who had Cabragena before grandpapa? Oh Captain Kyle, try and recollect, was your grandfather an Irishman? Would it not be diverting to a degree if it should turn out that he was the man that lost Cabra House to my grandpapa in a night at cards?"

Dorothea tried without success to restrain Jenny by a warning look. She could not imagine that if Captain Kyle should, by an odd coincidence, prove to be the descendant of the man whom her grandfather had directly ruined and indirectly driven to suicide, he would care to have such a tragic piece of family history disinterred and tossed at him in this unceremonious manner. But Captain Kyle was either insensitive or unusually complaisant. He admitted with a smile that he was of Irish extraction and that he was indeed descended from the last Kyle to own Cabragena House.

On hearing this startling information, Dorothea regarded him with renewed and almost apologetic interest. She hoped most sincerely that this sudden appearance of two members of a family whom he must have been brought up to regard as responsible for his disinheritance had not pained or embarrassed him. On the contrary, it seemed that he was as far from feeling embarrassment as Jenny herself, and that like her he welcomed this discovery as a means of establishing a kind of intimacy between them. He invited the ladies to warm themselves at the fire while his valet ("a Frenchman and as good as any chef though I say so myself") dressed the supper, and answered Jenny's volley of excited questions with equal zest. Yes, it was true, his grandfather had fled to France where he had shot himself. ("But pray don't let that spoil your ladyship's supper. I hope we are not responsible for the follies of our ancestors. I find my own quite boar enough!") His own father had been brought up in France and, though he had married an Englishwoman, had remained in Bordeaux, where he had built up a prosperous business as a wine merchant. Captain Kyle, as the youngest of four sons, had taken service in the British Army. He assured Jenny that though he had been brought up in France he did not consider himself in the least frenchified, and could enjoy a sirloin of beef and a tankard of ale as well as any home-bred Briton. In answer to Jenny's enquiries he gave a brief account of his military career; he had served in Ireland and the West Indies and now, eager to see some fighting, intended to apply for a transfer to cavalry reinforcements that were shortly to sail for America.

Jenny listened to all this with rapt attention, finally breaking out with "My sister Dolly here and Lord Mandlesham and their friends have not a good word to say for the American war, but if I was a man I should be of the same mind as you and mad to go wherever there was fighting."

Dorothea smiled deprecatingly; she had no wish to have her political views thrust upon this obliging young man, but he passed it off with a laugh and a polite, "I am sure that Lady Mandlesham will forgive me for putting my duty as a soldier before all else." For Jenny he reserved a warmer glance both appreciative and indulgent.

As the three of them sat over a choice little supper, Dorothea became pensive, partly because the lively persiflage between the other two almost excluded her from joining in the conversation, partly because the situation gave her cause for thought. She was accustomed to see Jenny admired openly, warmly, often extravagantly. There was nothing unusual about that. What was unusual was Jenny's interest in this young man whom she had not met an hour ago. As she looked at him and listened to him there was a look in her face that Dorothea had never seen there before; it was as though something had been lit up for the first time. This made her appear so extraordinarily beautiful that Dorothea, who had known and loved her face since childhood, gazed at it in wonder. It was not surprising that the young man who was the cause of it could not take his eyes off her.

Dorothea, however, could not understand why her sister was so taken with Captain Kyle. He was a very personable young man it was true, about 26 or 27 years of age, of middle height, sturdily built rather than elegant, with a high colour and a bold yet persuasive glance. He gave the appearance of being a man of pleasure and gallantry as far as the demands of his career permitted, for Dorothea judged him to be a zealous and ambitious soldier. He had declared himself inordinately fond of riding, and it was easy to imagine him as a dashing cavalry leader. No doubt he took his pleasures as he found them—women, cards, wine—and was prevented from being a rake more from lack of means and attention to his profession than from natural refinement. His manners lacked the polish to which Dorothea was accustomed, but there was a heartiness about them that was not displeasing. Certainly he could be described as a fine young fellow, with all that the phrase implied of robust and egoistical masculinity.

To Dorothea the name of Kyle had always been one of ill-omened and sinister import—whenever she had thought of it, that is to say, which was not often, for it was disagreeable to her to recall the dubious way in which the Lynchs had acquired Cabra House. Now a descendant

of that last doomed owner of Cabragena had turned up
and proved to be neither resentful, nor gloomy nor
mysterious, but a virile young man who was making love
as fast as he could to Jenny. This should have been reassuring, but for some strange reason it was not. The
name of Kyle still sounded a note of foreboding in
Dorothea's consciousness; in it she could feel the desolation
of her Irish home and hear the cry of the seagulls as they
wheeled about the haunted rocks of Ardnabannagh.

CHAPTER XIII

DISASTER

I

IN THE YEARS to come Dorothea was to ask herself
if by any means she could have saved Jenny from disaster.
Few loving minds, however firm and sensible, are proof
against this most poignant form of self-torture—the letter
that should not have been written, the advice that was
withheld, the sudden apparently trivial change of plan,
the insolvable mystery of the might-have-been. Could
Dorothea's sisterly devotion have prevailed against such
a strong infatuation, this sudden unsealing of the springs
of Jenny's emotional life? Probably not, but Dorothea
could not absolve herself from blame for not having made
a greater effort to advise and warn her sister.

Her journal reveals the honesty with which she
endeavours to understand her own shortcomings. All her
life she had been reserved and reticent; these qualities
were part of her pride. Though she had faced the larger
crises of her life with courage she had shrunk from too close
contact with her fellow beings. She remembered with

pain how in her girlhood she had avoided playing with or talking to Tishy; how laboured her dutiful kindness to her weak-minded sister was compared to Jenny's unforced tenderness! In her married life she had taken refuge in wounded silence when she discovered the relationship between her husband and Tessy Bellingham; an attitude which saved her pride from total humiliation, was infinitely convenient to her rival and unwittingly authorised Charles to continue the connection. Had she not harmed not only herself but Charles by this attitude of unnatural reserve? There were times now when she believed that Charles was no longer so completely under Tessy's spell, times when his pleasure in her own company was so spontaneous and whole-hearted that it seemed to exclude the possibility of a satisfying companionship elsewhere. Rumour said that Mrs Bellingham's temperament had grown even more exacting with success; though she was reported to be as amusing and as fascinating as ever her tantrums were celebrated. There was an air of fatigue, even exasperation, about Lord Mandlesham's expression sometimes when he had been in the actress's company; at such times he seemed to wish for nothing better than to spend an hour or two in his wife's boudoir, to sit idly and at peace admiring her tranquil beauty. Yet to some extent she had helped to commit him to this liaison; things had drifted on for so long that it seemed impossible for her now to attempt to unravel the tangle of her married life.

With Jenny, Dorothea's consciousness of her superior sense and intellect, if not her year's seniority, entitled her to play the part of a fond but admonitory elder sister. But partly from a dislike of interfering, partly because she would not admit to herself the extent of Jenny's folly, she had persuaded herself that Desmond Kyle was just another of her sister's innumerable admirers, that her infatuation for him was one of her many ephemeral flirtations.

Though personally modest and lacking in vanity, Dorothea, not surprisingly, had an unconscious confidence in the Lovely Lynchs' destinies. They had been snatched from obscurity and raised to dazzling heights through no effort of their own. It had been sufficient for them to walk into the Viceregal ballroom; in an instant they had been acclaimed as the loveliest pair of the age. Impossible that calamity should strike down one member of this bright partnership. Other women might be disappointed, betrayed, shamed. Lovely Jenny must always be adored.

The three years after the sisters' first visit to France were crowded and varied. A quantity of interests, social and political, cluttered up Dorothea's days, so that it was with difficulty that she kept aware of the pattern even of her own personal life, while she remained ignorant, except for moments of apprehension, of Jenny's danger.

The war in America—"this shameful war" as it was considered at Mandlesham House as at Devonshire House, those twin citadels of Whig principles—was like an ever-darkening cloud in the political sky. When the Duchess of Devonshire and the Marchioness of Mandlesham met— friendly and gracious rivals in beauty—at some social function, their conversation would pass rapidly from books and cards and the merits of Dick Sheridan's new play, to warm appreciation of their friend Charles Fox's latest and most brilliant speech against the war.

A man like Horace Walpole, whose patriotism no one could doubt, could declare in public that he had always been a zealot for liberty in every part of the globe and heartily wished success to the Americans. Fox's aunt, Lady Sarah Lennox, who might have been Queen of England, congratulated herself that the marriage had never come off, "for I should certainly go mad to think a person I loved was the cause of such a shameful war".

These and similar sentiments found an echo in all true

Whig breasts, even after the united Colonies had adopted the Declaration of Independence early in 1776. The British soldiers taking part in the campaign were pitied, not only for the amazing incompetence of the War Office, but also for being obliged to take part in what was regarded as an unnatural and even fratricidal conflict. Yet Lord Mandlesham, who had supported the cause of conciliation towards the colonists with sincerity and fervour in the House of Lords, rode down himself to Crome to bring Dorothea the first news of the capture of New York by British troops.

Dorothea shared his exultation, then asked him teasingly if they ought to rejoice over an event that would probably prolong the war. "I would stop the war to-morrow if I had the power", was his reply, "but so long as our soldiers are fighting, I shall hear of their victories over the Yankees with the greatest satisfaction."

Such divided feelings were common to many of the Mandleshams' friends, who, while they remembered that they were Whigs, could not forget that they were Englishmen or Englishwomen.

Lady Aintry was spared any such mental conflict. For her the war meant only one thing: the absence, the danger, and yet the possible aggrandisement of the man she passionately loved. "Jenny has become quite a strategist these days", wrote Dorothea to her mother, "and has looked up North America on the map so that she may know, as she says, where Captain Kyle has been fighting before she writes him a letter of gratulation, for it seems that he has distinguished himself in the campaign, and is promoted to Major. Jenny is as hot for the war as I am against it, which will show you how well we love each other!"

No doubt Mrs Lynch might be expected to share her daughters' interest in Desmond Kyle on account of his antecedents. There is a note however of indifference if not of actual hostility in Dorothea's phrase, "It seems that he has distinguished himself." Captain Kyle had been much in Jenny's company during the few weeks that he had spent in England before sailing for America. Lady Aintry was so thronged with admiring young men that one more passed unnoticed. The almost startling brilliance of her eyes and expression was attributed to her recent triumphs in Paris and her new toilettes. Dorothea had some suspicion of the true cause, but trusted that distance and time would effect a painless and lasting separation between her sister and Desmond Kyle.

She had written to her mother disparagingly: "Capt Kyle, though a very civil and obliging young man and tolerably agreeable in his person, is not the interesting figure that you imagine him to be. He is certainly not low-bred, but there is a certain lack of refinement, I think, not in his manners so much as in his disposition."

The war dragged on, and Dorothea, who did not care if Desmond Kyle was promoted or not, continued to disapprove of it, to be cast down over British defeats and secretly triumphant over British victories. The strain of the war began to be felt in Society. Houses were sold, coaches and establishments reduced. The fashionable world lost something of its carefree exuberance, though outwardly the same round of gaieties and social functions continued.

Dorothea and Jenny paid two more visits to France, in the summer of '76 and again in the autumn of '77. It was delightful to Dorothea to renew her friendship with the Duchesse de Lapalisse, and from now on they corresponded regularly. The Queen, too, welcomed her with sincere affection. It saddened Dorothea to find how unpopular Marie Antoinette had become. No longer was she the idol of the crowd; the carriage of "the Austrian", as she was called, passed uncheered through the streets. A stream of pamphlets, many of them from the private printing-presses of the Palais Royale, disseminated slander against the Queen. Her debts at cards, the sums she spent on the Trianon, even her fantastical head-dresses were denounced. The pensions and places that she distributed to members of the Polignac clique were a particular cause of discontent. Madame de Polignac's relations and friends seemed intent on sucking the Treasury dry. Their rapaciousness flabbergastered the King, but he could refuse the Queen nothing. "Her ascendancy over me is so complete", he told Maurepas. The married life of the royal couple was still unconsummated. Dorothea wrote in her journal, "Is this charming Queen to remain a virgin all her days?"

The first of these two visits was the gayest. Lord Mandlesham joined his wife and sister-in-law for a short time, bringing with him a string of race-horses, with which he gained several victories at Sablons. Though Dorothea was only too well aware of his personal attractions, she could not help remarking with wifely gratification how popular he was with the men and how sought-after by the women. But in spite of, or perhaps because of, Tessy Bellingham, Charles was not promiscuous. His attentiveness to his wife was commented upon. "Le beau Marquis est bien épris de sa belle Marquise; ils ont l'air de deux personnages d'une conte de Perrault," one lady wrote sentimentally. There was no Mrs Bellingham round the corner to spoil Dorothea's triumph here.

A melancholy that was not only due to the autumnal season seemed to permeate the later visit. The possibility of France actively assisting the American colonists had been foreseen since the beginning of the conflict. There were indications now that it would not be long before England and France were at war. When Dorothea invited the Duchess de Lapalisse to visit her at Crome in the spring, the latter smiled sadly: "Alas, my friend, I fear that by then we shall be enemies." "That we shall never be, whatever the politicians may do," replied Dorothea. Before leaving she gave Madame de Lapalisse a locket set in diamonds, containing a strand of her golden hair. Madame de Lapalisse in return gave Dorothea a little pomander, enamelled with tiny flowers, on a chain and ring. The delicate but distinctive fragrance inside survives to this day, token of the friendship between two women who lived a hundred and seventy years ago.

In this way Dorothea was made aware for the first time of the helplessness of the individual swept along in the turbulent flood of world events. She was still young enough to resent it. With all its faults she loved France, as one can only love a place where one has been happy and carefree. She had made good friends there and had experienced the pleasures of a highly cultivated and brilliant if decadent society. In some indefinable way France had altered her; the prevailing atmosphere of gallantry, more refined and subtle than in England, had drawn from her some hidden quality of femininity. In her girlhood someone had said of her unkindly, "The elder Miss Lynch is indeed beautiful—a white rose without a scent." It is significant that Lord Mandlesham's increased taste for his wife's society dates from the time of her visits to Paris.

Now a fog more dense than any provided by the Channel was to descend between the two countries. "When shall I see France again?" Dorothea asked in her journal. She would not have been reassured if she could have foreseen the answer.

2

The year 1777 ended on a sombre note for Dorothea and Jenny. Mrs Lynch died in November after a few days' illness. Her daughters were disconsolate. They had not seen her for nearly five years, and to modern ideas it

197

seems surprising that they did not make more effort to visit her at Cabragena. It is true that they had contemplated a journey to Ireland in the early spring of '77, but Dorothea at that time was expecting another child (her second son Edward was born in June of that year); at her mother's request she did not undertake the journey and the project came to nothing. Even so one might have expected at least an annual attempt to revisit their former home. It must be remembered, however, that in the eighteenth century even the most devoted relations were resigned to lengthy separations. The difficulties and hazards of travel do not altogether explain it. Life was lived at a different tempo. Visits were more infrequent and lasted longer (Mrs Lynch, when she was in England, spent five months with her daughters); bad news as well as good had to be awaited with patience; the naval husband or son who went to sea disappeared for years from the family circle; those who settled abroad seemed content to remain in voluntary exile for ten or fifteen years, relying on their friends' correspondence or occasional English travellers to keep them in touch with home affairs.

War-time exigencies forced us—grudgingly—to conform more closely to our ancestors' standards in this respect, but we could never resign ourselves to conditions that they accepted as natural.

There can be no question of Dorothea's and Jenny's affection for their mother. They wrote to her regularly several times a week—even Jenny in the midst of all her gaieties never failed to send an ill-spelt scrawl. Their letters betray their solicitude for their mother; no shadow of their matrimonial troubles is allowed to fall across these sunlit pages, which are a record of their social pleasures, their trivial daily occupations, and of their children's doings and sayings—fond prattlings which we may not call fatuous, for they were written not for the eyes of strangers living in another century, but for the delectation

of an affectionate grandmother . . . Cara is the merriest
little mouse imaginable. She will not be as great a beauty
as her aunt Jenny but she promises to be nearly as bewitching. Little Charles is very forward for his age. At four he
can read and play a game of cards with his mama. He
gets very indignant if he does not win. His father laughs
and tells him, "Your mother has the devil's own luck at
cards." The baby Edward grows very lusty and strong.
When he sees his sister and brother ride away on their
ponies, he shouts with envy and tries to leap out of his
nurse's arms. The little Minton boys seem somewhat
colourless compared to their cousins, or perhaps Jenny has
not the time to describe them. They send their "love and
dutie" to their grandmama. Horace has a pet squirrel.
Frederick is much prettier than he was. In the Gainsborough portrait of "Lady Aintry and her children" they
are shown leaning against their delicious mother, dark-
eyed, distinguished-looking little boys in white satin suits
and frills.

Now there was an end to these letters to Mrs Lynch
from her beautiful daughters, these letters which she must
have read and re-read with maternal pride and contentment as she sat by the fireside of an evening in the drawing-
room of Cabra House and heard the wild Atlantic gales
lash themselves relentlessly against the headland, or was
lulled on calmer nights by the drowsy murmur of the
ground-swell. Oliver Lynch, stupefied with sleep and
brandy, snored in his chair; Tishy in her corner mumbled
happily over the dolls sent to her by her sisters in London,
and her scraps of ribbon and lace. Mrs Lynch had only
these letters and the memory of two graceful young
figures sitting close together, golden and dark hair shining in the candlelight, but she did not complain. Her
daughters were happy, successful, renowned. Not in vain
had she given birth to this peerless pair. Their beauty had
been crowned with a deserved felicity. She died, peaceful

in this belief, and before the first anniversary of her death had occurred Dorothea was to have cause to be thankful that she had died when she did.

News travelled slowly in those days, a storm in the Irish Sea further delayed communications, and Mrs Lynch was buried in the family vault before her daughters had heard of their loss. What was to happen to Tishie? It was arranged that she should be brought to England and should spend her time between her two sisters. Jenny, in a letter which reveals the intrinsic sweetness of her nature under her giddy ways (for she was aware what a burden Dorothea would find Tishie) wrote: "I will have Tishie here mostly, sister, if that suets you. I am so nerely an idiot miself that I find it no trouble to play with her. When I am not gaming or raking (as my Lord Aintry calls my card playing and dancing) I am much alone and wil be gladd of her companie."

As it happened Tishie refused to leave Cabragena, declaring that she must be there to assist her mother out of the family vault at the Resurrection Day. No arguments or persuasions could move her, so it was finally decided that Kathie should keep house for Tishie and Oliver Lynch who, now that Mrs Lynch's restraining influence was removed, could settle down to drink himself to death on his nieces' allowance. Dorothea and Jenny could rest assured that their sister would be as happy as her condition allowed in Kathie's kindly care; but neither Kathie nor their uncle were letter-writers, and their only link now with their girlhoods' home were occasional letters from the local clergyman, who undertook the neighbourly office of sending them news of their imbecile sister.

It seemed indeed as though Cabragena House, desolate and bleak on its remote headland, had faded into the background of their lives. Yet, in fact, influences from its sinister past were now rising like a miasma around them.

The first intimation of danger (as Dorothea afterwards saw it) came in the summer of 1776, when Jenny came to Dorothea and asked her to persuade Lord Mandlesham to use his influence to procure the command of a regiment for Major Kyle. To Dorothea's eighteenth-century mind there was nothing strange, far less reprehensible, in this idea of a man forwarding his military career with the help of influential relations or friends. It was indeed the accepted way of advancement both in the Army and the Navy, and men of the highest probity did not scruple to use it. What caused her concern was to find that her sister was corresponding with Desmond Kyle, and was sufficiently intimate with him to exert herself in this way on his behalf (presumably at his request).

The conversation that she had with Jenny on the subject evidently made her very uneasy, for she recorded it in some detail in her journal. Jenny made her request in an airy and casual tone, at the same time blushing so deeply that Dorothea's attention was immediately fixed. Dorothea was distressed by her sister's air of confusion, but she overcame her natural dislike of probing into other people's affairs sufficiently to express her surprise that Jenny was so interested in the career of a young man who was neither a connection nor a friend of long standing. Jenny replied eagerly that, on the contrary, she considered Desmond Kyle to be almost a relation, "or near enough as makes no odds. Consider, sister, that if it were not for Grandpapa the Kyles would have been living at Cabra instead of being in exile in France. Major Kyle has been deprived of all the advantages of a family estate and a settled education. Surely the least that we can do is to exert ourselves to help him now that he has come our way." She added vehemently, "Is it fair, is it just that a gallant and zealous officer should be hindered in his career because he has no family interest?"

Dorothea would have been amused to notice how the bare and impoverished acres of Cabragena, and Bat O'Hallohan's schooling, had been transformed by Jenny's imagination into "a family estate and a settled education", had she not been both alarmed and annoyed by Jenny's attitude. She said rather unkindly, "If you feel so strongly about it why do you not engage Lord Aintry's interest for him?" In reply Jenny fixed her beautiful eyes on her sister with a look of reproach and sadness which cut Dorothea to the heart. She caught Jenny in her arms: "Jenny, love, I would do anything to please you so long as it did not harm you too. I am sure that Major Kyle is a deserving young man and a meritorious officer. I have nothing against him, provided that he does not endanger your happiness or respectability. But if it should come out that he has been promoted through your interest (or mine for that matter, for everyone knows how close we are) would it not look very odd? Surely it would be better that he should advance himself through his own exertions, which an officer of his energy and merit cannot fail to do in this war? You see how rapidly he has been promoted to Major."

Jenny looked unconvinced. She said quickly, "Yes, but we—I mean he was obliged to buy his majority. Such a large sum could not easily be found a second time."

Again her confusion was evident. Dorothea's suspicions were painfully aroused. In a flash of intuition she remembered a scene between Lord Aintry and his wife at a supper-party at Mandlesham House some months ago. Lord Aintry had asked Jenny what had happened to her diamond necklace that she never wore it nowadays, to which Jenny had replied evasively that she did not know, she believed that it might have been stolen by a maid who had been dismissed from her service. Lord Aintry had chided her for her carelessness in not informing him before of the loss of such a valuable ornament. Jenny had accepted his reproaches with unusual meekness. The matter had dropped; it seemed to be just another of the Aintry's continual bickerings. Only now did the recollection of it spring up in Dorothea's mind, endued with a new significance, for she felt as convinced as though her sister had confessed it to her that Jenny had sold her diamond necklace to buy Desmond Kyle's majority.

Something of her dismay must have shown itself on her face, for Jenny abruptly changed the subject as though Desmond Kyle and his promotion were a matter of complete indifference to her. Not long after this conversation, however, she informed Dorothea with an air both triumphant and defiant that she need not trouble Lord Mandlesham with the little matter that they had discussed, for Desmond Kyle had been promoted to the rank of Lt. Colonel, after distinguishing himself at the taking of New York.

After this Jenny never mentioned the name of Kyle to her sister, but through other sources Dorothea heard news of the man, for whom she could not help feeling an unreasoning but instinctive aversion that amounted almost to fear. Her estimate of him as an ambitious and able soldier had proved correct. The ups and downs of the American war, disconcerting as they were to civilians at home, provided him with opportunities for displaying his professional prowess of which he was quick to take advantage. He formed a body of cavalry known, from the colour of the uniform, as Kyle's Green Horse, whose exploits under their intrepid leader daunted the enemy, while their depredations terrified the countryside through which they passed.

There were acts of brutality on both sides in the

American war, more particularly among what would now be called the guerrilla troops. If more than one defenceless town was set ablaze at Colonel Kyle's commands, it is only fair to record that his renown rested on more creditable exploits, particularly on one fight when he and his "Green Devils", with no more than ninety cavalry and seventy infantry and unaided by artillery, routed some 1000 Americans posted on strong ground. He was lucky, but he was also energetic, bold, and dashing to the point of brilliance.

When he returned to England in the autumn of 1777 he was something of a hero, and certainly a far more notable and glorious figure than the unknown young captain who had sailed for America two years ago.

He was celebrated enough, at any rate, for Dorothea to be aware of his return, and to regard it with misgiving. But Jenny remained silent. If her eyes seemed unnaturally brilliant and large in her delicate face, if her cheeks flushed with too hectic a colour when Colonel Kyle's name was mentioned, Dorothea could attribute this to her health which was causing Dorothea increasing alarm. She coughed continually, she had grown very thin, there was an air of fragility about her that was frightening. She was very lovely still, but her radiant air had gone; it was as though her beauty were burning itself out like a too ardent fire.

Yet her frantic pursuit of pleasure never slackened, indeed its pace increased as her health grew worse. Like a child that grows more excited and noisy in its sport as bedtime approaches, so Jenny crammed her days and nights with aimless gaiety. Dorothea's anxious solicitude she evaded with a laugh or a kiss, her doctor's warnings she dismissed petulantly; she had long ceased to pay any heed to Lord Aintry's admonition or advice. They lived together under the same roof as strangers, an unspoken constraint and hostility between them and, on

Lord Aintry's part, a silent jealousy, the only reminder of their former intimacy.

Desmond Kyle had all the qualities that make a man popular in society: sufficient good looks, good humour, high spirits and a reputation for courage and success. He had not been back long from America before he was in demand in fashionable circles, and was to be seen at Devonshire House, Melbourne House and other social centres where Lady Aintry could not fail to meet him.

Soon after his return, however, Mrs Lynch's death put an end to Jenny's appearances in public. Decorum obliged her to cancel her engagements and to spend at least some months of her mourning in seclusion. Dorothea's fears were allayed. It seemed as though their mother, by the circumstances of her own death, had been allowed to protect her daughter.

So Dorothea persuaded herself, not remembering that those who have a perilous secret will endeavour most sedulously to conceal it from those they love the best.

4

The letter in which Jenny confessed to Dorothea that she and Desmond Kyle were lovers, and that she had left her husband and thrown herself on his protection, still exists. To this day the ill-formed handwriting betrays by its more than usual illegibility the agitation of the writer; the ill-spelt words still convey across the centuries their passionate message, still announce Jenny's headlong abandonment to her love and her ruin. There is a smudge at the bottom of the page. Did tears fall from Jenny's splendid eyes as she wrote? The paper is deeply creased, perhaps from the convulsive working of Dorothea's hand as she sat holding it, stunned and amazed with horror and grief.

It is undated but must have been written some time between March 5th–7th 1778. It reads:

"DOLLY,

I dred the shok this letter will give yr tender hart. But it must be writ. All must out. You must no all. Oh Dolly! have you never gessed the conexion between me and Desmond Kyle? I love him to maddness. I cannot live without him, truely I canot. I wd rather tramp in patterns besid him than live in afluence with a man I doe not love.

Oh Dolly, I no I use Lord Aintry very ill, he is two good for me, but if you knew the misery I have sufered these past three years since I first met my dearest Kyle your hart wd not be entirely shut against me. Dont despise me sweetest Dolly. If you cast me off my hart will be broke. God bless and preserve you prays your truely and loving sister,   JENNY LYNCH."

"Jenny Lynch." This signature more even than the breathless, incoherent phrases, must have shown Dorothea how irrevocably Jenny had broken with her husband and her married state. It was as though the nine years of her married life had never been, as though she had never lived with Lord Aintry and borne him children. Wifehood, motherhood, duty, prudence, honour, all had shrivelled away in the white flame of this consuming passion.

Dorothea was appalled, not so much at the consequences of her sister's flight, for her deep love for her swept away all that was superficial and conventional, as at the state of affairs it revealed, the piteous emptiness and frustration of Jenny's heart. Jenny, so full of life and love and sweetness, "a child walking in its sleep with a lighted candle in its hand"—all her best instincts thwarted and pent up, the tenderness that should have warmed and fructified her married life spending itself on this almost abject love

206

for a man whom Dorothea could not believe worthy of her. There was no word in Jenny's letter of Desmond Kyle's love for her, no guarantee that he was prepared to compensate her for her sacrifice of reputation and peace of mind by a constant and protective devotion. Jenny, the admired, the adored was now the adorer.

In her dire distress Dorothea turned to her husband for help. She was at Crome when Jenny's letter came, Lord Mandlesham was up in town. Without even waiting to change her dress she ordered her travelling chaise and drove to London. It was evening when she reached Mandlesham House, to find that Lord Mandlesham was out. So great was her need of his help and advice that even if he had been supping with Mrs Bellingham she might possibly have sought him out. Fortunately it was one of his more intellectual evenings; he was at the Turk's Head in Gerrard Street at a meeting of the Literary Club, a choice assemblage whose members at various times included Sir Joshua Reynolds, Burke, Sheridan, Charles James Fox, Dr Johnson and Topham Beauclerk.

It is easy to imagine the raillery which was directed at Lord Mandlesham when he was informed that a lady outside desired to speak to him privately, his surprise when the cloaked and hooded figure proved to be his wife, his concern when she beckoned him into the carriage and told him in whispered tones of her sister's disgrace.

The night-watchman has shuffled by with his lantern and staff, the prostitute in gaudy petticoat and tarnished buckles loiters at the street corner, accosts a tipsy buck and links her arm in his, a shapeless heap of rags in a doorway rises and reveals itself to be a beggar. In the darkness of the carriage, Dorothea's face is set and pale as a statue's; Charles, no longer debonair, regards her with compassion and solicitude, promises his immediate aid. All has passed, the shadowy, indifferent night-life of the street outside, the grief and tenderness that linked together for a few intensely felt moments the man and woman in the darkness of the carriage. Do such moments of deep emotion die or do they ripple on throughout eternity?

By a fortunate circumstance, as Lord Mandlesham pointed out to his wife, Lord Aintry was staying at Euston Hall for the Newmarket Races. It was just possible that he had not yet heard of Jenny's flight. This gave the Mandleshams a brief space of time in which to search for her and, if they found her, to endeavour to persuade her to return to her husband. "I will leave that part to you, Dolly," Charles told her. "If I were a handsome woman like Jenny I should be heartily sorry to have Aintry as a permanent bedfellow."

In spite of his poor opinion of Lord Aintry's attractions as a husband, Lord Mandlesham lost no time in setting forth on his dutiful task. To find Colonel Kyle's lodgings was his first endeavour. He judged rightly that the person who could give him the most up-to-date information on this point was Moll Lloyd, who kept a notorious bagnio in Covent Garden, and whose clientele was said to range from market-porters to dukes. This obliging lady assured Lord Mandlesham that she knew the gallant colonel well and gave him his address. But Colonel Kyle was no longer at his rooms in Leicester Fields; the landlady at first maintained an obstinate silence as to his whereabouts, but convinced at last that Lord Mandlesham was both the finer gentleman of the two and more lavish with his bribes consented to speak. Yes, a lady had arrived at the house several nights ago in a hired chaise, unannounced and (the woman gathered from Colonel Kyle's evident astonishment) unexpected. Colonel Kyle told the landlady that she was his sister. She spent the night there. Next morning they left, Colonel Kyle paying a month's rent in advance. It was an easy matter to trace the owner of the hired carriage, which had taken them to Richmond village. Lord Mandlesham returned to Mandlesham House to change his clothes, snatch a hasty breakfast and reassure the anxiously waiting Dorothea before setting off again for Richmond.

Here again the birds had fled. The respectable widow woman who had let her sitting-room and bedroom to the runaway pair had no suspicion that she was entertaining any other than a newly married couple, though she had been mildly surprised that the lady who was "as beautiful as an angel but very poorly looking" seemed so prone to tears. They had only stayed there a couple of nights, then had left—where for she could not say—she believed for London.

It was strange to think that only yesterday the rare and pampered Jenny had sat in this homely little room with its spotted china dogs on the mantelpiece and its rag hearth-rug. (Worried and preoccupied as he was, Lord Mandlesham had time to notice its furnishings with curiosity.) Jenny had sat there, a fugitive, tired, ill and in tears. The thought urged her kindly brother-in-law on to further efforts, but though he managed to trace the lovers as far as the Queen's Head, Southwark, he could find out nothing about their subsequent movements. In any case it was too late. By now everyone, including Lord Aintry, knew that Lady Aintry and Colonel Kyle had eloped.

The elopement was rather more than a nine days' wonder, providing society with a welcome and piquant change of topic from Lord North's conciliatory plan for making a treaty with the Americans, and the probable outbreak of war with France. There were some who condemned Jenny: "Lady Aintry has abandoned her husband and children and placed herself under the protection of Colonel Kyle. Such frenzy, folly, extravagance of passion —I know not what to call it—passes belief." Others drew

209

a moral lesson from it: "What lamentable proof Lady Aintry's ruin affords that beauty alone, unadorned by steadiness of principle, character and propriety, is of no lasting benefit, indeed rather a snare, to its possessor."

Others sneered: "So one of the Lovely Lynchs has run off with a soldier. When one considers all the fracas that she and her sister, the proud Marchioness, occasioned, 'tis a paltry enough ending. It seems that the Colonel is something of a rake, so it is to be hoped that the fair Jenny will not end in the gutter." But there were others again who sincerely lamented the disaster: "Poor Lady Aintry! Her folly and the impropriety of her conduct have exposed her to the just censure of the world, but I, for one, cannot forget her innumerable little acts of kindness. She said many a foolish thing but seldom an unkind one. The poor lovely creature deserved a more profuse and happier fate. She had a thousand graces; her equal for beauty and good nature will be far to seek."

Many people pitied Dorothea, whose devotion to her sister was well-known and whose character commanded general liking and respect, but Dorothea, who felt unequal to the commiseration of any but her intimate friends, and had no intention of allowing Jenny to be censured in her hearing, left London for the comparative seclusion of Crome.

A letter which she wrote to Lady Hannah, in answer to an invitation to stay, discloses her feelings: "You need not apologise, dear Lady Hannah, for offering me your sympathy. It would be a false and unworthy sense of pride indeed that could prevent me from accepting pity from so true a friend as yourself and one who loves Jenny so dearly. I admit that I feel unequal at present to moving in circles where Jenny's fate is nothing but an object of curiosity and scorn. But the solicitude of Lord Mandlesham and my close friends is my chief comfort in this misery. Oh Lady Hannah, what has become of her? We have no news (though Lord Mandlesham continues to make diligent enquiries) and I have no confidence in the man for whom she has sacrificed everything.

"Indeed I will gladly come and stay with you. I remember with gratitude how wise and comfortable I have always found your advice. But you will excuse me, I know, from seeing Lord Aintry. To the world at large he is an injured husband—I cannot deny the justice of this—but to me he will always be the man who married Jenny when she was an ignorant, confiding girl of seventeen, and had not the patience or sympathy to attach her to him and secure her happiness. I am ashamed, dear Lady Hannah, of my bitterness. I must strive against it, but I cannot hope to be anything but partial where Jenny is concerned."

Six weeks went by without news of Jenny—weeks of intense suffering for Dorothea. At last a letter came, not from Jenny but from Desmond Kyle. Dorothea wrote in her journal that when she saw the signature she believed Jenny to be dead, and for a few moments could not read the letter for the wild beating of her heart. She composed herself, saw that Kyle had written from Calais, and that Jenny was alive. Alive but desperately ill.

It was this circumstance alone, Kyle explained, which had induced him to write to Lady Mandlesham. He was well aware, he said, of the unfavourable light in which Lady Aintry's relations and friends must regard him (nor would he attempt now to defend himself), and on no account would he have exposed himself to the mortification of a rebuff from Lady Mandlesham did he not solemnly believe that Lady Aintry's welfare, nay her life, depended on it. Their happiness together he said had been cruelly curtailed by Lady Aintry's severe illness, which the fatigue of the journey and the agitation produced by too sensitive a nature in a delicate frame had brought on soon after their arrival in France. She had lacked no care that his devotion or the skill of the physicians could suggest, but her health had steadily declined under the strain of a racking cough with haemorrhages and feverish heats. Now he dared no longer conceal her danger from her family. His pecuniary circumstances obliged him urgently to go to Bordeaux, where he hoped to realise some money due to him under his father's will. No power on earth would have induced him to leave the sick-bed of the loveliest and dearest of women but this unhappy combination of events. He was confident that Lady Mandlesham, of whose generous and forgiving nature he had heard much from Lady Aintry, would fill his place at her sister's bedside.

At the bottom of the letter was scribbled in Jenny's handwriting, "Dolly, for God's sake com to me, if only to saye farewell."

Dorothea was not deceived by Colonel Kyle's letter. She went to her husband, laid the letter before him and said, "Jenny is ill—dying. Desmond Kyle has no further use for her. He has abandoned her."

Charles was incredulous. "Is it possible that any man could be such a scoundrel?" But when he had read through the letter he was obliged to agree with his wife.

It was painfully clear what had happened. As long as Jenny was the beautiful and admired Lady Aintry—in Horace Walpole's phrase an "Empress of fashion"—he was charmed to be her lover. Nor was her attraction for him lessened by the fact that she was able and eager to help him on in his career. He had utterly misunderstood Jenny. Too egoistical to be interested in the character of the woman whom he professed to love, he had imagined her to be just another sophisticated and rakish woman of quality. He had never guessed at the innate simplicity of her loving but undisciplined heart.

Her impulsive flight from home and arrival at his lodging had taken him completely by surprise, upsetting all his plans for his social and military advancement. He realised too late that what for him had been an exciting intrigue, highly gratifying to his vanity, was Jenny's first experience of love. To have repulsed her now would have demanded a strength of character or a control over his passions which he did not possess. Involved in an elopement which he had never intended, he took her to France. Here, he soon found himself with a sick, possibly dying woman on his hands, harassed by lack of money, his army career imperilled, his social position ruined.

To a man of his temperament it must have seemed to him that he was behaving with striking generosity in sparing her his reproaches, and in carrying out the uncongenial and unaccustomed role of a sick-nurse. When the state of her health and of his finances became equally critical he seized at the opportunity of escape, no doubt persuading himself that it was best for her, as well as for himself, that he should leave her, at any rate for a while.

When Lord Mandlesham had read the letter through a second time he said: "Someone should seek this fellow out and kill him. If Aintry will not do it I have a mind to do it myself."

Dorothea told him sadly, "That will not help Jenny. Let him go. He is unworthy even of our thoughts. We must think only of Jenny now and how we can save her."

They had no need to discuss the matter at length. Both agreed that Dorothea must go at once to Calais and, as soon as Jenny's health permitted, bring her back to Crome. To do this before Lord Aintry heard of her plight seemed to them both to be essential. Charles told his wife: "They are saying at Brooks's that Aintry has vowed to get Jenny back, as though she were a piece of statuary that had been stolen from him, or one of those confounded medals that he sets such store by. Mark my words, there is no fondness or pity there, only a frenzy of jealousy very near to madness."

Dorothea, no doubt, remembered her husband's words as she travelled to Dover as speedily as post-horses would convey her, and blessed the chance that had brought her news of Jenny's hiding-place before Lord Aintry had heard of it. She would not stop at the coaching inns on the road longer than was necessary to change horses; she needed no rest nor refreshment for herself but only to reach Jenny with the least possible delay. In an agony of impatience she counted the hours till she could kneel by her sister's bedside and, holding her in her arms, as she had done when they were children together at Cabragena, and Jenny had been scared by some night sound of their haunted home, assure her of the love and protection that awaited her at Crome.

There was a storm in the Channel and the packet boat was not sailing. Dorothea did not rest till she had found the captain of a small craft (a fishing boat by day, a smuggler by night, but Dorothea asked no inconvenient questions) who, if he were paid well enough, was ready to risk the crossing. Nine hours later Dorothea landed at Calais, so exhausted by sickness and the buffeting she had received that she could hardly stand upright, but sustained by the thought, "I am near Jenny."

She drove at once to the modest *auberge* whose address Desmond Kyle had given her in his letter. How she must have almost suffocated with impatience and apprehension as she enquired from the *patronne* if she had an English lady, "une malade", staying there. Oh yes, the woman told her, there had been an English lady there with her husband, a military gentleman, "comme elle était souffrante, la pauvre"—she tapped her chest significantly. The gentleman had gone away on business and the lady had been alone for a few days, but not unattended as her husband had arranged that a girl of fourteen should come and nurse her. She had told the *patronne* that she was expecting a relative to arrive shortly from England to take her home. And sure enough a gentleman had come and taken her away. The *patronne* only hoped that she would survive the journey.

Dorothea was stupefied. "A gentleman took her away?"

"Certainly. A grand gentleman—an English milord. Tiens! what was the name. Andrie—Antrie?"

Dorothea wrote in her journal that night: "I am too late. Lord Aintry has found her."

CHAPTER XIV

GOOD-BYE TO JENNY

EVERYONE—NEARLY EVERYONE that is to say, for Lord and Lady Mandlesham were prejudiced, and old Lady Hannah Martindale was mad—was greatly edified by Lord Aintry's goodness towards his erring wife. No one could have blamed him if, after being so openly betrayed and shamed by her, he had cast her off for ever. In doing so, he would have been well within his rights as an injured husband. But no—when he learnt that she had been abandoned by her lover and lay dying (as it was thought) at Calais, he went at once to find her and brought her back to Wing Magna, where she was languishing at present, somewhere between life and death, in the seclusion that her ruined health and reputation demanded, but surrounded, it was said, with every attention and care.

Even those who thought Lord Aintry haughty and unsympathetic were obliged to admit that it was a remarkable display of Christian forgiveness. As for Jenny, the spectacle of erring beauty brought low, broken in health and contrite, was one that made a special appeal to the eighteenth-century mind.

Lady Hannah Martindale would have none of this: "To forgive and to be forgiven is the most delicate of arts, requiring an excess of generosity and fine feeling in both parties if they are to live together in any comfort. My nephew Aintry knows nothing about it. Why did he not let poor little Jenny go to her sister and die in peace? Everyone tells me how handsomely he is behaving. Fine flummery! I say that he is behaving most barbarously."

Dorothea did not express herself so intemperately; in fact, though she disliked her brother-in-law, she had to admit that he had treated Jenny with surprising leniency; yet deep in her heart she knew that Lady Hannah, so wise and old, was speaking the truth. Not love, not the compassionate generosity that cannot bear to triumph through the suffering of another human being, had prompted him to pardon his wife, but his overweening sense of possession. Jenny had been his; he had once loved her ardently enough, but his passion had burnt out, for Jenny herself had withheld from him the fondness upon which it could be fed; nothing was left now but the ashes of disillusionment. But he could never forget that he had possessed Jenny Lynch in the perfection of her youthful beauty. Love had gone, but jealousy, love's baser self, remained. She had tried to escape from him and fate had cast her back, forlorn and broken, at his feet. Now he would keep her to the end.

Dorothea at least felt sufficient distrust of her brother-in-law's motives to write and beg him to allow her to have the care of Jenny. She must have known that she was exposing herself to a rebuff, but her love for Jenny was stronger than her pride. Her letter to Lord Aintry has disappeared—no doubt it was conciliatory—she wanted so desperately to have Jenny with her but, from her journal, it is clear that Charles helped her to compose it.

"Lord M. and me sate up till 2 o'clock in the morning writing my letter to Lord A." Dorothea kept Lord Aintry's reply locked up in her private letter-box, as though to accuse him to future generations. It is like the writer himself, polite, formal and correct, but as contemptuous as a door slammed in the face of this too fond and importunate sister:

"I have to thank your ladyship for the favour of your letter and am sensibly touched by the wish you express to be of service to my unhappy wife. If she was without other refuge in her melancholy situation, it would indeed be suitable that she should place herself under your ladyship's protection, as being her nearest female relation. But this is not the case. Lady Aintry may have forgotten her marriage vows; I am not wont so lightly to overlook my undertakings. Your ladyship may rest assured though it is not in my power to restore Lady Aintry to health or happiness, she shall not want the care which her distracted and enfeebled condition requires nor the respect to which her rank entitles her."

This was hardly a letter to reassure a loving and agonised sister. Dorothea lost no time in going down to Wing Magna to see Jenny for herself. There is no record of that first poignant meeting between the two sisters. One may be sure that no word of reproach or even of wounding pity passed Dorothea's lips. Her nature, so sensitive beneath its outward placidity, would give her the courage to conceal the frightful pang that Jenny's altered looks and spirits gave her, would even enable her to greet her with playful tenderness as though they were still the two Lovely Lynchs, standing hand in hand on the threshold of their golden destiny.

Her first visit was followed by many others. When possible she timed them to coincide with Lord Aintry's frequent absences; when he was there he made her feel neither welcome nor unwelcome; he was courteous, coolly solicitous and well-bred, and her antipathy to him deepened into something like hatred.

These visits to Wing Magna were indescribably melancholy, yet their performance was her one consolation during that spring and summer. Sometimes she would travel all night after some social function at Mandlesham House or elsewhere that she could not avoid, so that she might be with her sister as soon as possible. As she leant back in her carriage with closed eyes, or stood warming her hands by the fire of some roadside inn, a stately and inscrutable figure, she must have been racked with sad and anxious thoughts. Perhaps she would draw from her reticule and read Lady Hannah's latest report of Jenny's health: "I saw our dear Jenny yesterday. She has been complaining for some days of pain in her side and an oppression across her breast, but the doctor believes that he has found a medicine which will relieve this. I found her weak and sunk in a low spirited state, but she assured me, 'When Dolly comes I will do better. She does me more good than all these horrid medicines.'"

If the weather was fine, the contrast was painful between the fresh green foliage and lawns outside, the flowers and the bird-song, and the darkened sick-room where Jenny, her brilliant eyes like sapphires in her ravaged face, lay sunk in a deadly languor. If the weather was wet, how mournful Wing Magna seemed, as though already lamenting its mistress; rain dripped from the sodden trees, the statues on the terrace were ghostly in the failing light, a green gloom filled Jenny's room with its view down the tree-lined canal to the tomb-like Garden Temple.

Jenny never spoke of her elopement and only once, indirectly, of Desmond Kyle. She had lain silent for a long time, holding Dorothea's hand, suddenly she said, "Dolly, if you was a girl again you would marry Lord Mandlesham would you not, even if you could know what you know now?" Dorothea nodded, unable to speak, as the thought of those eight years of mingled happiness and bitterness flooded into her mind. Jenny sighed deeply. "Yes, I understand. You love him. It has made up for everything." She added, "I too know now what love is. At least I have not missed that." She burst into such a passion of weeping that when her sobs ceased she lay nearly unconscious in Dorothea's arms.

On the whole there was an air of indifference, too languid even to be called resignation, about her that alarmed Dorothea more than anything; it was so unlike the Jenny she had known all her life. Even the sight of her children (it was considered the supreme proof of Lord Aintry's magnanimity that he had not debarred them from the society of their prodigal mother) could not arouse in Jenny more than a flicker of pleasure or interest; their chatter soon exhausted her, or they would fall silent and stare at her, frightened and bewildered at the change that had come over their once gay and lovely mother. Jenny seemed to accept the fact that Lord Aintry had found her after the elopement as an inescapable decree of fate, to be no more grateful for nor resentful of his reassumption of his rights over her, than some woodland creature would be that had been caught in a trap and brought back to human habitation.

It was not till long afterwards, when it no longer mattered, that Dorothea learnt how Lord Aintry had traced his wife. It was Charles who told her and, though he did not say so, she guessed, rightly, that he had heard it from Tessy Bellingham. This is Mrs Bellingham's account of it from her memoirs:

"The chief topic of conversation in the early spring of 1778 was my performance as Clarinda in *The Suspicious Husband* and the elopement of Lady Aintry, Lord Mandlesham's sister-in-law, with an Irishman, Colonel Kyle. Lady Aintry had, on occasion, used me very uncivilly, allowing her sisterly jealousy to overcome her good breeding (of which indeed I must say she had a considerably smaller share than her sister). Had I not restrained my temper out of consideration for my noble lover we might several times have scolded together in public like two oyster women! However, prolonged resentment is not one of my faults, and consequently I did not triumph in her fall. She was certainly an exceedingly beautiful creature and, if she had applied herself as dilligently to studying men as she did to studying her appearance and dress, might have been as happy as she was beautiful. As it was her lover deserted her when her health began to fail, and though her husband took her back, it was to gratify his sense of revenge, it was said, more than his affection. Her sister would gladly have offered her shelter and nearly drowned herself in a fishing smack crossing to France to find her, but by ill luck a woman by the name of Harriet Swann, who was a courtesan and an actress, and successful at neither profession, had seen the runaway pair at Calais. Harriet who had been Lord Aintry's mistress, but had been dismissed by him and not very handsomely compensated at his marriage, revealed Lady Aintry's whereabouts out of malice, and so Lord Aintry came and carried her off before her sister could reach her."

It is hard to say what Jenny's thoughts were during those months as her strength gradually ebbed away before the onslaught of her fatal illness, hard even to get any consistent impression of her during this time. One day Dorothea was deeply distressed to find her looking through her personal jewels and trinkets with a view to their distribution to various relations and friends after her death. In vain Dorothea tried to turn her mind from this morbid trend of thought to some more cheerful subject. She begged Dorothea to see that each member of her household received some memento of her ("Dolly, they treat me with as much respect and affection *now* as when I first came here as a bride") and, giving Dorothea the ornament of jargons which she had worn the night of her debut at Dublin Castle, and which Lady Moffat had given her, asked that her niece Cara might wear it at her first ball. "They say that she is like me, but I pray she may be a thousand times happier and more sensible."

Yet soon afterwards she was writing to Lady Moffat, "My health is so much better for quiete and total idlness that I believe I shall sone be able to emerg from this bannishment and enjoy miself again." At first sight this pathetic attempt at jauntiness might seem to be prompted by courage or defiance but, from other sources, it seems that at moments Jenny actually cherished the illusion that she might regain her health and with it her place in society, and reign again a young queen of fashion. Though Dorothea realised with an aching sadness how illusory such hopes must be, she could not help snatching at these evidences of Jenny's renewed interest in life, persuading herself eagerly that they showed at least an improvement in her sister's health. All her reason, her common-sense, could not reconcile her to the thought that Jenny's brief splendour was over, all her frail triumphs at an end.

It seems as though Jenny's thoughts, emancipated at last from frivolity and triviality, were turning gradually to more enduring things. Lady Hannah, whose travels in the East had not undermined her faith in the Christian religion, wrote to Dorothea: "Jenny says that she likes this new young clergyman Mr Oswald vastly better than that gloomy old Mr Hare. He is most assiduous in his ministrations to her, and she declared to me yesterday with tears in her eyes that she derives the most solid satisfaction from his praying over her and readings from the Scriptures."

On the other hand from another visitor we learn that

even as Jenny's life moved into the shadows her vanity was unextinguished, and that when she was too weak to read or embroider she would draw a little mirror from beneath her pillow and for hours on end watch the changes in her face.

In January Jenny's health appeared to rally. A friend visiting her reported: "Poor Lady Aintry is by no means so fallen off in beauty as I expected. She is certainly very frail but I attribute this to the distresses she has undergone. I believe that she only needs to be happy to regain her bloom, for youth, cheerfulness and pleasing expectations are the best physics in the world. Her sister and Lord Mandlesham are enraptured by her improvement and flatter themselves, I believe with some reason, that if she can survive the winter the spring will see her on the way to recovery."

That Dorothea was in no immediate anxiety on Jenny's behalf is evident by the fact that she was in London at the beginning of February and not at Wing Magna.

Political circles just then were much excited over the court-martial of Admiral Keppel, a highly respected and popular officer who, at the instigation of his subordinate officer, Sir Hugh Palliser, had been accused of misconduct and neglect of duty at the indecisive action off Ushant in July of the previous year. In fact the blame lay partly with Lord Sandwich, the incompetent First Lord of the Admiralty, whose estimate of the strength of the French fleet had been at fault, and partly with Sir Hugh Palliser himself for failing to obey Admiral Keppel's orders and pursue the retreating French. Lord Sandwich and Palliser were Tories (Palliser being an M.P.); Admiral Keppel had powerful Whig connections. The court-martial therefore not only aroused feelings of natural indignation among all those who cared for justice, but was a call to battle for the Whigs.

Lord Mandlesham and other prominent Whig peers hurried down to Portsmouth to lend their support to the Admiral, while Dorothea drove daily to Spring Gardens to commiserate with the Admiral's mother, old Lady Albemarle, and on her return home wrote short notes to Jenny giving her the latest news of the affair.

On February 11th Admiral Keppel was unanimously and honourably acquitted. London was in a turmoil. The whole town was illuminated, squibs and crackers were let off. Fox and his friends triumphed uproariously, while the mob, always ready to break windows in a good cause, gutted Sir Hugh Palliser's house and chased Lord Sandwich and his mistress, Miss Ray, out of the Admiralty.

The following evening Dorothea and Charles gave a banquet and ball to celebrate this Whig victory. Dorothea was dressed in her ball gown and jewels and waiting to receive her guests, when a messenger brought a note from Lady Hannah. It read: "Dorothea, be brave! You must come at once to say good-bye to Jenny."

Dorothea, without speaking, showed the note to her husband. He said, "Go now, Dolly. Shall I come with you?" She pressed his hand. "No. Stay here and entertain our guests. I will go alone."

A carriage was ordered, her finery hidden beneath a cloak and hood and, as the first guests drove into the courtyard of Mandlesham House, Lady Mandlesham set off on her journey to Staffordshire.

It was dawn when she reached Wing Magna. Lady Hannah, her old face broken up with grief, met her in the hall. When Dorothea asked her, "Am I too late?" she shook her head, led her through the great, hushed house, past weeping servants, who did not remember their mistress's disgrace, but only her bright young beauty and the bewitching sweetness of her smile.

Lord Aintry was not there. Jenny's collapse had been so sudden that Lady Hannah, in her flurry of spirits, had totally forgotten to send word to him at Bath till two hours ago. So she told Dorothea, who thanked her with a look of silent gratitude.

The doctor and the young clergyman, whom Jenny had liked so well, withdrew from the curtained bedside as her sister approached. Lady Hannah softly closed the door. The Lovely Lynchs were alone.

Dorothea took Jenny in her arms, the golden and the dark tresses mingled as they had done long ago at Cabragena when the sisters lay together in bed, or whispered their little jokes and confidences in the firelight. Jenny looked at Dorothea before she died, said "Dolly" and, touching the glittering corsage of her gown, smiled as though with pleasure. . . .

When Jenny was dead Dorothea knelt for a long time by her side, not praying, not weeping, hardly thinking, only wondering in numb amazement if it was true that Jenny had gone and that from henceforth she would be alone.

At last she rose and, walking as though in her sleep, passed through the little group of watchers outside the room, through the lovely silent house, and out by a side door into the open air.

She saw the figure of a man in riding clothes approach her and shrank back, believing it to be Lord Aintry. But it was Charles, and as he took her in his arms and held her head against his breast her terrible frozen calm melted into tears.

PART II

CHAPTER XV

SUMMER'S DAY AT CROME

I

On May 25th 1787, Lord and Lady Mandlesham gave an entertainment at Crome to celebrate the seventeenth birthday of their daughter Lady Carolina Chessel. Those who were among the seven hundred guests agreed that it surpassed in splendour and gaiety any social event of the kind in recent years.

It was rumoured that Lady Mandlesham, whose sixteen years of social queenhood had not altered her innate simplicity, favoured a less elaborate and more intimate form of celebration. Cara was only seventeen. "If we fête her like an Empress when she leaves the schoolroom, however shall we wish her joy of her twenty-first birthday or of her marriage?" she asked her husband.

But Lord Mandlesham welcomed this double opportunity of expressing his devotion to his daughter, and exercising his taste for artistic and magnificent display. He reminded Dorothea of the irrefutable fact that Carolina's seventeenth birthday would never occur again. Let them make the most of it. Seventeen was a charming age —if the weather held good the birthday party would be a veritable festival of Spring. Cara's wedding would be a more solemn affair altogether; how could they rejoice wholeheartedly at an event which would deprive them of her companionship? As for her twenty-first birthday, who knew what might not have happened in four years' time?

Such unwonted forethought on the part of the insouciant Charles made Dorothea laugh, and when the children, from Carolina herself to the six-year-old Jonathan, clamoured, "Oh Mama, pray let Papa have his party!" she surrendered.

It was to be a comparatively small affair to begin with—"a matter of some fifty or sixty guests, with a few of the more ancient tenants and Dorothea's bits of orphans. There will be dancing on the lawn and some kind of a rout in the house afterwards."

But when the list of guests was made out Lord Mandlesham thought of more and more people who might be affronted if they were not invited, and the more general the party became the more people Dorothea thought of who must be included if they were not to be offended as well.

"My parents' hospitality and good nature is such", their eldest son the fifteen-year-old Lord Fulmer wrote to a school friend, "that I really believe they would have ended by inviting half England to my sister's birthday, but when they reached the seven hundredth guest *I* put my foot down and declared it must stop."

That matter being settled Lord Mandlesham was able to attend to his plans for the fête itself. The "dancing on the lawn" evolved into an elaborate pastoral, and the rout into a magnificent masque, "The Triumph of Spring", for both of which entertainments Lord Mandlesham wrote the music, arranged the dances and designed the costumes, while as an afterthought a Venetian carnival was to be held on the lake.

Hundreds of orange trees were sent down from the hothouses of Highframlington Park to supplement those already at Crome; festoons of flowers were to hang from tree to tree, and in the evening the park was to be illuminated throughout with coloured lamps. On the lake were to float a number of small craft built to resemble Venetian gondolas, filled with masked male and female singers in Venetian costumes. Water and music when combined greatly appealed to the taste of the eighteenth century, but on this occasion the floating music on the lake was only one of the pleasures which Lord Mandlesham had prepared for the ears of his guests. Crome, that memorable day, was to be like Prospero's isle, full of "sounds and sweet airs that give delight and harm not". From groves and garden temples were to come the dulcet sounds of flute and hautboys, harps and violins, or the sweet soprano of some hidden singer. That those guests who were not familiar with the vast lay-out at Crome might not lose their way, Lord Mandlesham had himself designed a plan of the grounds, beautifully engraved in the Bartolozzi manner.

Everything depended now on the weather. Lord Mandlesham alone did not worry about it; he was sure that it would be fine for Cara's birthday, and his optimism was justified. The dawn of the festive day was clear and untroubled, dissolving into the shimmering beauty of a fine May morning.

The celebrations began with a family breakfast; parents and brothers agreed that they must have Cara to themselves for a few hours at least. Though separated from it by over a hundred and fifty years, we may easily recreate the informal and joyous scene, seeing it in our imaginations as one of those family groups immortalised in many an eighteenth-century Conversation Piece. The gentle sunshine pours in through the long windows of the breakfast room with their brocade curtains, quivering in rivers of light on the painted ceiling and decorated wall panels, gleaming on satinwood chairs, gilded mirrors and Chippendale cabinets filled with oriental porcelain. Lady Mandlesham, beautiful and gracious, presides at the silver breakfast tray. Wearing a flowered morning gown, her profusion of blonde hair, already elaborately dressed for the day's entertainment, is confined under a muslin mob cap with coquettish bows under the chin. Her handsome consort leans against the carved marble mantelpiece, surveying his wife and family with proud satisfaction. Lord Fulmer, tall, fair and serious, with a look of his mother, stands by the window, a fishing-rod in one hand (for he has already been out on the lake), and holds a fish out to his sister. ("We made very merry over a trout which Fulmer caught, saying that it and a diamond bracelet was all Cara would get from him for her birthday.") Edward, a robust boy with ruddy colouring, struggles with a roistering spaniel puppy, which is his gift to his sister. Jonathan, pretty as an angel in his long pantaloons and frilled shirt ("the naughtiest rogue in Christendom" his fond mother has described him) proffers a birthday posy of flowers to Carolina. And Carolina herself bends over the new harp which is one of her father's and mother's presents, a graceful, girlish figure in her white muslin gown and green sash, her clustering bronzen curls falling down her shapely white neck on to her fichu. So let them exist for a moment, or for ever, wrapt in the bright and peaceful happiness of that far-away May morning.

The Chessel family were distinguished by their good looks, their good spirits and the strong devotion which bound them together. "I have been staying at Crome", an acquaintance wrote sententiously, "and felt great satisfaction in contemplating the handsome and interesting countenances of my host and hostess and of their offspring, and observing the ease and cheerfulness which regulate their family life."

This pleasure in each other's company permeated even the crowded splendours of that festal day, and was perhaps one reason why the fête was so much praised and so long remembered. It was a family party on a vast scale, but a family party all the same. As Lord and Lady Mandlesham stood side by side, "the finest couple in England" (Lady Mandlesham, superb though she was in her great hat ornamented with ostrich feathers, was thought to look remarkably young to be the mother of a seventeen-year-old girl), their delight in their daughter was touchingly apparent. Carolina herself had the sparkling air which never failed to remind Dorothea with a pang of tenderness and unassuaged grief of Jenny, while the boys, even the dignified Fulmer, were frankly out for a riotously good time.

As the stream of carriages and coaches flowed up the avenue, Dorothea looked out eagerly for the guests who ranked in her mind as more important and welcome than any others—not the Prince of Wales, nor the Duchess of Cumberland, the Duchess Georgiana, Lady Bessborough, Fox or Sheridan, pleased as she would be to see them, but her French friend of many years' standing, the Duchesse de Lapalisse and her twenty-one-year-old son Jules, the young Duc. So much in fact were they to be regarded as part of the family circle that she and Lord Mandlesham had invited them to come to Crome some days before the fête, but they had been delayed on the journey and were not able to arrive till the day itself.

When peace with France was signed in '83, Dorothea had hastened to resume her interrupted correspondence with Madame de Lapalisse, and had visited her in France on several occasions. The seven years of hostilities between the two countries had left little bitterness behind. England and France were natural enemies—it was an inescapable decree of Providence—but strong ties of culture and class solidarity linked their respective aristocracies, and it was pleasant when the tedious and rather senseless quarrels initiated by the statesmen had worked themselves out in slaughter and vast expenditure, and civilised relationships could be resumed.

This was Madame de Lapalisse's first and long promised visit to England, and Dorothea looked forward with an almost childish gratification to showing her the children and Crome. She was interested to see what kind of a young man Jules de Lapalisse had grown into. She had taken Carolina with her on a visit to France three years ago, and had herself been pleased with Jules's good manners and intelligence, but the young people had not taken the liking to each other which their mothers had fondly expected. The sophisticated youth of eighteen had not been able to simulate much interest beyond that demanded by politeness in the shy and gawky girl of fourteen. Cara was secretly mortified and inclined to be pert afterwards in conversation to her brothers about the young Frenchman. Dorothea flattered herself, with motherly complacence and some amusement, that Jules might not be so indifferent to her daughter now.

When people, anxious to please Dorothea, assured her that Carolina closely resembled the late Lady Aintry, Dorothea shook her head, silently, for even now, eight years after Jenny's death, she could not trust herself to speak of her sister to any except her intimate friends. Though she was a fond, almost adoring mother, she was too honest and had too high a standard of beauty to admit the comparison. Moreover, she deprecated this tiresome habit of comparing the younger generation to their elders. A face was a face, she used to say, and should be considered the exclusive property of its owner, not a patchwork of family features. Cara was not a beauty, but she was a very pretty and engaging girl. Her eyes, which were a peculiarly beautiful blue with long black lashes, her sweet temper and a certain radiant air which she had when she was happy or amused, no doubt reminded people of her aunt, but Dorothea, who had loved Jenny as she was and loved Cara as she was, was well aware that there the resemblance ceased.

In spite of her vivacity, there was a strain of gravity in Carolina which had been no part of her aunt's temperament. Tenderness and sensibility rather than coquettishness would be the characteristics, Dorothea believed, of her emotional life. Under her fresh gaiety there was an intensity about her that Jenny had lacked. She was fond of reading, and had a rather incongruous taste for draughtsmanship—the pretty insipid sketches of flowers and birds considered suitable expression for the artistic yearnings of young misses had never appealed to her. Instead she executed for her father (who was again contemplating sweeping alterations in the lay-out at Crome) careful and workmanlike plans of the park and gardens. It had been impossible to imagine Jenny growing old—it was as though she had been consumed by her own too brilliant youth—but Carolina would no doubt find mental interests to occupy her as youth waned. To Dorothea it seemed as though Jenny had typified the spirit of the period in which they had grown up—those giddy, glittering, carefree years of the late '60's and early '70's—or did one's youth always appear to one in retrospect in rainbow colours? Was Carolina the child of a new age—an age in some ways more refined and yet more ardent, an untidy age of sensibility rather than of reason, of burning hopes and vague unformulated dreams?

At last Dorothea saw Madame de Lapalisse descend from her carriage, assisted by a young man who must be her son Jules. A moment later the two women were clasped in each other's arms, Dorothea endeavouring to convey by the warmth of her embrace her tender sympathy for her friend who had lost her husband since they had last met. Dorothea was shocked at the change that sorrow and ill-health had wrought in Madame de Lapalisse's appearance. But her vivacity remained unimpaired, and she assured Dorothea that when she had changed her travelling clothes and eaten something she would be ready to join in the festivities.

While their mothers exchanged the happy, excited trivialities of two friends reunited after a long separation, Jules and Carolina stood and gazed silently at one another. The young man was so astonished at the transformation that three years had made in the young girl that he was unable to speak. What magic had turned the gauche *fillette*, whom he had dutifully entertained at his parents' château three summers ago, into this ravishing young woman? Carolina, surprised and deeply moved by his eloquent gaze, was equally confused. By the time that they had taken each other's hands in formal salutation they were well on the way to falling in love.

Their respective mothers, forgetting the extraordinary velocity of youthful emotions, only saw with satisfaction that their dear children were favourably impressed with each other. Jules de Lapalisse was not handsome but he had a well-made, elegant figure, a distinguished air, and a face which was prepossessing by reason of the intelligence, sincerity and firmness of character which it expressed. Though he had never been to England before he spoke excellent English, and seemed perfectly at his ease in this vast concourse of strangers, only asking Carolina with a smile if English parties were always conceived on such an immense scale.

His strangeness to the place gave him an excuse for keeping near Carolina of which he took full advantage. Indeed he could not take his eyes off her, and though she managed to carry out her obligations as a hostess, she was burningly aware of his attention. To both of them their former indifference added wonderfully to the piquancy of their present feelings. It was astonishing that those tedious hours at Châteaudoux, those gaping silences and half-baked conversations should have blossomed at a look into this delicious sympathy. The day was in league with them; the balmy air, the mild sunshine, the feathery green foliage of the trees, the early summer flowers, encouraged thoughts of happiness and love. Crome looked its best; its fine but rather overwhelming proportions formed an ideal background for the great throng of richly dressed visitors.

Jules told Carolina, as they watched the pastoral, how struck he had been with the prosperity of the English countryside as he travelled through it; the neat cottages with their little gardens, the tidy villages and well-thatched barns, the comfortably-dressed cottagers, had made a great impression on him, and he contrasted them painfully with the poverty of his native countryside. He had already had some experience of the rough independence of an English crowd. At Fenny Stratford, where they had stopped at an inn on their way down, the onlookers had jeered at him (in no way impressed by his fine equipage and clothes), calling out "Frenchie! Frenchie!" Yet the same people had good-humouredly and patiently assisted his postilions to adjust some of the luggage which had come loose.

In fact he was in a mood to find everything in England admirable. To a young man of his idealistic temperament and liberal views England was the home of liberty and good government; what was more important to him at the moment, it was the home of this adorable young girl.

To follow the pastoral, Lord Mandlesham had prepared a surprise, not only for his guests but for his children, in the form of a large balloon which was to ascend from the Cricket Field at 5 p.m. The excitement which this event caused can be imagined when it is remembered that balloon ascents were a recent innovation. Everyone watched entranced as the huge thing slowly soared into the air, and felt that they were assisting not merely at a display but at a portent of a new age of progress and scientific invention. Only Lady Mandlesham was too preoccupied to gape after it, for her youngest son Jonathan, who should have been watching it by her side, had disappeared. Even in such a large crowd he should have been safe enough in his parents' domain, but Dorothea had good reason never to feel safe about Jonathan unless he was actually in her sight.

All the same it was a shock to her when, as the balloon slowly descended half an hour later, a rosy and triumphant Jonathan scrambled out of the under-carriage amid shouts of laughter from the onlookers. Signor Leoni, the balloonist, was seething with apologies; he had had no idea that the young milord was concealed in the under-carriage till the balloon was up in the air. Jonathan declined to comment on the affair beyond saying, "Papa and Mama thought they would surprise me, but it was I, was it not, that surprised them?"

Evening brought no diminution of the day's enjoyment. The state drawing-room, hung with curtains of pale green satin edged with silver fringe, decorated with garlands of flowers and lit by hundreds of wax candles, was the scene of the masque, "The Triumph of Spring", in which some fifty friends of the Mandleshams took part, with Lady Mandlesham herself as Demeter (her golden hair plaited like a diadem across her forehead) and Carolina as Persephone. When the masque was over the guests sat down to a sumptuous supper, which, following as it did a series of collations throughout the day, caused the young Duc de Lapalisse to note with amazement and some apprehension as to his own digestive powers the formidable appetites of the English.

A display of fireworks ("superior in brilliance to anything to be seen at Ranelagh") brought the long day's entertainment to a close. It was time at last for the guests to make their farewells. The linkboys lighted them to their carriages. The torches were like fireflies as they moved to and fro, in apparent aimlessness, in the soft darkness of the summer night. One by one the equipages drew away from before the pale and lofty portico of Crome and down the three-mile avenue, till the rumble of their wheels, which sounded as though the artillery of an army was passing by, gradually faded away and at some imperceptible moment was transmuted into stillness. Inside the great house yawning men servants, moving as though they were sleep-walking, extinguished innumerable candles. At last silence and darkness took possession of Crome.

2

What were Dorothea's thoughts as at last, when the dawn was breaking, she lay beside her husband, in the great curtained bed? Probably she only had time before sleep engulfed her for a drowsy sense of relief that the festal day was over (for even with her fine physique she must have been conscious of some fatigue by the end) and of thankfulness that Cara and the boys and Charles had enjoyed themselves so well. Yet had she only known it that day in some sense marked the close of a phase in her life.

It had opened in bitter grief and bereavement. When Jenny died, Dorothea felt as though a part of her had died too. They had been so close to each other always, and had meant so much to each other since before the dawn of their conscious memories. It seemed unbelievable to Dorothea that Jenny, her gayer more fascinating self, had gone, that she was alone. When, in years to come, people praised her appearance she could have cried out in anguish, "Oh but if only you had seen my sister Jenny!" This was something more than personal loss. It was the haunting poignancy of vanished beauty, beauty that could be recalled in conversation or in gazing upon portraits and miniatures that could not do it justice, but that had gone—for ever gone.

Dorothea's nature was not one that forgot easily. It would be true in a way to say that she never got over Jenny's death. One of her grandchildren remembered that whenever she spoke of her sister a look of tenderness and grief passed over her face. But inevitably time, and her own prayers and mental strivings, drew the poison from her sorrow. She could at last think of Jenny without being swept by a tempest of misery and regret. She shut her mind as far as possible to the thought of Desmond Kyle and Lord Aintry, the two men who, to her way of thinking, had between them wrecked her sister's life. Both were comfortably settled. Kyle, risen to be a General, was married to the daughter of a rich City merchant. Lord Aintry too, a year after Jenny's death, had married; his new wife was the daughter of the Bishop of Woodstock, a good-looking, sensible young woman who made an excellent wife to him and a kind stepmother to his sons. Yes, they were alive and prosperous. Jenny was dead. Dorothea, devout Christian though she was, reserved to herself the right to hate them.

Her devotion to her children and the various and absorbing interests that make up family life kept her from brooding. And about eighteen months after her loss, another source of contentment was granted to her. Tessy Bellingham faded out of Charles's life. "Faded" is perhaps hardly the word. Her exit was as spectacular as the rest of her career.

For some time it had been apparent to Mrs Bellingham that she was losing the pre-eminent place in her lover's affections and, what was more, was losing it to his wife. "A man's wife may afford to become a habit, a man's mistress cannot," she commented in her Memoirs with her usual frankness. Dorothea had the qualities, both mental and physical, that wear well with time. Her constancy, her amiability and her integrity had gradually won not only Charles's admiration but his warm devotion, while her beauty, which had acquired an added grandeur with maturity and yet remained remarkably fresh, was a constant source of pleasure to his highly developed aesthetic sense. Who could help loving a woman who woke up every morning looking like a good-tempered rose?

Tessy had no intention of allowing her rival an open triumph. It was her boast that she had never yet been willingly deserted by a lover. Yet she must not discard Lord Mandlesham till she had found an equally influential protector. She might have tried her luck with the youthful Prince of Wales, but there she had been forestalled by Mrs "Perdita" Robinson.

The solution to her problem came to her in a singular manner in those frightening June days of 1780 when the Gordon riots were raging, a lawless howling mob, incited by the fanatical Lord George and his watchword "No Popery!", sacking the town, burning Catholic houses and chapels and threatening to attack the prisons and the Houses of Parliament. To the horror-struck watchers on the roof-tops on the night of June 7th, "Black Wednesday", it seemed as though London, blazing from a dozen huge fires, was doomed. The ferocious bestiality of the mob, numbers of whom died through wallowing in the casks of spirits that they had staved at the sack of a wine merchant's house, was an appalling disclosure of what lay beneath the surface of prosperous and fashionable London.

Not only the houses of Catholics but the properties of the prominent Whigs who had favoured the Act to rescind the old penal laws against the Roman Catholics, were menaced. Bedford House was sacked, Lord Mansfield's famous library burnt, and Devonshire House and Mandlesham House were in imminent danger. Lord Mandlesham refused to leave his library and art treasures and, as the children were safe in the country, Dorothea refused to leave him. Lord Mandlesham and the men servants prepared to defend the house with muskets.

Meanwhile Tessy who, though she could hardly be considered a devout Catholic, was in danger through the mere fact of being one at all, took refuge rather oddly at the French Embassy. Here she found herself in company with a French nobleman, the Marquis de St Aube Ferté, a studious, middle-aged man of distinguished manners and some literary attainments, who had already admired Mrs Bellingham from across the footlights. How Tessy succeeded in captivating him during those days and nights of terror must remain a mystery.

By June 8th, after a fierce battle at dawn between the military and the rioters, the city was quiet, the firing had ceased, dead bodies of rioters lay in pools of liquor in the gutters or among the smoking ruins of the houses they had pillaged. Horace Walpole was able to note the "fortunate circumstance" that "not a single person of any name" had been killed; Lord Mandlesham, embracing his wife, assured her that the danger was over; and Tessy Bellingham had been married in the drawing-room of the French Embassy (the chapel had been destroyed) to the Marquis de St Aube Ferté.

It was thought very entertaining at Brooks's and Boodle's that Mrs Bellingham, after being the kept mistress of one Marquis for years, should "make an honest man" of another one by marrying him. If Lord Mandlesham was mortified or grieved by her desertion he showed no sign of it.

Dorothea was thirty when her rival took herself off to France and respectability, in the heyday of her beauty and confident that having at last gained Charles's love she knew how to retain it. Those early years of her married life with their bitterness and disillusionment could never be expunged, but she would not waste her present happiness in regretting them. They were part of her life's experience and so of her soul itself.

The son Jonathan that she bore in 1781 seemed to her a living token of her complete reconciliation with her husband. A passionately devoted mother to all her four children, it would be untrue to say that she had favourites in the ordinary sense, but there is no doubt that for Carolina the child of her humiliation, and for Jonathan the child of her triumph, she felt a particular tenderness.

These years between 1780 and 1787 flowed smoothly for Dorothea. Besides the upbringing of her family she shared many social, political, artistic and philanthropic interests with her husband. It was some years now since she had discovered that he was in the habit of going secretly to the Marshalsea Prison at Easter and Christmas and releasing several debtors, and had asked him to allow her to contribute from her personal allowance towards the sum which he set aside for this charity. The gulf that yawns between the modern conception of charity, organised and administered by well-paid officials, and the haphazard, personal charity of former times, is typified by the picture this conjures up of the debonair young peer, wearing his plainest clothes (perhaps a bottle-green or mulberry-coloured suit), driving down to St George's Fields, passing through the foetid atmosphere of the prison (holding to his nose a sprig of lavender bought from the herb woman in St James's Market to ward off gaol fever), and choosing as the objects of his beneficence those debtors whose air of particular misery or dejection appealed most strongly to his compassion, without troubling to enquire whether they were especially deserving. He would feel no embarrassment in bestowing nor they in receiving charity, for it would occur to neither party that the Marquis of Mandlesham had not a God-ordained right to his vast wealth and privileges, only they entailed certain duties and obligations.

It was Charles's fortunate lot to be able to carry out the impulses of a generous nature on a generous scale. Dorothea never tired of St Chidwiddin Old Hall, and it seems that Charles sometimes went down there too, for there is a charming sketch among his drawings of Dorothea standing on the Cornish shore, looking out to sea, the wind blowing back her fair curls and the clinging folds of her white gown. But he felt a wish to provide her with a house to which she could retire when she wanted to live more simply than at Crome, and yet be within easy reach of him.

With this idea he entirely redecorated and refurnished a Palladian villa which he owned at Richmond and gave it to her as a birthday present. The note with which he announced his gift—"Now you will have no excuse for frisking off to Cornwall"—perhaps gave her as keen a pleasure as the house itself, lovely as it was with its well-proportioned rooms decorated in soft pastel colours, turquoise blue, lilac, blush rose and dove grey, their wall panels and ceilings painted by Angelica Kauffmann or, like Dorothea's bedroom, covered with a fine hand-painted Chinese wallpaper gay with fantastic birds and flowers; its shady garden, sloping down to the river, where Dorothea might walk among daffodils and primroses in the Spring, pick armfulls of white lilac in May, or later in the year sit and sun herself in a graceful, classical alcove in the rose garden.

There was an almost feminine elegance and grace about the whole house which told that it had been designed to give pleasure to a beloved woman. The ornamental device of a sheaf of wheat which Charles had chosen as Dorothea's emblem (no doubt by now classifying Tessy in his mind as a tare) appeared in various forms through the house, woven into the beautiful curtains of Spitalfields silk, introduced on the backs of chairs, on the entablatures of the marble chimney-pieces, in the delicate wall sconces for candles, and stamped in gold with her initials and coronet on the vellum covers of books. Even the set of pale green china cups and saucers that Dorothea used for breakfast had been specially produced for her by

Josiah Wedgwood, and later became celebrated as "Mandlesham Ware".

This Richmond villa typifies all that is most elegant, urbane and gracious in eighteenth-century taste, and Lord Mandlesham had good reason to write to Dorothea in modest gratification: "I am sensibly touched by the charming things you say about the villa. I intended it to be beautiful and I think I have not been altogether unsuccessful." He continues on a suddenly impassioned note whose sincerity cannot be doubted, "But you are mistaken when you say it is *too* beautiful. No material object, however beautiful, could be altogether worthy of a woman who is in all respects the paragon of her age."

3

Dorothea and Madame de Lapalisse were happy together. As they sat in the Little Drawing Room, their fingers busy with the needlework that overflowed their silken laps, drove on fine days in a phaeton through the park, or on wet days strolled up and down the picture gallery, their conversation rippled on, affectionate, easy and intimate. They talked of their children, of their houses and of their friends.

With concern Dorothea heard that, though the birth of her children had increased her domestic happiness, Marie Antoinette was harassed and saddened by her unpopularity and the gross insults of the lampoonists. The notorious affair of the Diamond Necklace, innocent though her part in it had been, had done her untold harm. Shortly before her thirtieth birthday the Queen had announced to her dressmaker her intention of changing her style of dress; she had finished with the fantastic feathers, the preposterous head-dresses and extravagant gowns of her early youth. The impression that she gave now was no longer of brilliant frivolity but of gracious dignity. She found all her solace in her children, in the Petit Trianon with its fairy-tale hamlet and its miniature blue and golden theatre, in the company of a few intimate friends, among whom Madame de Polignac and her hangers-on were no longer to be counted, and above all in the loyal and unselfish devotion of the handsome and gallant young Swede, Count Axel de Fersen. The Queen's altered mode of life had not placated her subjects. Every national misfortune was attributed to the hated Austrian.

On her side, Dorothea was able to give her friend an account—more comic than pathetic—of the Prince of Wales's matrimonial tangles, his secret marriage to a virtuous and well-born Roman Catholic widow, Maria Fitzherbert. Her position was ambiguous—the marriage had been denied by Fox in the House of Commons while soon afterwards the bewildered members had heard Sheridan speak in glowing terms of her virtue—but her character was generally respected, and Dorothea, like other prominent Whig ladies, visited her and invited her to her parties.

While their mothers chatted away peacefully, Jules and Carolina rode together through the park, practised archery together and taught one another French and English songs. They talked a great deal too, exchanging the light, laughing, foolish badinage of happy youth, and then, growing serious, would discuss with deep solemnity and eagerness the future of the world, the dawning of that age of reason and liberty for which Jules looked (and which was to release mankind in general and France in particular from the dead hand of custom and tyranny), and of course of their own personal aspirations and feelings. All the time they were really talking about themselves because they were in love, and so everything had taken on an intensely personal meaning.

Sometimes a sudden silence would fall between them, more interesting and exciting than any words. Then a glance, a touch of the hand, became a wonderful experience. Cara knew that she was in love because she jumped out of bed in the morning all aglow with the idea of meeting Jules at the breakfast-table. Jules knew that he was in love because every morning when he looked at Carolina, sitting in her muslins and ribbons eating muffins, he thought that she looked if possible even prettier and more desirable than she had done the evening before. The length of the English dinner, lasting as it did for some four or five hours, had at first confounded him, but after the ladies retired he enjoyed the conversation of Lord Mandlesham and the other men, their frank discussion of politics, their lively and bawdy humour. Now every day he found himself waiting with great impatience for the moment when a servant would announce that tea was ready and that they could rise and join the ladies. Lord Mandlesham would perhaps be expounding to him the science of breeding race-horses. Jules, who as a rule had a passion for acquiring information, found his thoughts wandering from his host's brood mares to his host's daughter; it was all he could do not to leap out of his chair when the welcomed summons arrived.

In August, a few weeks before he and his mother were due to return to France, the young Duc de Lapalisse asked Lord Mandlesham for permission to propose to his daughter. Everyone was astonished, except Jonathan who, with the diabolical perspicacity common to younger brothers, had long ago sized up the situation, and had discovered that by dogging his sister's and her admirer's footsteps, he could be sure of being richly bribed with sweets by Jules to make himself scarce.

Charles and Dorothea found themselves in a predicament. Though, according to the standards of the age, Carolina was of fully marriageable age, the thought of losing her so soon filled them with dismay, still more the prospect of her leaving not only her home but her country.

Yet on what grounds could they justifiably oppose the match? Jules was not only of ancient lineage, high rank and considerable wealth (considerations which the Mandleshams as eighteenth-century parents would have thought themselves most negligent to have ignored), but was an attractive young man of honourable character, amiable and sincere. What more could any parent demand in a son-in-law? That the young people were tenderly attached to each other was now glaringly apparent. What was more, not only the mutual attraction of youth but an evident similarity of interests and outlook seemed to make them ideally suited to one another. To oppose a marriage which promised their daughter not only a position worthy of her rank but the fairest prospects of happiness, merely because of the accident of nationality, would have been an act of parental capriciousness and harshness of which Charles and Dorothea were incapable.

Some objection might have been felt, and indeed was felt, by the Mandleshams, both of whom were firmly attached to the Protestant faith, on the score of religion. The de Lapalisses were nominally Catholics, but Madame de Lapalisse was no bigot, while Jules frankly confessed that he deplored the superstitious practices which had grown up round the doctrines of the Church, and that he hoped one day to see the end of clerical as well as of aristocratic privilege and immunity. A belief in a benevolent Deity, revealing Himself not through priestcraft but in nature and through men's consciences, was the groundwork of his own faith. There was obviously nothing here to prevent him from living comfortably with a Protestant wife.

The Mandleshams, after consulting with Madame de Lapalisse, gave their consent to the courtship; Carolina's radiant face when she announced to them that Jules had proposed and been accepted was their reward.

To both Jacqueline de Lapalisse and Dorothea this love match between their beloved children was a romantic and auspicious culmination to their long friendship. They could hardly doubt now that fate had brought them together for this very purpose. Charles could not be expected to take this sentimental view of the affair. The thought of losing Cara filled him with a gloom which he strove valiantly to conceal. He was accustomed to a surplus of feminine devotion; aunts, mistress, wife, daughter, they had all loved him and how warmly he had loved them in return! It was hard to have to relinquish his claim to Cara's undivided attention when she had barely emerged from the schoolroom. He did not know which he regretted most, the delicious moppet in tiny mob cap and apron that he had dandled, so short a time ago it seemed, on his knee and that was now, amazingly, grown up and in love, or the charming girl whose companionship he and Dorothea had hoped to enjoy for a few years at least. But he was too genuinely devoted to his daughter, and too desirous of seeing everyone cheerful and comfortable to give way to his feelings. He admitted to Dorothea that he had no fault at all to find with Jules (whom he liked exceedingly) except that he was not an Englishman, and that, he supposed, must be accounted more his misfortune than his fault.

Dorothea and he consoled themselves, as parents must, by contemplating not their own loss but their daughter's gain, and by commenting a great deal on the narrowness of the English Channel. If Madame de Lapalisse accepted Carolina with joy as a cherished daughter they, for their part, were soon able to regard Jules, in all sincerity, as a dear son.

The engagement was not a long one. It was Madame de Lapalisse's dearest wish to see her son and Dorothea's daughter united, and the precarious state of her health seemed to make any unnecessary postponement of the

245

marriage inadvisable. Christmas was spent happily together at Crome, and early in the New Year of 1788 Monsieur le Duc de Lapalisse and Lady Carolina Chessel were married and left for France.

CHAPTER XVI

SEPTEMBER NIGHT IN PARIS

I

JULES AND CAROLINA left for France. Enraptured with love and happiness they moved confidently towards their destiny. The glow on the horizon which to us, watching from this vantage-point in time, heralds the coming conflagration, is to them the sunrise of their married life. 1788. To Jules and Carolina it was a golden date, marking their union. To us it has the fearful significance of water swirling for a breathless moment before the plunge of the cataract.

To understand how the Mandleshams allowed their daughter to merge her personal fate with the fate of France at such a time, it is necessary to realise that to them, too, the year of her marriage was just another year like all others; not, as we may see it, the end of the old order and the prelude to a new age's volcanic birth.

Two trends of thought probably influenced their outlook. On one side it was generally admitted, especially among people of liberal or advanced views, that the world was in a sad way. Horace Walpole, some ten years previously, had been greeting his correspondents with such cheering phrases as: "I think I shall outlive the storm and talk over the ruins; but in truth they will be considerable." "I cannot expect to live to see England

revive. I shall leave it at best an insignificant island."
"Adieu, Madame, if we are digged out alive when the
conflagration is over, we will chat over old times."

This unsatisfactory state of affairs had lasted so long
that it had ceased to be very alarming. The young took it
for granted, the middle-aged talked and worried about it,
the old lamented a golden age of plenty, good government
and good conduct (naturally coinciding with their youth)
which, in reality, only existed in their imaginations.

The common people, the "mob", were dimly appre-
hended as a new, disturbing force, threatening with its
turbulence and unrest the foundations of polite society,
but there seemed no guarantee that England (with its
recent experience of the Gordon riots) would be more
immune than France from an outbreak of mob violence.

Side by side with this fear of the future there also
existed, particularly among those of the Whig persuasion,
unbounded hope in the destiny of mankind. "Reform—
liberty—the rights of the individual"—these were words
which were as trumpet-calls to the younger and more
ardent spirits of the age; while aristocrats like the
Mandleshams, secure in their enchanted garden of privilege
and wealth, yet not altogether forgetful of the enthusiasms
of their youth, regarded them as interesting guests to be
admitted to their friendship and honourably entertained
so long as they did not overstep the bounds of good breeding and good sense.

Symbolic of this attitude were the Mandleshams'
relations with Tom Paine. The philosopher, who had
begun life as a staymaker, was already celebrated for his
writings and work on behalf of American independence,
and when he returned to England in the late Summer of
1787 he became the pet of Whig society. The Duke of
Portland, Burke, Lord Landsdowne, Lord Fitzwilliam and
Fox hastened to pay him respect, hoping thereby to lay
the foundations of friendly political and commercial

relations with America when they themselves should come to power. He was entertained at all the great Whig houses, called "my esteemed friend" by highborn ladies, and showered with compliments, which left him unmoved, for he already had an unbounded opinion of his own merits.

The Mandleshams were not behindhand in their hospitality, and the sturdy figure of the philosopher, in his snuff-coloured coat with drab breeches (his pockets stuffed with sweets for Jonathan, for he was very fond of children), was frequently to be seen at Crome. His brilliant conversation and the startling originality of his views (among other reforms he advocated the abolition of war and slavery, and denounced injustice to women and cruelty to animals) interested Lord Mandlesham, who could appreciate good quality in any form. Dorothea liked him for his idealism, his honesty and his essential benevolence. His eccentricity amused them both. He never said "How d'ye do?", only "What news?", and resented any personal questions. This was considered droll, but his intolerance for other people's opinions, and dogmatic belief that those who did not agree with him must be dishonest, was harder to endure.

It was edifying when he hailed the American War of Independence as "the birthday of the New World", or when he laid down the axiom that "Society in every state is a blessing, but government, even in its best state, is a necessary evil. . . . The design and end of all government should be freedom and security." It was entertaining, even, to hear him describe a monarch as "a worm who in the midst of his splendour is crumbling into dust"; but surely when he was sitting at Lord Mandlesham's table sipping his port it was tactless, to say the least, to maintain that "Aristocracy is a kind of fungus growing out of the corruption of society", and that if he had been obliged to accept a title it would have been a knighthood

so that the infamy of it should not descend on his family?
Nor did the Chessels, who considered themselves with
some reason to be gifted mentally as well as physically,
enjoy hearing the nobility described as the "no-ability".

Though he exalted reason as a prime virtue, no one
could be more unreasonable than he in an argument.
While he was holding forth no one must interrupt or even
show inattention. A dropped poker, a cough or the rustle
of a piece of embroidery was sufficient to throw him out of
temper.

It dawned on the Mandleshams, as it had done on his
other aristocratic friends, that the ex-staymaker not only
thought himself their equal but their superior. They
flattered themselves that they were progressive, but this
was more than they could stomach. Tom Paine's appearances at Crome became infrequent and then ceased
altogether.

2

Carolina and her husband visited Crome at the end of
the summer. It was a joyful family reunion. Charles and
Dorothea were able to congratulate themselves that they
had not delayed through selfish motives a marriage that
had so evidently brought happiness to their daughter.

Dorothea wrote to Madame de Lapalisse: "There is
nothing but laughter and gaiety at Crome since our dear
young couple arrived. I have never known Jules in
better spirits nor Cara look more blooming. Her brother
Fulmer teases her and says that it is indecent for an old
married couple of seven months' standing to be so dotingly
fond of each other! In good truth their feeling for one
another is all tenderness and sensibility, yet is founded on
such good principles and mutual esteem that I have no
fears that it will not endure. I am excessively delighted
to hear of Cara's hopes, and look forward as eagerly as
you do to being a grandmother. You are right! there

will be no keeping Johnny in order when he becomes an uncle!"

The family party at Crome, absorbed in their domestic felicity, probably did not discuss outside events very intently. Carolina would have much to tell her mother of Marie Antoinette and the royal family. Though Jules's liberal views excluded him from the Court party, he adhered steadfastly to the tradition of loyalty to the King's person which was part of his family heritage. He had nothing but contempt for the treacherous intrigues of the Duc d'Orleans and the Palais Royal clique, and blamed not the King and Queen but their advisers for the chaotic state of France's finances and administration. The Queen had been gracious and welcoming to the daughter of her friend Lady Mandlesham, and had written to Dorothea praising Carolina's charming candour and sweetness.

Jules might tell his father-in-law of the widespread hailstorm which had swept France in July and which it was feared would ruin the harvest. Prices were rising alarmingly, unemployment was increasing; Paris was crowded with destitute peasants.

It was pleasant to turn from these depressing topics to the more congenial one of English methods of farming, a subject upon which Jules was eager to acquire information. To the young Frenchman it was significant and wholly admirable that in England an aristocrat, like Lord Mandlesham, could devote his attention not only to the beautification of his house and pleasure grounds but to the improvement of his cattle, and could discourse as knowledgeably about manures and crops as upon pictures and books.

The year came to an end peacefully enough as far as the Chessel and de Lapalisse families were concerned, though Dorothea's letters were full of the shocking news of the King's madness.

To Dorothea the approach of the year 1789 was interesting mainly because it would, she hoped, see the birth of her first grandchild. She went to France in February to be present at Carolina's confinement, and by the end of the month a gossip was writing: "The news from France is that the young Duchesse de Lapalisse, Lady Mandlesham's daughter, is brought to bed of a fine son. This appears to give a new meaning to the word 'grandmother', for her ladyship, who is not yet turned 39, is considered one of the handsomest women of the age, and has retained the perfection of her hair, complexion and figure to a remarkable degree."

By April Dorothea was back at Crome but the letters, which she wrote several times a week and received as regularly from Cara, kept her in touch with her dearly loved daughter.

The newly-born François naturally had chief place in this correspondence, but on May 1st an event of such importance took place that Carolina, in announcing it to her mother, relegated her infant son, for the first time, to a postscript. The King, confronted by a ruined treasury and a clamorous country, on the advice of Necker summoned the States General to Versailles.

To Carolina, to Jules, to a thousand sanguine hearts throughout France, this seemed an occurrence of more than political significance. Surely it was the first pale light of dawn after centuries of night? Joy was widespread throughout France, unreasoning, ecstatic. Strangers embraced each other when they heard the news, the "divine rescript" was read out from every pulpit to congregations tearful with joy.

Carolina wrote to her mother: "It is impossible to describe the happiness and hope that is felt by everyone. At last we shall have the reforms which are needed. Jules writes that the solemn procession of the deputies to St Louis Church was impressive to a degree. The Third

251

Estate were hailed with loud applause, there was silence for the nobles and clergy, but more applause for the King who ended the procession. I wish I had been there but my little tyrant keeps me to my duties here. When I hold him in my arms I wonder how he will be affected by these stirring events. Perhaps he will have fewer privileges than his ancestors enjoyed, but what will that signify if he is the citizen of a free and happy land?"

Dorothea shared her daughter's satisfaction, though to a less rapturous degree. "I sincerely hope, my love, that all your and Jules's brightest hopes will be justified, and that France will acquire that free constitution with which England has been blessed these last hundred years. (Fulmer who is looking over my shoulder says '101 years, Mama'—tiresome boy!) I trust though that matters will not be rushed on too fast. The ignorance of the mob and the sad corruption and greed of many of their betters must not be discounted when planning for the future. But I must not croak at you, my darling child! My hopes are hardly less ardent than yours. I have loved France for years. Now that it is *your* country, how earnestly I desire its prosperity and peace."

3

Summer brought disillusionment to France. What had appeared to be the daybreak of the Age of Reason was now seen to be an uneasy transition period between a dying past and a threatening future.

The National Assembly, middle-class enthusiasts without political experience, were too progressive for the Court and the reactionary nobles, too slow-moving for the hungry discontented populace which was beginning to feel its power. As the props of the ancient régime were removed one by one, the great imposing edifice of the State, and with it law and order, was crumbling into ruin. Thanks to the grain monopolists bread was scarce in Paris that summer, the army was disaffected, the city was full of rumours; something resembling mass hysteria was in the air.

The atmosphere was charged with explosive, and on July 11th the King and his advisers threw a firebrand into it by dismissing Necker. When the Paris mob heard the news they rose. By the 13th they had seized the Arsenal of the Invalides; on the 14th they stormed the fortress of the Bastille. In a frenzy of destructive energy men, women and children surged to and fro in the glare of its flame. The Governor of the prison and several officers were massacred. The King, confronted by this terrible unknown force, surrendered, recalled Necker and, on the balcony of the Hôtel de Ville, publicly donned the tricolour.

The chief excitement in England that summer had been King George's sudden and unexpected return to sanity. This put an abrupt end to the rival parties given by ladies of the Whig and Court factions, where the former wore Regency caps in honour of the Prince of Wales, and the latter wore dresses of garter blue and decked their hair with ribbons inscribed with "God save the King". Instead there were thanksgiving services, fireworks and rural jollifications. Even the Mandleshams, staunch Whigs as they were, rejoiced, for they were not intimates of the Prince of Wales', and general loyalty to the throne and compassion alike made them prefer a sane to a mad king.

Lord Mandlesham treated his tenants to a roasted ox. Dorothea, who had taken Jonathan to Weymouth to recover from an attack of measles, joined the cheering crowds and, from her carriage, fluttered a handkerchief as the King and Queen arrived for their annual holiday.

Next day the King, after taking a dip before a concourse of loyal subjects to the strains of "God save Great George our King" from a band concealed in a bathing machine, went for a stroll along the promenade and meeting Jonathan, who was running ahead of his mother, stopped him, gave him a gingerbread and asked him what he was going to be when he grew up. "A man", said the literal-minded Jonathan. "What—what? A man. Quite right. Quite right," said the King very pleased. "How d'ye do, Lady Mandlesham. Your son, eh? He shows a very good spirit. Very good spirit indeed."

While Dorothea wrote an account of this homely scene to her daughter, news of the astonishing events in France was on its way across the Channel. The taking of the Bastille was described by Charles James Fox as the greatest event that had ever happened, and others, as enthusiastic as he, overlooked the bloodshed which had accompanied it and thought of it only as a symbol of the revolt of free men against arbitrary rule. More cautious people were dubious. This was not the way in which things were done in England. One must wait and see.

Dorothea wrote in some alarm to her daughter, but Carolina, from the peaceful seclusion of Châteaudoux, replied reassuringly. The murder of the poor Marquis de Launay and the others was horrible, and could not be too strongly condemned. Undoubtedly the populace had got out of hand, but this was the consequence of years of despotic government which reduced men to the level of beasts. The people were drunk with their new freedom. Jules was hopeful that reason and good feeling would prevail. He had great faith in the Comte de Mirabeau, a man who in spite of his disreputable past had a statesman-like grasp of the realities of the situation, and was working for a moderate revolution based on the English revolution of 1688.

Carolina added the news that the Polignacs had fled to Switzerland at the Queen's request; the Comte d'Artois, the Prince d'Henin, the Comte de Vaudreuil and many other former members of the Queen's circle had left too.

Carolina announced her intention, now that the baby was weaned, of accompanying Jules to Versailles to pay her respects to the Queen. "Now that so many are in flight one can appear at Court without suspecting oneself or being suspected by anyone else of toadying. It will be a pleasure to attempt to repay by my sympathy and duty some of the kindness which the Queen showed my dearest mother."

Dorothea was only partially reassured by her daughter's calm. On August 4th the Assembly abolished all feudal privileges—a Declaration of the Rights of Man was proclaimed and many nobles, the Duc de Lapalisse among them, voluntarily renounced their rights. There was a solemnity and nobility about this break with the past which Dorothea could admire, even though she might feel glad that the more elastic social system of England had made any such renunciation on the part of the Marquis of Mandlesham unnecessary. It was less comfortable to learn that in many districts the peasants were plundering their landlords' châteaux, burning the title-deeds and sometimes killing an unpopular seigneur.

Carolina was not nervous. "Jules and my mother-in-law have made themselves so beloved with the peasants round here by their benevolence that I am convinced no harm will come to us. I do not say this from complacency or from indifference to other people's misfortunes, only to reassure you, dearest Mama."

For several months there was a lull, and then in October the news came that the Paris mob had marched on Versailles. At daybreak they broke into the Palace, killing the sentries; the Queen, half-clothed, fled with her children to the King's apartments. Maternal love wrung from her proud lips the cry, "O mes amis, sauvez moi et mes enfants!" The arrival of Lafayette and the National Guard alone saved the situation. The King showed himself on the balcony and was cheered; the people demanded the presence of the Queen. When she appeared with the children there were cries of "Point d'enfants!" She came out alone and faced the accumulated hatred of years with a superb and haughty courage. Lafayette kissed her hand and the people, swept by a sudden emotion, shouted "Vive la Reine!" Then there was a roar, "À Paris!"

The vast crowd, exultant, ribald, jeering, tramped before and behind the royal carriage, swarmed round it, shouting in mocking allusion to the bread shortage: "We are bringing back the baker, the baker's wife and the baker's boy!" The humiliated royal family were lodged in the Tuileries, a palace that had been unoccupied for over a century. The power and glory of the monarchy was at an end.

To the Mandleshams, with their personal interest in French affairs, these events could not fail to be alarming, and indeed many more impartial observers in England began to be distrustful of the course that the revolution was taking. Yet, after the march on Versailles, the Assembly, mostly composed of members of the upper-middle class and of the more liberal nobles, managed to gain control and to keep some semblance of order with the aid of the National Guard.

While the Assembly was framing a new Constitution the King and Queen, in the gloomy and rambling palace of the Tuileries, held a shadowy court which, with its diminished entourage, and its etiquette often disturbed by the appearance of popular delegations and members of the Assembly, bore only a faint and disheartening resemblance to the lost splendours of Versailles.

Noble emigrés were leaving the country in hundreds, but a little group of friends had rallied round the royal couple, foremost among them the favourite of the Queen's youth, the Princesse de Lamballe. The young Duchesse de Lapalisse was also often in attendance on the Queen.

Jules had by no means lost hope that Mirabeau, by gaining the confidence of the King and the middle classes alike, might steer France into the calm waters of liberalism. The Queen had grown very attached to Carolina, and Jules implored his wife to use her influence to overcome the Queen's distrust of the man whom Jules was convinced could alone save the monarchy. But Carolina soon perceived that this was a task beyond her powers. All she could do was to lighten by her gaiety and sympathy the anxious monotony of the Queen's existence. Marie Antoinette, daughter of an Imperial house, neither could nor wanted to understand the Revolution. She could only move with stubborn heroism towards her fate. Carolina grieved for her obduracy, loved and revered her for her courage.

4

Carolina and her little boy spent several months of the Summer of 1790 with her parents. It was obvious to them, more by what she left unsaid than by what she said, that she was disillusioned at the course of events in France. But they had too much regard for her feelings to probe them on this point. When all was said and done, what did it matter exactly what form of government prevailed in France as long as Cara's safety was not threatened? They saw no reason to be apprehensive on this score. Politics in France seemed to have reached a condition of stalemate; the idealism of the Third Estate had expanded itself in a froth of theoretical talk. Visitors from England travelled peacefully through France. The Duchess of Devonshire had even stayed in Paris for the birth of her long-desired son.

Carolina was more communicative about the personal side of her life in her adopted country. Dorothea was anxious to hear news of the Queen and of her other friends at Court. It was astonishing to hear that the

Queen's apartments had dwindled to a bedroom, a salon, a billiard-room and a dining-room. Her life was as simple now as even she, in the days of the youthful rebellion against etiquette, could have wished—her religious duties, needlework, a game of billiards with the King, conversation with her intimates, this was all her life. But what a difference between the Arcadian simplicity of her own devising which she had indulged in at the Petit Trianon, and this dreary seclusion, in the immense, sombre palace, whose dark corridors were full of spies. Permission had been granted to the royal family to spend the summer at St Cloud, but even here Lafayette's aides-de-camp followed the King and Queen everywhere. Perhaps the brightest aspect of life at the Trianon was the devotion of the Queen's friends—the Princesse de Lamballe, the Princesse de Chimay, the Comtesse d'Ossun, the Duchesse de FitzJames, these and a few others who had remained with her. Carolina spoke of them with admiration, never considering, her mother noticed with pleasure, that she herself was also to be commended for devoting as much of her time as she could spare from her child to the Queen's service.

On the whole the Mandleshams felt that Jules and Carolina had acted prudently as well as rightly in remaining in their country, and not joining in the panic flight of the emigrés. The future was uncertain but not alarming. Meanwhile it was happiness enough to have Cara back again in the family circle, to hear her laugh and joke with her brothers, to be able to admire with her the charming audacity of her toddling son.

In May 1791 Carolina was back at Crome. It had been an understood thing that she should return that Summer, if possible with her husband, but this sudden arrival, several months earlier than had been arranged, had implications which somewhat overclouded her parents' pleasure at seeing her. Jules had been unable to leave Paris, but Carolina had brought little François with her, with the intention of leaving him with her parents when she returned to France. This could surely only mean one thing—she was alarmed for the future. What had happened during this last year to undermine her and Jules's optimism?

In England opinion was now sharply divided about the changes in France. Burke, declaring that he hated tyranny but that he hated it most when most were concerned in it, had written his prophetic *Reflections on the French Revolution*. After a painful scene in the House, he and Fox had severed their long friendship. Tom Paine, in answer to Burke, had published his revolutionary book, *The Rights of Man*. His views commanded a large following among the Nonconformists and lower middle classes. But though a general uneasiness prevailed, there was as yet no definite signs of the gathering storm. Carolina admitted to her parents that when the Comte de Mirabeau had died that April, the Queen had wept bitterly and said, "Our last chance has been taken from us." She did not tell them that, in her husband's opinion, power was passing from the Assembly to the Republican Clubs and that in the end this would mean mob rule.

It was her aim to quieten her parents' fears, to conceal from them her increasing distrust of the future, to make them believe that she was leaving her child with them for a while because her attendance on the Queen took up so much of her time, and that therefore it was a good opportunity for him to get to know his grandparents and English ways. As she watched them, her handsome loving parents, leading their serene English life, her heart yearned over them, as though she were the parent and they her unsuspecting children. Her father might shake his head over the working-men's Jacobin clubs in Manchester, her mother regret the lost glories of Versailles; but how could

they, in the midst of this lovely peace and security, understand the volcanic forces that were boiling below the
surface of France's life?

Something happened late in June that shocked them and
all England into greater awareness. The royal family fled
in disguise, were detected at Varennes, and brought back
in ignominy to Paris. The position of the King and Queen
was now greatly worsened. The lack of confidence in the
people which their flight had disclosed deepened the
people's distrust of the monarchy. From henceforth
they were, to all intents and purposes, prisoners in the
Tuileries.

To the Mandleshams all this was proof that they should
try and persuade Carolina to postpone her departure; to
Carolina it was a summons to return. Jules would never
leave France while there remained any hope of moderate
counsels prevailing; he was not of the stuff of which
emigrés were made. It would be unbearable for him to
lounge about in London drawing-rooms, the object of
sympathy from fashionable hostesses, while his country
needed his services. Whatever the disappointments and
dangers that he was to endure in the near future, she
must be by his side to share them. He needed her more
than her parents, more even at the moment than her
child.

Another consideration demanded her return. The
thought of the Queen, whose dignity and courage seemed
to increase with every fresh humiliation, appealed to a
chivalrous strain in Carolina's ardent young nature. Now
was the time to prove her gratitude and loyalty to her
royal mistress.

Her decision distressed the Mandleshams beyond
measure. They were unable to bring forward any cogent
reasons why she should not go back to France. Though
there had been some republican agitation following the
flight of the royal family, the moderate party had re-

mained in control. Cara declared herself confident (as indeed she was since no outbreak had taken place) that by the autumn she would be able to come back to Crome to fetch her son. A dread which she could not put into words oppressed Dorothea and, anxiety being contagious, also infected her husband. Yet Dorothea knew that her daughter was only doing what she herself would have done in her place. Would she have left Charles at such a moment? Certainly not—though to tell the truth it was hard to imagine the insouciant Charles as an idealistic reformer.

Sadly, yet trying to conceal their sadness, the Mandleshams let their daughter go without distressing her by further persuasions. As Carolina kissed her little boy once more, and then again, she admonished him gaily to have that tooth through by the time Mama came back. But suddenly her voice faltered, her eyes brimmed with tears; she dared not look at him any longer, she ran from the room.

She was very white as she bade her father and mother farewell. As Dorothea clasped her in her arms Cara said, "It has been heaven to be with you both. I will be back soon. Why of course I will be back."

But from the inn at Dover she wrote: "Do not be anxious, dearest mother, or let my father fret about me. You have often told me that nothing can happen to us without the permission of God. I want to tell you that I believe this with all my heart."

5

It was a September evening at Crome, 1792. Dorothea was walking up and down the Temple Glade. It was growing chill; the glowing colours of the trees were muted, a mist crept round the steps of the Temple of Psyche at the end of the long avenue, the earth struck damp

261

through Dorothea's thin slippers, the smell of burning leaves filled the air with the fragrance of melancholy finality. It was the season and the hour to sit indoors by a cheerful fire. Yet Dorothea continued to walk up and down. The house, immense as it was, could not contain the immensity of her torment.

Her agony of mind had been so long drawn out, first a dull, slowly increasing anxiety, swelling like a cancerous disease during these last weeks to such anguish that at moments she found herself dazed, feeling it almost as a physical pain, hardly knowing what it was all about. She would wake in the middle of the night, believing drowsily that it was a dream, that Cara was a child again sleeping in her crib in the nursery wing. Or, finding forgetfulness for a few minutes in a book, she would look up and see Charles's eyes fixed on her in miserable compassion. Then the fear rushed back again like a huge wave engulfing her, or rather, like a ferocious beast that tore at her heart and stomach with fangs and claws.

The stages that had led up to this present nightmare had been so deceptively gradual. It was just over a year now since Carolina had left England. A few months after her return the Legislative Assembly had passed a decree confiscating the property of the emigrés and, soon afterwards, another pronouncing sentence of death on those who failed to return to France before the year was out. These were, in fact, vetoed by the King, but they were indications of the temper of the nation. To the Mandleshams they had the sound of an iron door clanging between them and their daughter.

Yet had Carolina not chosen wisely in returning voluntarily to her adopted country? When a stable government was established, would not the aristocrats like the de Lapalisses, who had chosen to share France's fortunes rather than to plot with foreign powers against her from beyond the frontiers, be honoured for their loyalty?

Opinion in England was growing more and more conservative, but a little group of Whigs, notably, Charles Grey, Charles Fox, Lord Launderdale and Lord Edward FitzGerald, still proclaimed their faith in the Revolution. Cara herself wrote cheerfully; her parents were not to worry, the times were difficult but all would come right in due course.

Foreign affairs were absorbing the attention of the Assembly. The Austrian Emperor's interference gave the Girondins the excuse to launch a crusade against despotism abroad which alone could unite the nation behind the Revolution. In April 1792 the French Assembly in the name of the King declared war on Austria. The French army, by now reduced to an undisciplined rabble, invaded Belgium and was routed. Relief was widespread throughout Europe, and in England was mixed with derision. It was felt that this abject defeat would effectively quench both France's war fever and her revolutionary ardour.

That the Mandleshams shared in this delusion is shown by Dorothea's journal, which during the months of May and most of June is written in an optimistic tone. In reality the opportunity had come for the Jacobins—the *enragés*—to strike. In July Prussia declared war on France. The Duke of Brunswick's manifesto was an arrogant threat to the Revolution. The nation rose in fury. The volunteers from Marseilles poured into Paris singing a new song, the "Marseillaise", which was soon to be on everyone's lips. On the night of August 9th the great bell of the Cordeliers began to toll. Next day the mob attacked the Tuileries. The Swiss Guards were butchered; the royal family fled to the Assembly. The King was deposed and imprisoned. France was declared a republic. The Austrian-Prussian invaders advanced. Danton in the Champs de Mars called on the nation for "De l'audace, et encore de l'audace et toujours de l'audace".

Rumours, followed by dependable news of these terrifying

events, came to a bewildered England, but to Dorothea and Charles waiting day by day in an agonised companionship at Crome or Mandlesham House no news came from Carolina. They wrote to Lord Gower, the British Ambassador in Paris, urgently commending their daughter to his protection; they used all their influence to get in touch with her but without result. Lord Mandlesham and his elder son decided to go to France to seek for her. Then as the flood of pitiable refugees, aristocratic and clerical, poured into the southern ports of England, a dreadful story spread around. It was said that as the invaders had advanced on Paris the Paris Commune had conducted a massacre in the overflowing prisons. . . .

Dorothea and Charles assured one another that Cara was safe at Châteaudoux far from the scene of these horrors. How could they doubt it? But Lord Mandlesham made all preparations for leaving at once for France.

He was up in London on this very business this September day, and Dorothea found it easier to wait for him out in the autumn twilight than indoors in the great echoing rooms. This day was no different from the days that had preceded it—a day of feverish plans, of resolute hope rent with fear, all ordinary interests or thoughts seen through a fog of sickening apprehension.

Yet when Dorothea saw Charles appear at the end of the glade on horseback, and dismount and walk towards her, a deadly faintness seemed to envelop her very soul. Perhaps it was because he walked so very slowly with bent head and shoulders as she had never seen him walk before in all their married life. His face when he drew near to her was quite changed; she saw how he would look when he was very old. He held a letter in his hand, and raising his head looked at her in anguish as though imploring her to guess what he could not say. She took the letter gently from him, and read the strange incomprehensible words. It was from the British Embassy in Paris and contained the news that the Duc and the Duchesse de Lapalisse (née Lady Carolina Chessel) had perished in the prison massacres on the night of September 3rd.

CHAPTER XVII

TIME PRESENT AND TIME PAST

I

ONE AFTERNOON in October 1795, a carriage drew up outside the portals of Mandlesham House. A lady, handsomely dressed in deep mourning, alighted and, announcing herself as the Marquise de St Aube Ferté, was shown upstairs to Lady Mandlesham's boudoir.

Lady Mandlesham was awaiting her. For the first time in their lives Dorothea and Tessy Bellingham met face to face, shook hands and exchanged words of conventional greeting.

The moment was so charged with emotion and irony that through excess of embarrassment it ceased to be embarrassing. Dorothea seated herself at a tea-table and poured out a dish of tea for her visitor. With surprise and even amusement she noticed Tessy's changed style and appearance. Was this the saucy painted enchantress whose formidable rivalry had poisoned her early married life—this widowed lady, sombrely but elegantly swathed in veils and crepes and jet bugles, a fine gold cross on her voluptuous bosom, who without any looks to speak of had an air of alluring animation? Tessy, for her part, fully conscious as she was of the drama and tragedy of the occasion, observed how well—provokingly well—Lady Mandlesham had kept her complexion and figure, nor

I I   265

could she help admiring her composure which, she was to discover later in the interview, came from good breeding rather than lack of feeling.

This visit was no surprise to Dorothea and she had had ample time in which to prepare herself for it, for it was more than a month since she had received this letter from the Marquise de St Aube Ferté:

"Your ladyship will doubtless be surprised and perhaps affronted at receiving a letter from me, but a sacred charge laid upon me, almost on the last day of her life, by your ladyship's late lamented daughter, the Duchesse de Lapalisse, obliges me to place to one side the natural delicacy which I feel at obtruding myself upon your ladyship. Madam, the Duchesse de Lapalisse and I shared a cell in the prison of La Force in Paris from August 20th to the evening of September 1st, two days before her death, when only my fortuitous removal to another prison saved me from sharing her fate.

"When the Duchesse discovered my nationality and that I had some slight acquaintance—as I told her—with her parents, she honoured me with her friendship and confidence. To me she confided her tender love for her parents, her husband and her child, spoke often of her happy family life with her brothers, and allowed me some glimpses of the faith and courage which sustained her innocent soul. Your ladyship will perhaps feel doubtful of my worthiness or suitability to be the recipient of confidences which, hallowed as they now seem to me, must to your mother's heart be inexpressibly sacred. Fate chose me however for this role and I endeavoured to give what comfort and succour I could to my endearing young companion.

"A few days before the fatal massacre she begged me, if any harm should come to her and I should escape to England, to visit her parents and to assure them of her eternal devotion. Moreover, as though granted a premonition of her fate (for at the time we seemed to be in equal jeopardy) she confided to me a lock of her hair, and a jargon ornament which she had contrived to hide about her person, and which she told me had belonged to her aunt the late Lady Aintry, she herself having worn it at her marriage, and charged me to give it to your ladyship with a request that it might eventually belong to her son's wife. Honour and good feeling, as well as the sincere affection that I felt for the Duchesse, demands that I should endeavour to acquit myself of this trust.

"How I survived the terror (in which my dear husband perished under the guillotine) and eventually, after many perils and hardships, escaped to Italy and from thence in a British man-of-war to England would be of no interest to your ladyship. It is enough to say that I am now in London, residing at this address in Portman Square with the Hon. Mrs Carolside, the sister of my preserver, Captain Frederick Craddock, R.N., who has done me the honour to ask me to become his wife. If your ladyship's recollection of past events should give you an invincible repugnance to meeting me, I shall be neither surprised nor offended. But if you accord me an interview I shall endeavour to give you as exact an account of your daughter's last week on earth as your mother's heart may demand or can endure."

The feelings with which Dorothea received this letter were extraordinarily mixed. First there was the shock of finding that the companion and comforter of Cara's last days had been the woman whom she, Dorothea, had regarded for years as her enemy. In a wave of bitterness Dorothea recalled her unhappiness at the time of Carolina's birth. Tessy's triumphant maternity had seemed to make a mock of her own pregnancy. She had been so disillusioned and sick at heart that at moments she had hoped that she would not survive her own confinement. Only when the pangs of childbirth had engulfed her had she forgotten everything, her whole mind and body engaged in the tremendous task of bringing a child into the light. With what consoling pride she had held Cara to her breast for the first time! Now she learnt that it was Tessy, of all people, who had filled a mother's comforting role during the closing days of Cara's life, no doubt had been the last woman to hold her in her arms. This was hard to bear. Then, reproaching herself for her stubborn pride and selfishness, Dorothea was thankful that her daughter had had a woman of her own race and class, a sympathetic and no doubt courageous companion, to sustain her during her imprisonment. She could even derive a spark of amusement from the scrupulous delicacy with which Tessy had spared Carolina's innocence—"I had some slight acquaintance with her parents."

In the end her yearning to hear all that Tessy could tell her of her daughter overcame every other feeling. It had been no small part of her parents' agony that they had known so little of her end—just the bare facts of her and Jules's imprisonment and murder. Had she been lonely, dismayed, terrified, before death released her—their bright and darling child? Not her death itself, but the hideous circumstances leading up to it had filled them with a grief which for a long time had found no assuagement except in comforting one another and their children.

Dorothea, writing from St Chidwiddin where she had received Tessy's letter, assured her that she would gladly receive her.

Now as they sat face to face, the thought of their past relationship and of Cara's death heavy between them, Dorothea said with a simplicity that eased the tension: "Madame, talk to me about my daughter. Pray tell me everything."

Tessy, with her histrionic sense, was keenly aware of the emotional value of the moment. Moreover, she had been genuinely attracted to Carolina. A more upright but less imaginative woman might have brought less comfort to a sorrowing mother. With delicacy and address she gave Dorothea an image of Carolina as she had been during those last tragic weeks, her courage and gentleness shining out more brightly against the background of squalor and fear, which Dorothea would cherish all her days.

Jules and Carolina had been in attendance on the King and Queen when the Tuileries was attacked. In the prevailing chaos their personal loyalty to the fallen monarchy was all that was left to them. When the royal family took refuge with the Assembly the de Lapalisses accompanied them. For seventeen stifling hours the royal party sat in the Recorder's box listening to the members crying out for the King's destruction, while outside the air was torn with musket and cannon fire and the clang of the tocsin. The Queen ate a little bread with her children and drank some water; the King, amazingly apathetic, his huge appetite unimpaired, chewed away at a chicken.

The King and Queen were then led to Les Feuillants, and here Jules and Carolina were parted, the former being taken away under arrest, while Carolina was left with the royal family. A few days later the royal party were conducted to the Temple, where they were kept under lock and key in a little tower beside the keep. No letters, visitors or newspapers were allowed. The drunken laughter of the soldiers guarding them was their only contact with the outside world. Carolina was racked with anxiety on her husband's account but—she told Tessy— "each one of us was in the same plight and so we endeavoured to bear it with patience and to comfort one another and the Queen."

On August 20th two commissioners from the Commune arrived with orders to remove those persons who did not belong to the royal family. It was a cruel moment for the Queen. Now she must part with the Princesse de Lamballe, the favourite friend of her youth—how the Polignacs had laughed at her absurd sensibility, but her fidelity had outlasted theirs—must part too with the young Englishwoman whose gaiety and sweetness had brightened these last unhappy few years.

Madame de Lamballe and Carolina were taken to La Force, and here Carolina had the joy of being reunited with her husband for a few moments. Again they were separated, Carolina being lodged in the same cell as Tessy, but at least they had the consolation of being in the same prison, and of being able to smuggle messages to each other.

Of the twelve days that she spent with Carolina, Tessy had much to tell, nor could Dorothea hide her painful longing for every detail. Tessy was too intelligent to conceal from Dorothea the grimness and squalor of that prison cell, but dwelt only on those things which Dorothea must wish to hear—Carolina's courage and cheerfulness, her courtesy even to the rough gaolers, her thoughts withdrawing more and more from the brutal present to happy memories of her family and Jules and her child.

She had spoken to Tessy of her belief in a future life, and she had said fervently more than once, "Here in France everything has gone wrong, because they have mistaken disorder for liberty, but that does not shake my faith in liberty."

Tessy had parted with her on September 1st with regret. Of the last dreadful scene two days later she could only give a vague outline, gathered from an account from one of the survivors of the massacre whom she had met in Italy. It seemed that Jules and Carolina de Lapalisse had died together and that their end had been swift. She did not tell Dorothea that many of the victims had been literally hacked to pieces by the mob. She assured Dorothea of her conviction that Carolina had met her death with the steadfast fortitude which had upheld her during her imprisonment. It was not in Tessy's nature to understand the quality of the light which had burned in Carolina's soul, but she could recognise its effect.

When she had said all that she could say, she handed over to Dorothea a casket containing the ornament of jargons and a lock of Carolina's hair. Dorothea sat with the casket in her hand, looking with a kind of amazement at these relics — the wine-red jewel which had glowed on Jenny's dark hair the night (a thousand years ago it seemed) of the Viceregal ball—the lock of bronzed hair, so silky soft and alive, though Cara herself was dead.

A profound silence fell between the two women: both with greatly varying degrees of pain were thinking of a fair young face.

For Tessy this was perhaps one of the more satisfying moments of her career. She sat there, titled, impeccably and tragically widowed, yet betrothed to a gallant British naval officer, having generously offered comfort to the proud and virtuous woman whom above all others she had reason to dislike. It was a noble gesture of a kind for which Tessy had not had many opportunities in her life.

For Dorothea the situation was less satisfactory. It was hard to have to feel gratitude towards Tessy Bellingham, yet gratitude she must feel, if mixed with some wonder at the ways of Providence who had seen fit to send her comfort in such a curious and embarrassing guise.

As Lady Mandlesham said good-bye to the Marquise de St Aube Ferté, thanking her sincerely for all that she had meant to Carolina and assuring her of the consolation that her visit had brought her (adding with an effort that she would repeat all that the Marquise had told her to Lord Mandlesham), she pressed into her hand a miniature of Cara as a child.

"She was such a pretty lamb," she murmured, and

271

turned away abruptly that Tessy might not see her weep.

Some time before this interview, on Cara's twenty-fourth birthday, Dorothea had written in her journal, without any other comment, the words—"I have accepted the will of God."

Resignation is not the fashionable virtue nowadays that it was in former times. Its heroic quality is not perhaps generally recognised; it is a state of mind more easily attained to by strong than by weak souls.

Dorothea's submission to the Divine Will was no empty platitude. She had passed through unspeakable anguish before she achieved this victorious surrender. So intense had been her grief at losing Cara and at the brutal manner of her death that only the necessity of comforting Charles who, faced with the first real sorrow of his life, was for a time quite distraught with grief and anger, enabled her to keep her mental equilibrium.

The loss of the young has an inexpressible poignancy for their elders, robbing them of the vicarious youth which they enjoy in their company and making them mournfully conscious of the approaching shadows of age.

The sunshine which Carolina's death had taken from her family's life could never be restored. Yet in time Dorothea became aware that her sorrow at Cara's loss was different from the sorrow that she had felt when Jenny died, though the circumstances surrounding her daughter's death had been even more tragic and heart-breaking than those connected with her sister's end. In Jenny she had mourned a life wasted and unfulfilled, its fair promise scattered like blossoms by an unseasonable wind. Though Cara had been so savagely torn from existence at a still earlier age, Dorothea had the curious conviction that she had fulfilled her destiny. Her light, according to mortal reckoning, had not burnt for long, but it had burnt with a bright

flame to the very end. Dorothea bore her grief with fortitude, even with pride, for when it threatened to become
unbearable she reminded herself that she had given birth
to an immortal soul.

2

The inexorable passing of time, flowing on like the in-
coming tide, is a source both of pain and of healing to the
bereaved. There must be sadness in every fresh event in
the family in which the beloved dead has no part, each
new springtime pierces the heart with a renewed sense of
loss. Yet the need for action, for the carrying on of daily
tasks and duties, is sorrow's only cure, though at the
time it seems to add unbearably to its burden.

So it was with Dorothea. The world did not come to an
end, affrighted, on the night that Carolina was slaughtered.
Her death and that of Jules and their fellow victims was
precursory of thousands of similar crimes. The Terror
raged in France like a fearful plague. Thousands perished
every month in Paris under the guillotine, thousands were
beheaded, drowned and shot in the provinces. News came
in January 1793 of the King of France's execution; in
June Dorothea learnt that her friend Jacqueline de
Lapalisse had been guillotined; by October Marie
Antoinette had suffered the same death. The time came
when Dorothea was thankful that if Jules and Carolina
had had to die they had gone before they saw the monstrous thing, gorged with blood, into which the Revolution
had grown.

Refugees poured over to England, and the Mandleshams
gave shelter at Crome to at least half a dozen aristocratic French families. Some of them were charming
and touching in their gratitude, others drove even their
indulgent host and large-hearted hostess nearly distracted
with their squabbles and intrigues. On one occasion Lord
Mandlesham wrote to his eldest son from the villa at

Richmond: "Your mother and I are emigrés in our turn. We have fled here for a few days to escape the French civil war which is raging at Crome between our various guests. Poor devils, they have lost all and I should not grudge them one of the few privileges that is left to them—that of quarrelling together in a foreign land!"

Soon after King Louis' execution the French republic declared war on England and Holland. Pitt had striven long for peace but, as the Foreign Secretary told Chauvelin, Britain could not stand by and allow any nation to make herself "sovereign of the Low Countries or general arbitrator of the rights and liberties of Europe".

Britain, unprepared as usual, girded itself for the conflict like a drowsy giant awakening from sleep.

To Dorothea the Christmas of 1793 was the saddest she had ever spent—her daughter and son-in-law murdered, her friends Madame de Lapalisse and the Queen of France guillotined, the France she had known and once loved given over to an orgy of slaughter and materialism, Ireland seething with disaffection, England hampered by the complacency of her government and the greed of her allies, blundering on through months of war. Yet Dorothea was not without consolations. Though she had lost Cara who was a part of herself, the boy François who was a part of Cara had been committed to her charge. He was a lively affectionate child, the darling of his grandparents and much petted by his young uncles.

The glorious First of June brought cheer to the nation in the Summer of 1794 (for in the general exultation at this resounding naval victory it was hardly noticed that the grain fleet had arrived in France, thus saving her from disaster).

The following month a National Administration was formed, the Whigs joined the Government, and Lord Mandlesham accepted a post as one of the Civil Lords of the Admiralty. He threw himself into his duties with a zeal and earnestness that surprised everyone who knew him. Only Dorothea realised that a passionate longing to avenge his daughter's death was the driving-power which inspired with extra energy his patriotism and sense of duty. This personal hatred of the Jacobins animated (though they never spoke of it) the whole Chessel family. Edward, the Mandleshams' second son, was now a captain in the Brigade of Guards, and took part in the disastrous campaign in the Low Countries in the winter of '94–'95, when the British Army retreated in arctic cold across Gelderland, six thousand men perishing in four days. But when Edward arrived home, wounded but otherwise in his usual robust health and spirits, he (in his mother's words) "made light of his hardships, which seem to have been dreadful beyond words, and is impatient to get well and be fighting the French again".

Even young Jonathan, who had been destined, or more precisely had destined himself, for the Navy since he was seven years old and, seeing the Grand Fleet at anchor at Spithead, had stood gazing at it entranced with admiration and wonder, pestered his parents to allow him to go to sea. They had promised him that he should join the Service when he was fourteen, a concession which he accepted with meagre gratitude, reminding them (till his father forbade him to mention the subject again on pain of a whipping) that many boys of his age were already midshipmen and had been in action.

As for Lord Fulmer, years later, when he had become the eminent reformer of early Victorian days, he was to write: "This is a matter where I make no pretence to reason or fairness. I am constitutionally unable to trust the French."

Now, in these last years of the eighteenth century, this personal hatred of Jacobinism, which endured long after the Jacobins had been superseded by the corrupt but less bloodthirsty Directorate, was merged in the larger activities of the nation preparing itself clumsily but stubbornly for a life-and-death struggle. After the collapse of the Grand Alliance, Britain had to strain her resources to the utmost to raise an army for her own protection. Voluntary enlistment proceeded apace, "voluntary" being a term which included such unorthodox methods as kidnapping and trepanning. All over the country, under the aegis of the aristocracy and county gentry, volunteer corps sprang into being. They chose their own uniform, arranged their own terms of service and, if their marching was not always up to Guards' standards and their officers sometimes escorted them in post-chaises, their spirit was admirable.

The Mandlesham volunteers wore a grey uniform with mulberry facings, and Dorothea in a becoming riding habit of the same colouring, and looking "exceedingly handsome", rode beside her husband as he inspected his men at a review at Crome.

To eighteenth-century ideas England was passing through a time of unparalleled stress, and indeed we may not minimise the deadly peril in which the country stood then and for some years to come. But if a modern observer, accustomed to the rigours of life in England during a total war, could be transported back to the late years of the eighteenth century he would be surprised at the apparent prosperity and indeed unwarlike appearance of the country. The misery of the poor was certainly appalling and was on the increase. But London was spreading; fashionable new districts were growing up in Bloomsbury and Marylebone; the country towns with their inns and bustling market-places reflected the prosperity of the farmers and the countryside. The mounting prices mainly affected the poor, the rich and even the well-to-do still ate enormously, and lived their accustomed leisurely and comfortable lives.

Even in the midst of his public duties, which he carried

out with vigour and conscientiousness, Lord Mandlesham found time to supervise the alterations to the demesne at Crome which had been his favourite hobby for some years, and which had recently received impetus from the publication of Sir Uvedale Price's *Essays on the Picturesque*. In this book Price ruthlessly condemned the tame and monotonous lay-outs of "Capability" Brown. The canvases of the romantic artists, Claude, Salvator Rosa and Poussin should, in his opinion, be the landscape gardener's guide, whose work should give the impression of being designed by nature alone. Crags, waterfalls, overhanging banks, paths thick with undergrowth, boulders, ivy-decked stumps of trees, and of course if possible a ruin—all these picturesque objects became as desirable in Lord Mandlesham's eyes as formerly they would have been abhorrent. His own tastes had been moving for some time in the direction of the picturesque. Now, in his letters from London to Dorothea, after acquainting her with news of the war, he begged her to tell him if the grounds at Crome were beginning to look as "savage, wild and melancholy" as he desired.

"How is the waterfall progressing? Does it give you a sensation pleasingly awful? I have an idea for a grotto to be set in the midst of a natural wilderness which I will discuss with you when I am down next week. It is a pity our French have left or we might have induced the old Duc to play the part of a hermit and sit in it!"

That Dorothea was not as enthusiastic as her husband about these schemes is evident from a letter she wrote to her eldest son: "Would you not think the times were terrible enough without your dear father wanting to introduce all this gloom and horror into Crome? I recollect that he used to teaze me because I loved (and still do) the savage wildness of St Chidwiddin. Now it is my turn to laugh! Frankly I do not believe that with all his enthusiasm and cleverness he will be able to give poor

Crome that awfully magnificent effect that he desires. However, it takes his mind off his worries at the Admiralty and does no one any harm, so though I do not precisely encourage him, I do not discourage neither!"

3

The "worries at the Admiralty" to which Dorothea made such casual allusion were not only to develop into one of the most alarming domestic crises that England had experienced for years, but also brought a curious echo from the past into Dorothea's life, and for this reason should be mentioned in her biography.

The British Navy in the eighteenth century, as now, was the pride and darling of the nation. More even than in present times, with Air power as a major factor in war, the Navy was felt to be Britain's bulwark. As long as the Navy held firm all was well with England. Yet though the nation took a sentimental pride in its jolly tars with their hearts of oak, it did not occur to anyone that these jolly tars might have grievances and be living in conditions that would put a strain on the sturdiest loyalty.

Naval pay not only still remained the same as it had been a century and a half ago, though prices had risen out of all proportion, but was often months, sometimes years, in arrears. Conditions on board ship at the best were hard, at the worst were indescribably brutalising and degrading. A good captain was regarded as a father by his crew; a drunken, flogging captain could turn his ship into hell afloat.

A trickle of petitions from the lower deck had reached the Admiralty in recent years and had been shelved. Their Lords of the Admiralty and the general public continued to expect their seamen to perform prodigies of valour and to "face the Enemy with a Cheerful Heart", an expectation which seemed fully justified when the news of the great naval victory against Spain off Cape St Vincent reached London early in March 1797.

Was there a prouder woman then in England than Dorothea Mandlesham? It is to be doubted. Not only had Jonathan, her "naughtiest rogue in Christendom", taken part in the battle (thus receiving his baptism of fire at the—to his ideas—scandalously mature age of $14\frac{1}{2}$), but he had been highly commended for his gallantry by his commanding officer, Commodore Horatio Nelson.

Yet only a few weeks later, on April 17th, Dorothea was writing in her journal the stark words, "The Fleet is in Mutiny. God help England!"

Her consternation was shared by the whole country. If the news was not quite such a shock to her as to the less well-informed public, it was none the less scarifying. She was aware through Lord Mandlesham of the petition, begging in the most respectful terms for fairer treatment and better conditions, which the men of the Channel Fleet had sent to Lord Howe before they sailed for the Spring cruise, and which the gallant but ailing old Admiral had forwarded to the Admiralty. Here it had met with the fate of the other pathetic and illiterate appeals. In the state of the national finances, Whitehall felt that a rise in naval pay was out of the question, and the matter was ignored. Lord Mandlesham, generous by habit and sympathetic by nature, confided to his wife his private conviction that this attitude was a mistake and might lead to trouble, but as a landsman he did not profess to understand the niceties of naval discipline. Lord Bridport was ordered to take the Fleet to sea. On the morning of April 16th he gave the signal to weigh anchor. His signal was ignored as totally as the men's petition had been ignored by the Admiralty. This was the horrifying fact which burst on an incredulous nation that black Easter Monday.

Dorothea's journal gives a vivid if rather sketchy picture

of the course of events. On the 17th Charles had accompanied the First Lord of the Admiralty, Lord Spencer, and other colleagues to Portsmouth. The Board was sitting at the Fountain Inn, and from here Charles sent her a hasty and reassuring note. She was not to be unduly alarmed. The situation was anxious enough to be sure but he, personally, did not believe that Jacobin influences were responsible for it. The men, though in mutiny, were behaving with exemplary discipline, and had even declared their willingness to sail if the French Fleet put to sea. Their demands seemed reasonable enough. "Can you credit it—the poor fellows are accustomed to eat weevils with their biscuits, and cheese full of red worms? Would not such a diet be enough to turn any stomach Jacobin?"

Dorothea, knowing her husband's genial optimism, was still profoundly uneasy. The opinion in London was that to surrender to the men's demands at such a time (Bonaparte advancing on Vienna, and an invasion fleet, probably destined for Ireland, gathering in Holland) might be the first slide towards revolution, massacre and ruin.

Yet on the 21st Dorothea noted with astonishment that the Prince of Württemberg, the Princess Royal's betrothed, had arrived at Portsmouth and had been cheered and saluted by the men as Lord Spencer had escorted him round the mutinous fleet.

Next day the news was bad again. Admiral Gardner, after abusing the delegates, had been bundled out of his flagship. The royal pardon, secured in haste by Lord Spencer, saved the situation. The men invited Lord Bridport, "the Father of the Fleet", to resume command. The mutiny appeared to be at an end.

To Dorothea's surprise it was Lord Mandlesham's turn to be uneasy. "It is to be hoped that the Government will honour their promises of redress to the seamen with the least possible delay. There is no want of loyalty to the King and Constitution among the men that I can perceive, but when simple and ignorant minds have been in a ferment, the least suspicion may set them boiling again."

His judgment was sound. By May 7th, maddened by the Government's procrastination, the Fleet at Spithead were again in mutiny. Dorothea wrote in her journal: "I am so agitated I can scarcely hold my pen. The mutineers at Portsmouth are flying the red flag and turning their captains and other officers out of the ships. Ad. Colpoys was near hanged in a broil on his flagship. Thank God, Johnny is away from it all with the Mediterranean fleet. Oh, why cannot the Government act quickly and with magnanimity! I am persuaded that the seamen are good and honest at heart though misled."

At last the authorities realised that prompt and speedy action was essential, and a Bill providing for increases of seamen's pay was hustled through Parliament. Lord Howe, the venerable hero of the Glorious First of June, was sent down to Portsmouth to treat with the men, to redress their grievances and to grant them the royal pardon. In six days his mission had succeeded, and on May 15th Dorothea, tired but joyful, was writing an account of a dinner at the Governor's House at Portsmouth which Lord Howe had given to the delegates and which she and Lord Mandlesham had attended:

"What a wonderful ending to all our terrors and alarms! Good old Lord Howe—'Black Dick' the sailors call him—was quite exhausted after being rowed and cheered round the fleet for twelve hours, but a look of intense satisfaction softened his stern countenance. The noise of the cheering and *feux de joie* as the aged hero was carried on the shoulders of the delegates to Sir William Pitt's house was almost deafening. I am sure if I have heard 'Rule, Britannia' once to-day I have heard it a hundred times, as well as countless other patriotic songs and naval ballads and ditties. Every kind of loyal toast was drunk after dinner, and Lady Howe's health and mine which compliment (I am vexed to have to confess it at my age!) made me blush, and also brought the tears to my eyes, for the honest fellow who proposed it called me, 'the mother of a young naval hero'."

Lord Mandlesham enlarges on this episode in a letter to his son Lord Fulmer: "I wish you could have seen your mother blush, a habit which she had never lost and I hope never does, for it is very becoming to her, when one of the delegates suddenly proposed the health of 'the Beautiful Lady sitting on the Admiral's port side, herself the mother of a gallant young naval officer.' Your mother declares that he must have been tipsy, but indeed she is as handsome as ever she was."

The relief felt by everyone at this reconciliation between the Navy and the nation was short-lived. The festivities were hardly over before it was learnt that the mutiny had broken out among the ships at the Nore and in a more virulent form. Of this second outburst—"the Floating Republic" as it has been called—under its excitable ex-schoolmaster leader Richard Parker, it need only be said that, lacking the justification of the first outbreak since the settlement made at Portsmouth, it was condemned by both the Government, the public, and even the men at Spithead. It was doomed to disaster, and was crushed with harshness by the authorities. By June 15th it had collapsed and, on the last day of June, Parker was hanging from the yard-arm of H.M.S. *Sandwich*.

The punishment handed out to the ringleaders, excessive as it may seem to us, was lenient according to the standards of the age. Out of a total of 412 men court-martialled, fifty-nine were sentenced to death but only twenty-nine actually executed, though others suffered imprisonment and flogging.

It was some weeks after the end of the mutiny, when the

recollection of its nightmare excitement was passing from people's minds (events on the Continent, with the formal surrender of Austria to France at Campo Formio providing an unpleasant distraction), that Dorothea was astonished to receive this letter written in an uneducated hand on a dirty slip of paper:

"To the Right Honourable Marchionness of Mandlesham.

"May it please your ladyship!

"That I your ladyship's humbl servant and foster-brother, at present lying under sentance of death under the infamous charge of partsipating in the recent mutney, but being guilty of no sutch thing—God help me!—do ernestly and humbly intreat your ladyship to cast your eyes compassionately upon your petitioner. Honoured Lady and dear Miss Dolly, I hope your ladyship will belev that I am not and never was a rebellious or mutnous person, as Capt Lackie will testify under who I served for two years in H.M.S. *Tyger*, and a finer gentilman never stepped, and was able to save his life on the glorious 1st June, as he will tell your ladyship, only nessessity and being exposed to the scoffs and jests and charges of cowerdliness from my shipmates forced me to join in said mutney. Therefore I most humbly beg your ladyship to assist me and preserv my life.

"And your respectful petitioner and foster brother will ever pray for your ladyship's health in this world and the next, dear Miss Dolly.

CONN McCARTHY."

Dorothea was painfully moved by this letter. Most vividly she remembered her foster-brother—beautiful, grave, with the unconscious dignity and pride of a fine young animal. She could not recapture now the shy and tentative emotion that she had felt for him, but she knew that it had been innocent, sincere and, for a time, deeply felt—a foreshadowing of her enduring passion for Charles. She was sadly aware of the unfairness of life. Thirty years ago she and Conn, both of whom had been nourished at Kathie's generous breasts, had been two young people, equal in health, hope and the capacity for happiness, and but loosely separated by class and education. Who could say that she, Dorothea, was in any way worthier or better than Conn? Yet now she was the great lady, secure and honoured, and he the suppliant, a rough seaman lying in a filthy prison under condemnation of death.

She went at once to Lord Mandlesham and showed him the letter. She said: "He is my foster-brother. If there are any extenuating circumstances, if there is any possibility of saving him without flouting justice, I beg you to do it for my sake. I owe it to Kathie. Yes, to Conn himself, for he was the only brother that I ever had. I do not know what he has become now, but he was a fine, good young man then."

She paused and, to her mortification, blushed. Lord Mandlesham regarded her intently, then said with a smile: "Fine and good—and handsome too, eh Dolly?"

She answered with the candid simplicity which always amused Charles: "Yes, he was the handsomest young man I ever saw—handsomer even than you, Lord Mandlesham!"

Soon afterward her husband was able to give her the good news that Conn McCarthy had been pardoned. Enquiries showed that he had indeed taken only a passive part in the mutiny, and his former captain, Captain Lackie, when applied to had spoken up handsomely for him, giving him the character of an honest and gallant seaman, adding, "Though an Irishman I certainly never did discover any seditious complexion in him."

In answer to a letter of thanks from Conn, Dorothea gave him a generous sum of money and arranged for him to be given leave to visit his mother at Ardnabannagh (their first meeting since he had been carried off by the press-gang thirty years ago). She did not suggest that he should come to Mandlesham House to offer her his thanks in person. How little of the noble-looking, dignified lad that she had known would have survived thirty years of degrading hardship on the lower deck? He should remain in her imagination as he had been that last night at Cabra House when they had said good-bye.

So the mutinies, terrifying as they had been and shocking to the complacency of the authorities, faded into the past, and later were seen to have been productive of much-needed reforms in the Navy. In October of the same year the British Fleet won a resounding victory over the Dutch at Camperdown, and Britain knew that her wooden walls still held firm.

CHAPTER XVIII

GOOD-BYE TO CABRAGENA

LADY MANDLESHAM's coach drew up at the bottom of the steep hill that led up to the headland of Ardnabannagh, for December mud slippery upon the deeply rutted surface of the road (if it could be called a road) made it impassable for wheeled traffic. Lady Mandlesham's English coachman was shocked at the idea of his mistress taking this lonely walk unattended—would she not have one of the postilions with her? But Lady Mandlesham thanked him and shook her head. She knew the way perfectly, though it was so long since she had been there. She would prefer to be alone, she would not be gone above an hour.

As she walked up the hill, the mud squelching over her fine kid shoes—conscious all down her back of the disapproval of her servants (for mercy's sake, what had possessed her ladyship to drive all the way from Youghal just to go trapezing up a hill to see a burnt-out house?)—she asked herself why indeed, after all these years, she was, for the first time, revisiting her girlhood's home. No personal tie survived to bring her back to Cabragena. Her mother was dead these twenty years; Uncle Oliver had drunk himself some years ago into his grave; Kathie and Tishie, since the fire which had destroyed Cabra House during last year's rebellion, had been living at Youghal; the house was gutted, deserted, abandoned at last to solitude, to its legendary ghosts, and to the relentless Atlantic gales.

It was the destruction of Cabra House more than a year ago which had brought her to Ireland now in the last month of 1799. Kathie, warned of the approach of the rebels, had escaped with her imbecile charge a short while before the house was plundered and given over to the flames. The local clergyman had given them shelter, and through him Dorothea had arranged for them to be boarded out at Youghal in the house of another clergyman and his wife who were distant connections of the Lynch family. Here they were comfortable and well looked-after. Unfortunately Tishie, whose wandering wits showed surprising concentration when she discussed Protestant beliefs and doctrines (to which she was a staunch adherent), so worked upon the nerves of her clerical host by her argumentativeness and dogmatism on a subject which he naturally regarded as his own preserve, that he was at length obliged to ask Lady Mandlesham to terminate the arrangement.

To find some other suitable place where Kathie and Tishie might stay, and to settle up various financial affairs, had been the object of Dorothea's visit. Her reunion with her old nurse had been extremely touching. Kathie in her eighties was as lively, as warm-hearted, as full of shrewd sayings and gossip as ever. She greeted her nursling (for so she still regarded Dorothea) with joy, as well as with heartfelt gratitude for Conn's preservation, invoking on her head enough blessings (Dorothea told her) to waft her at once to heaven. She exclaimed in astonishment and delight on Dorothea's beauty. Shure, wasn't it true what the priests said that purity of soul (and —Kathie added on her own—the love of a fine man) were the best preservatives of female looks? Dorothea shook her head and laughed. She believed indeed that she and Charles had kept their freshness tolerably well, but at forty-nine her appearance only interested her in so far as it gave pleasure, and seemed to cause a fond foolish pride, to her husband and family.

It was less agreeable to see Tishie again. Dorothea was ashamed to find that a feeling of slight repugnance and exasperation still mingled with her pity for her unfortunate sister. Tishie for her part, though carefully primed by Kathie, seemed unaware that this magnificent lady was her sister Dolly. She had forgotten Dorothea but—and this smote Dorothea's heart with a sense of merited self-reproach—she had remembered Jenny. What was more, she believed that Jenny was still alive. "Where is my sister Jenny? I want her to dress my doll for me. She promised she would come and play with me. What have you done with Jenny?" And yet perhaps her errant wits had partly grasped the fact of Jenny's death, for later she said, with a look of childish cunning, her voice and manner sending an uncontrollable shudder through Dorothea: "Ah, you think you have shut Jenny up in a box and put her away in the ground, but I know better, for I saw her last night, smiling and beckoning to me, so pretty, so pretty, with green ribbons in her hair."

Certainly the visit, in spite of the compensation of

seeing Kathie, had had its painful moments. Why then, now that her business had been successfully concluded and arrangements made for her old nurse and sister to lodge with a maiden lady at Lismore, had she deliberately added to them by making this doleful pilgrimage to her forsaken home? She could not explain to herself the motives that impelled her to do so, for she was not given as a rule to morbid retrospection. Some obscure but profound instinct called her back to Cabragena. She must see it again, acknowledge to herself all that the happiness and sorrow of the thirty years that had passed since she had lived there had wrought in her, and then say good-bye to it for ever.

Thirty years—and yet how familiar everything around her was, and yet again how strange, more dream-like in its long unseen familiarity than an unknown landscape could ever be. There was the partly ruined church with its round tower, left behind her as she toiled up the hill, there by the roadside the holy well or spring, there the tumbledown cabin, and there surely a blackthorn tree, stunted as the trees were in this district, that had hardly grown since she had last set eyes on it.

The weather even was of the kind that she remembered as typical of Ardnabannagh. There was a drizzling rain and some wind, but as she reached the crown of the hill and turned down the track that led to Cabra House the mizzle cleared, a rent was torn in the clouds, and a stream of watery sunshine poured its light down upon the sea, turning the leaden waves to an angry blue.

With beating heart Dorothea turned in at the broken gates, walked up the dark and gloomy avenue of firs and wind-tormented oaks and, coming in sight of the house, paused in sad amazement. To what an ultimate desolation of rooflessness, of scorched and crumbling walls and gaping windows Cabragena had been reduced! Moving forward cautiously, as though by the mere fact of being

288

alive she was more of an intruder in this haunted place than any phantom would have been, she stepped over the ruined threshold, gazed with painful wonder at the blackened shell of what had once been her home. Here, in what remained of the drawing-room, the fireplace still stood; on this side her mother had sat in her high-backed, winged chair busy at her needlework. There, where nettles and rank grass already sprouted, Jenny and she had sat together sewing and exchanging their silly, merry jokes and confidences. Were these charred stones all that remained of the study, once so full of her father's boisterous presence, the walls hung with his sporting trophies, his writing-desk littered with unopened bills? The dining-room which had witnessed such scenes of gross and lavish revelry was almost entirely destroyed. Two of the round corner towers still stood. The shattered staircase led up into emptiness.

The house seemed to her to exhale a sinister defiance, as though aware that it had at last fulfilled its unblessed destiny. She felt herself unwelcome and, leaving it in haste, went to the garden, reassuring with its high and stalwart wall. But here the door—its rusty latch hard to lift as though it had never expected and even resented another visitor—opened to disclose a desolation caused, not by the hostility of man, but by nature untended and unchecked. All was surprisingly tangled and overgrown. The desiccated remnants of the flowers and weeds of two summers littered the beds, the paths were green with grass, the autumn crop of apples still rotted on the ground. Dorothea—between a laugh and a sigh—thought that Charles would have found all the picturesque melancholy here that even he could desire.

Skirting the ruined, forbidding house she made her way on to the cliffs and here, pacing up and down for a while on the rough grass, the salty wind, the misty rain beating against her face, the waves fretting in their never-ending strife against the rocks below, the low, unappeasable roaring of the ground-swell marking their advance and retreat, she struggled with the flood of memories that surged over her.

Memories of Jenny—how near she seemed to her here on this spot where they had often walked and stood together! Perhaps this was the reason why an urgent instinct had sent her back to Cabragena. She could almost see her, hear her, touch her; not the hectic, fashionable, benighted Jenny of the London years, but Jenny in all the radiant sweetness and spring-like gaiety of her early girlhood. It was as though she was standing by her side now on the cliff's edge, her arm round Dorothea's waist, the wind blowing back her dark curls, whipping the folds of her shabby white dress round her shapely young limbs, bringing the bright, exquisite colour to her delicate cheeks, her deep blue eyes glistening with mischief between the long black lashes: "Look, Dolly, there goes poor old Bat. Shure, wasn't he mad with us to-day?"

Dorothea wept a little. "Oh Jenny, Jenny," she sighed to the heedless wind, to the seagulls tossed like lost souls in the stormy air. Yet as her tears fell, something of the soreness that had been in her heart ever since Jenny's death was drawn away. Might she not dare to hope that wherever Jenny was now, she had become again the Jenny of Dorothea's bright and tender memories?

Many other recollections, some pleasant, some unhappy, crowded in on her. How long ago it seemed—another life—and yet so vividly recalled, when she and Jenny and her mother had set out (in a country cart, for the badness of the roads) on the first stage of their journey to Dublin. How brilliant and fugitive, with the evanescent sparkle of a firework, had been the triumph that their much lauded beauty had brought them. To Jenny indeed it had brought ultimate disaster. To Dorothea it had often proved a source of secret mortification and frustration. Even now the thought of Tessy was a stab to Dorothea's pride—and then she laughed, for was there not something irresistibly droll about the idea of Tessy as a British Admiral's wife?

All that was satisfactory in her life—her love for Charles and their children—she owed not to her looks, but to the simple and kindly emotions of the heart. Charles was proud of, had always admired her beauty, but it had availed her nothing against the impudent fascinations of Tessy Bellingham. He had loved her in the end for her fidelity and her companionship, just as his kindness and generosity had helped her to forget the bitterness of their early married life. In the end he had wanted to be with her more than with any other woman; she had always preferred his company to that of any other man. To such a simple and unexciting formula the secret of a happy marriage could be reduced. She thought of her children, too—she had little guessed, as she had stood laughing on the cliffs with Jenny, what potentialities for bliss and anguish lay hidden in her maiden body—her sons of whom she was so proud, and Cara—lost to her in the flesh but, she believed, eternally alive and young in the unfading summer of her immortality.

The eighteenth century was passing—the century that had given her birth and seen the brief splendours and sorrows of her youth. Soon she would be writing the strange and intimidating numerals "1800" at the head of her letters. What would the new century bring to her loved ones, and to England, still in the grip of a long and wearisome war but with her fighting spirit wonderfully restored? The future was uncertain, even threatening, but Dorothea could face it with serenity and courage. Though she herself was unaware of it, for simple and direct in her emotions she was not given to introspection, she had fulfilled the prediction of the old woman, so many years ago at St Declan's pardon—she had loved much and had been richly loved in return—she had "made her own soul".

DOROTHEA MANDLESHAM was to live well into the nine-teenth century, to enjoy a peaceful and honoured old age, and to be granted the supreme felicity of surviving her husband for only a few months before she died in her sleep in the autumn of 1838. It would be too great a strain on the reader's patience to trace in detail the events of her later life, interesting though many of them were both from a national and a domestic point of view. Nor is there any need, for now at the time of her good-bye to Cabra House (she was to revisit Ireland but never the ruins of her former home) she had reached her full spiritual develop-ment. From now on she was to reap where she had sown.

Two pleasant incidents, however, can be briefly re-corded. One is a description of Dorothea visiting her son Jonathan's ship after Trafalgar (for his gallantry under fire he was promoted to captain during the action) and being heartily cheered by the sailors—in middle-age as in youth she was a queenly and lovely figure. The other is her attendance at the Coronation of the young Queen Victoria, on which occasion a descendant commented: "I really believe that the finest complexion in the Abbey belonged to dear Grandmama."

It is sufficient now to take leave of Dorothea as she takes leave of Cabragena, turning once more as she emerges from the sombre avenue to see the sun breaking through the clouds. Cabra House itself, forsaken and for ever uninhabitable, is untouched by its rays—a fine rain that is half mist passes over it—but the distant headlands are illuminated with a strange and unearthly light, and there is a gleam on the horizon of the hyacinth sea.

Then without another backward glance Dorothea walks away on the first stage of her journey home.